The Postal Service Guide To U.S. Stamps

**United States
Postal Service
Washington, D.C.
20260-6811
Item No. 8893**

D0104953

20th Edition

**1994
Stamp Values**

Library of Congress Catalog Card Number 87-656545
ISBN: 1-877707-03-1
Printed in the United States of America

Editorial and Design: Mobium Corporation for Design and Communication, Chicago, IL
Printing: R.R. Donnelley & Sons Co., Crawfordsville, IN
Cover Photography: Howard Ash Photography
Inside Photography: Morrison Photography

Table of Contents

Stamp Collecting Basics

A Symphony of Stamps: An Introduction
  to Stamp Collecting   4
Words and Phrases   14
Organizations, Publications and Resources   18
Philatelic Centers   22
Significant Stamp Details   34
Explanation of Catalog Prices   42

Stamp Feature Story

Elvis Mania!   28

Values for Stamps

Commemorative, Definitive and
  Special Stamps   44
1993 Issues   314

Stamp Products

Commemorative Stamp Collections   328
Topical Stamp Collections   334

Subscription Services

First Day Ceremony Programs   327
Standing Order Subscription Service   330
Commemorative Stamp Club   332
Souvenir Pages Subscription Program   336
American Commemorative Panels
  Subscription Program   337

Values for Stamps (continued)

Airmail and Special Delivery Stamps   338
Registration, Certified Mail and Postage
  Due Stamps   354
Official and Penalty Mail Stamps   358
Parcel Post and Special Handling Stamps   362
Duck Stamps   364

Values for Stationery

Stamped Envelopes   368
Postal Cards   378

Values for Collectibles

Souvenir Pages   384
American Commemorative Panels   388

Subject Index   391

A symphony of stamps

Just as music takes many different forms, stamps also come in a variety of entertaining styles. Like music, postage stamps are created by artists who interpret and give life to their subjects.

W.C. HANDY
Father of the Blues

6c

UNITED STATES

4

Stamp collecting is a fun hobby that is not only rewarding but inexpensive as well. You don't need a lot of money to start your collection, just a lot of imagination!

Few popular songs keep their appeal for many years. But your stamp collection can endure for decades!

With this guide to starting your own collection, you'll be doing the "stamp collector rock" in no time!

What is philately?

The word philately (fi-lat-el-lee) means the study and collecting of stamps and other postal materials. Stamp collectors are called philatelists.

How do I start collecting stamps?

It's easy. You can start by simply saving stamps from letters, packages and postcards. Ask your friends and family to save stamps from their mail. Neighborhood businesses that get a lot of mail—banks, stores, travel agencies—might save their envelopes for you, too.

Or, start your collection by choosing one or two favorite subjects. Then, collect only stamps that fit your theme—art, history, sports, transportation, science—whatever you choose! This is called topical collecting. See the boxes on page 7 and 13, and the stamps pictured in this article for ideas to get you started on a music theme.

Will it cost me a lot to start a collection?

No! Start with used stamps and a few inexpensive accessories (such as a small album and a package of hinges), and you can have a great time on a limited budget. Remember to put stamps, albums and hinges on your birthday and Christmas wish lists, too!

Definitive

Commemorative

Special

Airmail

Booklet

Coil

What kinds of stamps are there?

-Definitive
-Commemorative
-Special
-Airmail
-Booklet
-Coil

Definitive stamps are found on most mail. They feature former Presidents, statesmen, prominent persons and national shrines. Their denominations range from 1 cent to 14 dollars. Definitives are usually available for several years, since they're printed in large quantities for specific postal rates.

Commemorative stamps are usually larger and more colorful than definitives. They honor important people, events or subjects. Only a limited number of each commemorative is printed, and most post offices only have them for a few months. The U.S. Postal Service's Philatelic Fulfillment Service Center also offers commemorative stamps by mail order for about one year after they are issued.

Special stamps supplement each year's regular stamp issues. They include the Christmas and Love stamps.

Airmail stamps are mainly used for sending mail overseas.

Booklet stamps come in small folders that contain panes of 3 to 20 stamps each. Each booklet stamp has at least one straight edge.

Coil stamps are issued in rolls. Each coil stamp has two straight edges and two edges with either slit-like cuts or little holes, called perforations.

How do I remove stamps from envelopes?

If you wish, you can save whole envelopes with stamps on them and store them anywhere—from shoe boxes to special albums. But if you want to remove stamps from envelopes, it pays to be careful. The best way to remove stamps from envelopes is to soak them. Here's how:

1. Tear or cut off the upper right-hand corner of the envelope.

2. Place it, stamp side down, in a small pan of warm water. After a few minutes, the stamp will sink to the bottom.

3. Wait a few more minutes for any remaining gum to dislodge from the stamp.

4. Lift the stamp out with tongs (a metal tool, like tweezers) if you have a pair. It's better to handle stamps with tongs because oil from your skin can damage stamps.

5. Place the stamp between two paper towels and put a heavy object, such as a book, on top. This will keep the stamp from curling as it

Who are America's Country Music pioneers?

Before Garth Brooks, Reba McEntire and Billy Ray Cyrus, there was Hank Williams, Patsy Cline, Bob Wills and The Carter Family. These music pioneers helped make Country and Western music famous.

A type of American music associated with rural culture and the Southern region of the United States, Country music was developed in the 1800s. It combines the elements of folk music from Great Britain, the blues of blacks in the rural South, popular songs of the late 1800s and religious music.

Country & Western stamps are the third installment in the Legends of American Music. Look for these in the "1993 Issues—Commemoratives and Special" section of your book.

Who decides which subjects will become stamps?

The USPS's Citizens' Stamp Advisory Committee meets four times a year to discuss new stamp designs. This committee, established more than 30 years ago, consists of historians, artists, business people, philatelists and others interested in American history and culture.

The advisory committee receives hundreds of suggestions every week. Just a few of these can be recommended because only a limited number of stamps is issued each year. The committee keeps all postal customers in mind as it makes its decisions.

If you think a story should be told on a stamp, submit your idea at least 36 months before the date when it should logically be issued. Send your suggestions and any helpful background information to:

United States Postal Service Citizens' Stamp Advisory Committee

*Room 5301
475 L'Enfant
Plaza West SW
Washington, DC
20260-2420*

dries. Leave the stamp there overnight.

6. If the stamp is a newer one with "invisible" gum, dry it face down with nothing touching the back, and flatten it later if necessary. Otherwise, it may stick to the paper towel when drying.

How should I organize my stamps?

However you want to, of course—it's your collection. But be sure to protect them so they don't get damaged or lost. You can attach your stamps to loose-leaf paper and put them in a three-ring binder. Or, arrange them in a more formal album, which you can buy in stores.

What kinds of stamp albums can I buy?

Some stamp albums feature specific categories with pictures of the stamps that should appear on each page. You may want to select one with loose-leaf pages so you can add pages as your collection grows. A stock book is an album with plastic or paper pockets on each page. There are no pictures of stamps, so you can organize the album your way.

How do I put a stamp in the album?

It's best to use a hinge—a small strip of thin plastic with gum on one side. Unlike tape or glue, hinges let you peel the stamp off the page without damaging it. Hinges come either folded or unfolded. Here's how to use a folded hinge:

1. Moisten the short end of the hinge lightly. Press it to the back of the stamp, placing the fold about 1/8 inch from the top of the stamp.

2. Place the stamp in the album and press down to secure it.

3. Using your tongs, gently lift the corners of the stamp to make sure it's not stuck to the page.

Instead of a hinge, you can insert the entire stamp into a mount—a small, clear plastic sleeve. Mounts are more expensive than hinges, but they protect stamps from air, dirt and moisture.

Here's a list of other equipment you may find helpful:

Glassine envelopes are made of a special thin, see-through paper that protects stamps from grease and air. You can use them to keep stamps until you put them in your album.

A **stamp catalog** is a reference book with illustrations to help you identify stamps. It also lists the values of used and unused stamps.

A **magnifying glass** helps you examine stamps by making them appear larger.

A **perforation gauge** measures

9

H
ow do I collect First Day Covers?

The fastest way to get a First Day Cover is to buy the stamp yourself (it will usually go on sale the day after the first day of issue), attach it to your own envelope (or cover), and send it to the first day post office for cancellation. You can submit up to 50 envelopes, up to 30 days after the stamp's issue date. Here's how:

1. Write your address in the lower right-hand corner of each first day envelope, at least 5/8" from the bottom. Leave plenty of room for the stamp(s) and cancellation. Use a peel-off label if you prefer.

2. Insert a piece of cardboard (about as thick as a postcard) into each envelope. You can tuck the flap in or seal the envelope.

3. Affix your stamp(s) to your first day envelope(s).

4. Put your first day envelope(s) inside another, larger envelope and mail it to "Customer-Affixed Envelopes" in care of the postmaster of the first day city. Your envelopes will be canceled and returned.

Or, you can purchase a plain envelope with the stamp(s) already affixed and canceled. These are now sold directly by mail order through the U.S. Postal Service.

perforations along the edges of stamps. Sometimes the size and number of perforations (perfs) are needed to identify stamps.

A **watermark tray** and **watermark fluid** help make watermarks on stamps more visible. A watermark is a design or pattern that is pressed into some stamp paper during manufacturing.

How can I tell what a stamp is worth?

Ask yourself two questions: "How rare is it?" and "What condition is it in?" The price listed in a stamp catalog gives you some idea of how rare it is. However, the stamp may sell at more or less than the catalog price, depending on its condition. Always try to find stamps in the best possible condition.

How should I judge the condition of a stamp?

Stamp dealers put stamps into categories according to their condition. Look at

the pictured examples to see the differences among categories. A stamp in mint condition is the same as when purchased from the post office. An unused stamp has no cancel but may not have any gum on the back. Mint stamps are usually worth more than unused stamps.

You can begin to judge the condition of a stamp by examining the front of it. Are the colors bright or faded? Is the stamp clean, dirty or stained? Is the stamp torn? Torn stamps are not considered "collectible." Is the stamp design centered on the paper, crooked, or off to one side? Are all the perforations intact? Has the stamp been canceled? A stamp with a light cancellation is in better condition than one with heavy marks across it.

Now look at the back of the stamp. Is there a thin spot in the paper? If so, it may have been caused by careless removal from an envelope or hinge.

The values listed in this book are for used and unused stamps in Fine-Very Fine condition that have been hinged.

Light Cancel–Very Fine

Medium Cancel–Fine

Heavy Cancel

Superb

Very Fine

Fine

Good

Where else can I find stamps?

Check the classified ads in philatelic newspapers and magazines at your local library. Also, there is a listing of philatelic publishers on page 19 of this book. These publishers will send you one free copy of their publications. Then you can decide if you'd like to subscribe.

What other stamp materials can I collect?

Postal stationery products are popular among some collectors. These have the stamp designs printed or embossed (printed with a raised design) directly on them.

Stamped Envelopes were first issued in 1853. More than 600 million of them are now printed each year.

Postal Cards were first issued in 1873. The first U.S. multicolored commemorative postal cards came out in 1956. Several different postal cards are issued each year.

Aerogrammes (air letters) are designed to be letters and envelopes all in one. They are specially stamped, marked for folding and already gummed.

Other philatelic collectibles include:

Plate Blocks usually consist of four stamps from the corner of a pane, with the printing plate number in the margin (or selvage) of the pane.

Copyright Blocks feature the copyright symbol © followed by "United States Postal Service" or "USPS" in the margin of the pane. The USPS began copyrighting new stamp designs in 1978.

Booklet Panes are panes of three or more of the same stamp issue. Panes are affixed inside a thin folder to form a booklet. Usually, collectors of booklet panes save the entire pane.

First Day Covers are envelopes bearing new stamps that are postmarked on the first day of sale. For each new postal issue, the USPS selects one location, usually related to the stamp subject, as the place for the first day dedication ceremony and the first day postmark. There is even an annual First Day Cover Collecting Week. See the article on page 10 for information on how to collect these covers.

Souvenir Programs are given to persons who attend first day ceremonies. They contain a list of participants, information on the stamp subject and the actual stamp attached and postmarked.

Are there any stamp groups I can join?

Yes! Stamp clubs can be a great source for new stamps and for stamp collecting advice. These clubs often meet at schools, YMCAs and community centers. Write to

**LINN'S CLUB CENTER
P.O. BOX 29
SIDNEY, OH
45365-0029**

for the locations of clubs near you.

Doing the "Stamp Collector Rock"

The Rock and Roll, Rhythm and Blues artist series is not the first set of stamps to acknowledge musicians and their music. There are many other music-related stamps featured throughout The Postal Service Guide. Conductors, composers, singers, musicians and their instruments have all been honored for their outstanding achievements. Check out some of these "melodious" stamps:

Scott No.	Description	Issue Date
1252	American Music	1964
1372	W.C. Handy, American Blues Musician	1969
1613-1615C	Musical Instruments	1976-79
1705	Centennial of Sound Recording	1977
1755	Jimmie Rodgers, Country Music Performer	1980
1756	George M. Cohan, American Composer	1980
1845	Igor Stravinsky, American Composer	1982
2110	Jerome Kern, American Composer	1985
2211	Duke Ellington, Bandleader and Composer	1986
2411	Arturo Toscanini, Conductor	1989
2550	Cole Porter, American Composer and Lyricist	1990

Also see "Composers" (1940) Scott 879-883
Stephen Foster, John Philip Sousa, etc.

AMERICAN MUSIC

U.S. POSTAGE 5 CENTS

Stamp Collecting Words and Phrases

Accessories
The tools used by stamp collectors, such as tongs, hinges, etc.

Adhesive
A gummed stamp made to be attached to mail.

Aerophilately
Stamp collecting that focuses on stamps or postage relating to air mail.

Album
A book designed to hold stamps and covers.

Approvals
Stamps sent by a dealer to a collector for examination. Approvals must either be bought or returned to the dealer within a specified time.

Auction
A sale at which philatelic material is sold to the highest bidder.

Block
An unseparated group of stamps, at least two stamps high and two stamps wide.

Black Jack
The nickname for the very popular U.S. two-cent black Andrew Jackson stamp, which was issued in various forms between 1863 and 1875.

Bogus
A completely fictitious, worthless "stamp," created only for sale to collectors. Bogus stamps include labels for nonexistent values added to regularly issued sets, issues for nations without postal systems, etc.

Booklet Pane
A small sheet of stamps specially cut to be sold in booklets.

Bourse
A marketplace, such as stamp exhibition, where stamps are bought, sold or exchanged.

Bluish Paper
Used to print portions of several issues in 1909; the paper was made with 35 percent rag stock instead of all wood pulp. The color goes through the paper, showing clearly on back and face.

Cachet (ka-shay')
A design on an envelope describing an event. Cachets appear on first day of issue, first flight and stamp exhibition covers, etc.

Cancellation
A mark placed on a stamp by a postal authority to show that it has been used.

Centering
The position of the design on a postage stamp. On perfectly centered stamps the design is exactly in the middle.

Classic
An early stamp issue. Most people consider these to be rare stamps, but classic stamps aren't necessarily rare.

Coils
Stamps issued in rolls (one stamp wide)

for use in dispensers or vending machines.

Commemoratives
Stamps that honor anniversaries, important people or special events.

Compound Perforations
Different gauge perforations on different (normally adjacent) sides of a single stamp.

Condition

Condition is the most important characteristic in determining a stamp's value. It refers to the state of a stamp regarding such details as centering, color and gum.

Cover

An envelope that has been sent through the mail.

Cracked Plate

A term used to describe stamps which show evidence that the plate from which they were printed was cracked.

Definitives

Regular issues of postage stamps, usually sold over long periods of time.

Denomination

The postage value appearing on a stamp, such as 5 cents.

Directory Markings

Postal markings that indicate a failed delivery attempt, stating reasons such as "No Such Number" or "Address Unknown."

Double Transfer

The condition on a printing plate that shows evidence of a duplication of all or part of the design.

Dry Printing

Begun as an experiment in 1953, this type of printing results in a whiter paper, a higher sheen on the surface, a thicker and stiffer feel and designs that stand out more clearly than on more standard "wet" printings.

Duplicates

Extra copies of stamps that can be sold or traded. Duplicates should be examined carefully for color and perforation variations.

Entire

An intact piece of postal stationery, in contrast to a cut-out of the printed design.

Error

A stamp with something incorrect in its design or manufacture.

Exploded

A stamp booklet is said to be "exploded" when it has been separated into its various components for show.

Face Value

The monetary value or denomination of a stamp

Fake

A genuine stamp that has been altered in some way to make it more attractive to collectors. It may be repaired, reperfed or regummed to resemble a more valuable variety.

First Day Cover (FDC)

An envelope with a new stamp and cancellation showing the date the stamp was issued.

Franks

Marking on the face of a cover, indicating it is to be carried free of postage. Franks may be written, handstamped, imprinted or represented by special adhesives. Such free franking is usually limited to official correspondence, such as soldier's mail.

Freak

An abnormal variety of stamps occurring because of paper fold, over-inking, perforation shift, etc., as opposed to a continually appearing variety or a major error.

Grill

A pattern of small, square pyramids in parallel rows impressed or embossed on the stamp to break paper fibers, allowing cancellation ink to soak in and preventing washing and reuse.

Gum

The coating of glue on the back of an unused stamp.

Hinges

Small strips of gummed material used by collectors to affix stamps to album pages.

Imperforate

Indicates stamps without perforations or separating holes. They usually are separated by scissors and collected in pairs.

Label
Any stamp-like adhesive that is not a postage stamp.

Laid Paper
When held to the light, the paper shows alternate light and dark crossed lines.

Line Pairs (LP)
Most coil stamp rolls prior to #1891 feature a line of ink printed between two stamps at varying intervals.

Miniature Sheet
A single stamp or block of stamps with a margin on all sides bearing some special wording or design.

Overprint
Additional printing on a stamp that was not part of the original design.

On Paper
Stamps "on paper" are those that still have portions of the original envelope or wrapper stuck to them.

Packet
A presorted unit of all different stamps. One of the most common and economical ways to begin a collection.

Pane
A full "sheet" of stamps as sold by a Post Office. Four panes typically make up the original sheet of stamps as printed.

Par Avion
French for mail transported "by air."

Perforations
Lines of small holes or cuts between rows of stamps that make them easy to separate.

Philately
The collection and study of postage stamps and other postal materials.

Pictorials
Stamps with a picture of some sort, other than portraits or static designs such as coats of arms.

Plate Block (PB) (or Plate Number Block)
A block of stamps with the margin attached that bears the plate number used in printing that sheet.

Plate Number Coils (PNC)
For most coil stamps rolls beginning with #1891, a small plate number appears at varying intervals in the roll in the design of the stamp.

Postage Due
A stamp issued to collect unpaid postage.

Postal Stationery
Envelopes, postal cards and aerogrammes with stamp designs printed or embossed on them.

Postmark
A mark put on envelopes or other mailing pieces showing the date and location of the post office where it was mailed.

Precancels
Cancellations applied to stamps before the stamps were affixed to mail.

Registered Mail
First class mail with a numbered receipt, including a valuation of the registered item. This guarantees customers will get their money back if an item is lost in the mail.

Reissue
An official reprinting of a stamp that was no longer being printed.

Replicas
Reproductions of stamps sold during the early days of collecting. Usually printed in one color in a sheet containing a number of different designs. Replicas were never intended to deceive either the post office or the collector.

Reprint
A stamp printed from the original plate after the issue is no longer valid for postage. Official reprints are sometimes made for presentation purposes, official collections, etc., and are often distinguished in some way from the "real" ones.

Revenue Stamps
Stamps not valid for postal use but issued for collecting taxes.

Ribbed Paper
Paper which shows fine parallel ridges on one or both sides of a stamp.

Se-tenant
An attached pair, strip or block of stamps that differ in design, value or surcharge.

Secret Marks
Many stamps have included tiny reference points in their designs to foil attempts at counterfeiting and to differentiate issues.

Selvage
The unprinted paper around panes of stamps, sometimes called the margin.

Series
All the variations of design and value of a particular issue.

Set
A unit of stamps with a common design or theme issued at one time for a common purpose or over an extended period.

Souvenir Sheet
A small sheet of stamps with a commemorative inscription of some sort.

Speculative
A stamp or issue released primarily for sale to collectors, rather than to meet any legitimate postal need.

Strip
Three or more unseparated stamps in a row.

Surcharge
An overprint that changes the denomination of a stamp from its original face value.

Sweatbox
A closed box with a grill over which stuck-together unused stamps are placed. A wet, sponge-like material under the grill creates humidity so the stamps can be separated without removing the gum.

Thematic
A stamp collection that relates to a specific theme and is arranged to present a logical story and progression.

Tied On
Indicates a stamp whose postmark touches the envelope.

Tongs
A tool, used to handle stamps, that resembles a tweezers with rounded or flattened tips.

Topicals
Indicates a group of stamps with the same theme—space travel, for example.

Unhinged
A stamp without hinge marks, but not necessarily with original gum.

Unused
The condition of a stamp that has no cancellation or other sign of use.

Used
The condition of a stamp that has been canceled.

Want List
A list of philatelic material needed by a collector.

Watermark
A design pressed into stamp paper during its manufacture.

Wet Printing
Has a moisture content of 15-35 percent, compared to 5-10 percent for "dry" printings; also, has a duller look than "dry" printings.

Wove Paper
A uniform paper which, when held to the light, shows no light or dark figures.

Organizations, Publications and Resources

For Your Information ...

Here's a list of philatelic resources that can increase your knowledge of stamps as well as your collecting enjoyment.

Organizations

Please enclose a stamped, self-addressed envelope when writing to these organizations.

American Air Mail Society
Stephen Reinhard
P.O. Box 110
Mineola, NY 11501-0110

Specializes in all phases of aerophilately. Membership services include Advance Bulletin Service, Auction Service, free want ads, Sales Department, monthly journal, discounts on Society publications, translation service.

American First Day Cover Society
Mrs. Monte Eiserman
Dept. USG
14359 Chadbourne
Houston, TX 77079-8811

A full-service, not-for-profit, noncommercial society devoted exclusively to First Day Covers and First Day Cover collecting. Offers information on 300 current cachet producers, expertizing, foreign covers, translation service, color slide programs and archives covering First Day Covers.

American Philatelic Society
Keith A. Wagner, Exec. Dir.
P.O. Box 8000, Dept. PG
State College, PA
16803-8000

A full complement of services and resources for stamp collectors. Annual membership offers: library services, educational seminars and correspondence courses, expertizing service, estate advisory service, translation service, a stamp theft committee that functions as a clearinghouse for philatelic crime information, intramember sales service and a monthly journal, The American Philatelist, *sent to all members. Membership 57,000 worldwide.*

American Society for Philatelic Pages and Panels
Gerald Blankenship
P.O. Box 475
Crosby, TX 77532-0475

Focuses on souvenir pages and commemorative panels, with reports on news, varieties, errors, oddities and discoveries; free ads.

American Stamp Dealers' Association
Joseph B. Savarese
3 School Street
Glen Cove, NY 11542

Association of dealers engaged in every facet of philately, with 11 regional chapters nationwide. Sponsors national and local shows. Will send you a complete listing of dealers in your area or collecting specialty. A #10 SASE must accompany your request.

American Topical Association
Donald W. Smith
P.O. Box 630
Johnstown, PA
15907-0630

A service organization concentrating on the specialty of topical stamp collecting. Offers handbooks and checklists on specific topics; exhibition awards; Topical Time, *a bimonthly publication dealing with topical interest areas; a slide loan service, and information, translation and sales services.*

Booklet Collectors Club
Jim Natele
P.O. Box 2461-U
Cinnaminson, NJ 08077

Devoted to the study of worldwide booklets and booklet collecting, with special emphasis on U.S. booklets. Publishes The Interleaf, *a quarterly journal.*

Bureau Issues Association
P.O. Box 1047
Belleville, IL 62223-1047

Devoted to the study of all U.S. stamps, principally those produced by the Bureau of Engraving and Printing.

Council of Philatelic Organizations
P.O. Box COPO
State College, PA
16803-8340

A nonprofit marketing and public relations organization comprised of more than 400 national, regional and local stamp clubs, organizations, societies and philatelic business firms. Membership is open only to organizations. COPO uses a variety of methods to promote stamp collecting, including an ongoing publicity campaign, occasional newsletters and joint sponsorship (with the USPS) of National Stamp Collecting Month.

Junior Collectors Society
11505 Brodie Lane
Austin, TX 78748

Promotes junior philately. Adults also may join, as Associate Members who are assigned a maximum of five juniors to correspond and trade with, etc.

Junior Philatelists of America
Central Office
P.O. Box 850
Boalsburg, PA
16827-0850

Publishes a bimonthly newsletter, The Philatelic Observer, *and offers auction, exchange, pen pal and other services to young stamp collectors. Adult supporting membership and gift memberships are available. The Society also publishes various brochures on stamp collecting.*

Linn's Stamp Club Center
P.O. Box 29
Sidney, OH 45365-0029

Write for the address of a stamp club near your ZIP Code. Will also provide information on specialized national societies.

Mailer's Postmark Permit Club
Florence M. Sugarberg
P.O. Box 5793
Akron, OH 44372-5793

Publishes bimonthly newsletter, Permit Patter, *which covers all aspects of mailer's precancel postmarks, as well as a catalog and two checklists.*

Modern Postal History Society
Bill DiPaolo
404 Dorado Court
High Point, NC 27265

Emphasizes the collection and study of postal history, procedures and rates beginning with the early 20th century and including rates as shown by use of definitive stamps on commercial covers, modern markings such as bar codes and ink-jet postmarks, and auxiliary markings such as "Return to Sender," etc. Publishes the quarterly Modern Postal History Journal.

Philatelic Foundation
501 Fifth Avenue
New York, NY 10017

A nonprofit organization known for its excellent expertization service. The Foundation's broad resources, including extensive reference collections, 5,000-volume library and Expert Committee, provide collectors with comprehensive consumer protection. Slide and cassette programs are available on such subjects as the Pony Express, classic U.S. stamps, Confederate Postal History and collecting basics for beginners. Book series include expertizing case histories in Opinions, Foundation seminar subjects in "textbooks" and specialized U.S. subjects in monographs.

Postal History Society
Kalman V. Illyefalvi
8207 Daren Court
Pikesville, MD 21208

Devoted to the study of various aspects of the development of the mails and local, national and international postal systems; UPU treaties; and means of transporting mail.

Souvenir Card Collectors Society
Dana M. Marr
P.O. Box 4155
Tulsa, OK 74159-4155

Provides member auctions, a quarterly journal and access to limited-edition souvenir cards.

United Postal Stationery Society
Mrs. Joann Thomas
P.O. Box 48
Redlands, CA
92373-0601

Universal Ship Cancellation Society
David Kent
P.O. Box 127
New Britain, CT
06050-0127

Specializes in naval ship postmarks.

Free Periodicals

The following publications will send you a free copy of their magazine or newspaper upon request:

Linn's Stamp News
P.O. Box 29
Sidney, OH 45365-0029

The largest weekly stamp newspaper.

Mekeel's Weekly Stamp News
P.O. Box 5050-ff
White Plains, NY 10602

World's oldest stamp weekly, for intermediate and advanced collectors.

Stamps etc.
Philatelic Fulfillment
Service Center
United States Postal Service
Kansas City, MO
64144-9997

Published quarterly; includes every philatelic item offered by the USPS.

**Stamp Collecting
Made Easy**
P.O. Box 29
Sidney, OH
45365-0029

An illustrated, easy-to-read, 96-page booklet for beginning collectors.

Stamp Collector
Box 10
Albany, OR
97321-0006

For beginning and advanced collectors of all ages.

Stamps Auction News
85 Canisteo Street
Hornell, NY
14843-1544

The monthly financial journal of the stamp market.

Stamps Magazine
85 Canisteo Street
Hornell, NY
14843-1544

The weekly magazine of philately.

Museums, Libraries and Displays

There is no charge *to visit any of the following institutions. Please contact them before visiting because their hours may vary.*

**American Philatelic
Research Library**
P.O. Box 8338
State College, PA
16803-8338

Founded in 1968; now the largest philatelic library in the U.S. Currently receives more than 400 worldwide periodical titles and houses extensive collections of bound journals, books, auction catalogs and dealer pricelists. Directly serves members of the APS and APRL (library members also receive the quarterly Philatelic Literature Review). The public may purchase photocopies directly or borrow materials through the national interlibrary loan system.

**Cardinal Spellman
Philatelic Museum**
235 Wellesley St.
Weston, MA
02193-1538

America's only fully accredited museum devoted to the display, collection and preservation of stamps and postal history. It has three galleries of rare stamps, a philatelic library and a post office/philatelic counter. Telephone: (617) 894-6735.

The Collectors Club
22 East 35th St.
New York, NY
10016-3806

Bimonthly journal, publication of various reference works, one of the most extensive reference libraries in the world, reading and study rooms. Regular meetings on the first and third Wednes days of each month at 6:30 p.m., except July, August. Telephone: (212) 683-0559.

Hall of Stamps
United States Postal Service
475 L'Enfant Plaza
Washington, DC
20260-0001

Located at USPS headquarters, this exhibit features more than $500,000 worth of rare U.S. stamps, a moon rock and letter canceled on the moon, original stamp design art, etc.

National Postal Museum
Smithsonian Institution
2 Massachusetts Ave. NE
Washington, DC 20002

Houses more than 16 million items for exhibition and study purposes. Research may be conducted by appointment only on materials in the collection and library. This new museum, which is housed in the old Washington, D.C. Post Office next to Union Station, opened to the public in mid-1993. Telephone: (202) 633-9360.

**The Postal History
Foundation**
Box 40725
Tucson, AZ 85717-0725

Regular services include a library, USPS contract post office, philatelic sales, archives, artifacts and collections and a Youth Department. Membership includes subscription to a quarterly journal, The Heliograph. Telephone: (602) 623-6652.

**San Diego County
Philatelic Library**
4133 Poplar St.
San Diego, CA
92105-4541

Western Philatelic Library
Sunnyvale Public Library
665 West Olive Ave.
Sunnyvale, CA 94087

**Wineburgh Philatelic
Research Library**
University of Texas at Dallas
P.O. Box 830643
Richardson, TX
75083-0643

Open Monday-Thursday, 9 a.m.– 6 p.m.; Friday, 9 a.m. – 5 p.m.; first Saturday each month (except May and June), 1 p.m. – 5 p.m.

Literature

Basic Philately
Stamp Collector
Box 10
Albany, OR 97321-0006

**Brookman Disney Stamp
Price Guide**
Arlene Dunn
Brookman Stamp Company
10 Chestnut Drive
Bedford, NH 03110

Illustrated, 128-page, perfect-bound book.

**Brookman Price Guide of
United States Stamps**
Arlene Dunn
Brookman Stamp Company
10 Chestnut Drive
Bedford, NH 03110

Illustrated, 304-page, perfect-bound catalog.

Brookman Price Guide of U.S., U.N. and Canada Stamps
Arlene Dunn
Brookman Stamp Company
10 Chestnut Drive
Bedford, NH 03110

Illustrated, 304-page, spiral-bound catalog.

Brookman Price Guide of U.S. First Day Covers, Souvenir Cards, USPS Panels and Pages
Arlene Dunn
Brookman Stamp Company
10 Chestnut Drive
Bedford, NH 03110

Illustrated, 206-page, spiral-bound catalog.

Catalogue of United States Souvenir Cards
Washington Press
2 Vreeland Road
Florham Park, NJ
07932-1587

Commemorative Cancellation Catalog
General Image, Inc.
P.O. Box 335
Maplewood, NJ
07040-0335

Catalog covering all pictorial cancellations used in the U.S. during 1988 to 1990 is available. Please send self-addressed, stamped envelope for prices and description.

Compilation of U.S. Souvenir Cards
P.O. Box 4155
Tulsa, OK 74159-4155

First Day Cover Catalogue (U.S.-U.N.)
Washington Press
2 Vreeland Road
Florham Park, NJ
07932-1587

Includes Presidential Inaugural covers.

Fleetwood's Standard First Day Cover Catalog
Fleetwood
Cheyenne, WY
82008-0001

The Fun Of Stamp Collecting
Arlene Dunn
Brookman Stamp Company
10 Chestnut Drive
Bedford, NH 03110

Illustrated, 96-page, perfect-bound book.

The Hammarskjold Invert
Washington Press
2 Vreeland Road
Florham Park, NJ
07932-1587

Tells the story of the Dag Hammarskjold error/invert. FREE for #10 SASE.

Linn's U.S. Stamp Yearbook
P.O. Box 29
Sidney, OH 45365-0029

A series of books providing facts and figures on every collectible variety of U.S. stamps, postal stationery and souvenir cards issued since 1983.

Linn's World Stamp Almanac
P.O. Box 29
Sidney, OH 45365-0029

The most useful single reference source for stamp collectors. Contains detailed information on U.S. stamps.

19th Century Envelopes Catalog
P.O. Box 48
Redlands, CA
92373-0601

Postage Stamp Identifier and Dictionary of Philatelic Terms
Washington Press
2 Vreeland Road
Florham Park, NJ
07932-1587

1992 edition, with new country listings.

Precancel Stamp Society Catalog of U.S. Bureau Precancels
P.O. Box 926
Framingham, MA 01701

Precancel Stamp Society Town and Type Catalog of U.S. Local Recancels
P.O. Box 926
Framingham, MA 01701

Scott Specialized Catalogue of United States Stamps
P.O. Box 828
Sidney, OH 45365-8959

Scott Stamp Monthly
P.O. Box 828
Sidney, OH 45365-0828

Scott Standard Postage Stamp Catalogue
P.O. Box 828
Sidney, OH 45365-8959

The 24¢ 1918 Air Mail Invert
Washington Press
2 Vreeland Road
Florham Park, NJ
07932-1587

Tells all there is to know about this famous stamp. FREE for #10 SASE.

20th Century Envelopes Catalog
P.O. Box 48
Redlands, CA
92373-0601

U.S. Postal Card Catalog
P.O. Box 48
Redlands, CA
92373-0601

The United States Transportation Coils
Washington Press
2 Vreeland Road
Florham Park, NJ
07932-1587

FREE for #10 SASE.

Exchange Service

Stamp Master
Box 17
Putnam Hall, FL 32685

An "electronic connection" for philatelists via modem and computer to display/review members' stamp inventories for trading purposes, etc.

Philatelic Centers

In addition to the more than 20,000 postal facilities authorized to sell philatelic products, the U.S. Postal Service also maintains more than 470 Philatelic Centers located in major population centers. These Philatelic Centers have been established to serve stamp collectors and make it convenient for them to acquire an extensive range of current postage stamps, postal stationery and philatelic products issued by the Postal Service. Centers are located at Main Post Offices unless otherwise indicated.

Alabama
351 North 24th Street
Birmingham, AL 35203

Philatelic Center
Space 102
2000 Riverchase
Galleria
Birmingham, AL 35244

307 North Oates Street
Dothan, AL 36302

615 Clinton Street
Huntsville, AL 35801

250 St. Joseph
Mobile, AL 36601

Downtown Station
135 Catoma Street
Montgomery, AL
36104

Alaska
Downtown Station
3rd & C Streets
Anchorage, AK 99510

Downtown Station
315 Barnette Street
Fairbanks, AK 99707

Arizona
2400 N. Postal Blvd.
Flagstaff, AZ 86004

Osborn Station
3905 North 7th Avenue
Phoenix, AZ 85013

General Mail Facility
4949 East Van Buren
Phoenix, AZ 85026

1501 South Cherrybell
Tucson, AZ 85726

Arkansas
30 South 6th Street
Fort Smith, AR 72901

600 West Capitol
Little Rock, AR 72201

California
Holiday Station
1180 West Ball Road
Anaheim, CA 92802

2730 W. Tregallas Road
Antioch, CA 94509

Cerritos Branch
18122 Carmencita
Artesia, CA 90701

General Mail Facility
3400 Pegasus Drive
Bakersfield, CA 93380

2000 Allston Way
Berkeley, CA 94704

135 East Olive Street
Burbank, CA 91502

6330 Fountains
Square Dr.
Citrus Heights, CA
95621

2121 Meridian Park
Blvd.
Concord, CA 94520

2020 Fifth Street
Davis, CA 95616

8111 East Firestone
Downey, CA 90241

401 W. Lexington Ave.
El Cajon, CA 92020

Cotten Station
3901 Walnut Drive
Eureka, CA 95501

600 Kentucky Street
Fairfield, CA 94533

1900 E Street
Fresno, CA 93706

313 East Broadway
Glendale, CA 91209

Hillcrest Station
303 East Hillcrest
Inglewood, CA 90311

5200 Clark Avenue
Lakewood, CA 90712

300 Long Beach Blvd.
Long Beach, CA 90801

Terminal Annex
900 North Alameda
Los Angeles, CA
90052

Village Station
11000 Wilshire Blvd.
Los Angeles, CA
90024

407 C Street
Marysville, CA 95901

2334 M Street
Merced, CA 95340

El Viejo Station
1125 "I" Street
Modesto, CA 95354

Civic Center Annex
201 13th Street
Oakland, CA 94612

211 Brooks
Oceanside, CA 92054

281 E. Colorado Blvd.
Pasadena, CA 91109

4300 Black Avenue
Pleasanton, CA 94566

1647 Yuba Street
Redding, CA 96001

General Mail Facility
1900 W. Redlands Blvd.
Redlands, CA 92373

1201 North Catalina
Redondo Beach, CA
90277

Downtown Station
3890 Orange Street
Riverside, CA 92501

330 Vernon Street
Roseville, CA 95678

2000 Royal Oaks Drive
Sacramento, CA 95813

Base Line Station
1164 North E Street
San Bernardino, CA
92410

2535 Midway Drive
San Diego, CA 92199

Rincon Finance Station
180 Stewart Street
San Francisco, CA
94119

1750 Meridian Drive
San Jose, CA 95125

St. Matthews Station
210 South Ellsworth
San Mateo, CA 94401

Simms Station
41 Simms Street
San Rafael, CA 94901

Spurgeon Station
615 North Bush
Santa Ana, CA 92701

836 Anacapa Street
Santa Barbara, CA
93102

201 East Battles Road
Santa Maria, CA 93454

730 Second Street
Santa Rosa, CA 95404

Hammer Ranch Station
7554 Pacific Avenue
Stockton, CA 95210

4245 West Lane
Stockton, CA 95208

200 Prairie Court
Vacaville, CA 95687

15701 Sherman Way
Van Nuys, CA 91408

Channel Islands Station
675 E. Santa Clara St.
Ventura, CA 93001

396 South California St.
West Covina, CA
91790

Area Mail Processing
Center
3775 Industrial Blvd.
West Sacramento, CA
95647

Colorado
16890 E. Alameda
Pkwy.
Aurora, CO 80017

1905 15th Street
Boulder, CO 80302

201 East Pikes Peak
Colorado Springs, CO
80901

1823 Stout Street
Denver, CO 80202

222 West Eighth Street
Durango, CO 81301

241 North 4th Street
Grand Junction, CO
81501

5733 South Prince Street
Littleton, CO 80120

421 North Main Street
Pueblo, CO 81003

Connecticut
141 Weston Street
Hartford, CT 06101

Meridian & Waterbury
Tpk.
Marion, CT 06444

11 Silver Street
Middletown, CT 06457

50 Brewery Street
New Haven, CT 06511

27 Masonic Street
New London, CT
06320

469 Main Street
Ridgefield, CT 06877

421 Atlantic Street
Stamford, CT 06904

Stratford Branch
3100 Main Street
Stratford, CT 06497

135 Grand Street
Waterbury, CT 06701

Delaware
55 The Plaza
Dover, DE 19901

Federal Station
110 East Main Street
Newark, DE 19711

General Mail Facility
147 Quigley Blvd.
Airport Industrial Park
New Castle, DE 19720

Rodney Square Station
1101 North King St.
Wilmington, DE 19801

District of Columbia
Headsville Postal Station
National Museum
of American History
12th & Constitution
NW
Washington, DC 20560

National Capitol Station
North Capitol Street &
Massachusetts Avenue
Washington, DC 20002

Pavilion Post Office
Old Post Office Bldg.
1100 Pennsylvania NW
Washington, DC 20265

USPS Headquarters
475 L'Enfant Plaza SW
Washington, DC 20260

Florida
824 Manatee Ave. West
Bradenton, FL 33506

100 South Belcher Road
Clearwater, FL 33515

Downtown Station
220 North Beach Street
Daytona Beach, FL
32015

1900 West Oakland
Park
Fort Lauderdale, FL
33310

2655 North Airport
Road
Fort Myers, FL 33906

1717 Orange Avenue
Fort Pierce, FL 34950

401 SE 1st Avenue
Gainesville, FL 32601

1801 Polk Street
Hollywood, FL 33022

Corporate Service
Center
4150 Belfort Road
Jacksonville, FL 32256

1110 Kings Road
Jacksonville, FL 32203

210 North Missouri
Ave.
Lakeland, FL 33802

50 8th Avenue SW
Largo, FL 33640

Suntree Branch
6105 N. Wickham Road
Melbourne, FL 32940

2200 NW 72nd Avenue
Miami, FL 33101

1200 Goodlette
Naples, FL 33940

1111 E. Nebraska
Avenue
New Port Ritchey, FL
34653

400 SW First Avenue
Ocala, FL 32678

1335 Kingsley Avenue
Orange Park, FL 32073

46 East Robinson Street
Orlando, FL 32801

421 Jenks Avenue
Panama City, FL 32401

1400 West Jordan St.
Pensacola, FL 32501

99 King Street
St. Augusta, FL 32084

3135 First Avenue N.
St. Petersburg, FL
33730

Open Air Postique
76 4th Street North
St. Petersburg, FL
33701

1661 Ringland Blvd.
Sarasota, FL 33578

2800 South Adams St.
Tallahassee, FL 32301

5201 W. Spruce Street
Tampa, FL 33630

850 East Lime Street
Tarpon Springs, FL
34689

3200 Summit Blvd.
West Palm Beach, FL
33406

Georgia
575 Olympic Drive
Athens, GA 30608

Downtown Station
101 Marietta Street
Atlanta, GA 30301

Perimeter Branch
4400 Ashford-
Dunwoody Road
Atlanta, GA 30346

Downtown Station
120-12th Street
Columbus, GA 31908

3470 McClure Bridge
Road
Duluth, GA 30136

364 Green Street
Gainesville, GA 30501

451 College Street
Macon, GA 31201

257 Lawrence Street
Marietta, GA 30060

5600 Spaulding Drive
Norcross, GA 30092

2 North Fahm Street
Savannah, GA 31401

904 Russell Parkway
Warner Robins, GA
31088

Hawaii
3600 Aolele Street
Honolulu, HI 96819

Idaho
770 South 13th Street
Boise, ID 83708

220 East 5th Street
Moscow, ID 83843

730 East Clark Street
Pocatello, ID 83201

Illinois
909 West Euclid Ave.
Arlington Heights, IL
60004

525 North Broadway
Aurora, IL 60507

Moraine Valley Station
7401 100th Place
Bridgeview, IL 60455

1301 East Main Street
Carbondale, IL 62901

Loop Station
211 South Clark Street
Chicago, IL 60604

433 West Van Buren St.
Chicago, IL 60607

1000 East Oakton
Des Plaines, IL 60018

In addition to these Philatelic Centers, some larger Post Offices have dedicated "Philatelic" Windows with many current stamps and products.

23

1101 Davis Street
Evanston, IL 60204

2359 Madison Avenue
Granite City, IL 62040

2000 McDonough St.
Joliet, IL 60436

1750 W. Ogden Avenue
Naperville, IL 60566

901 Lake Street
Oak Park, IL 60301

123 Indianwood
Park Forest, IL 60466

North University Station
6310 North University
Peoria, IL 61614

5225 Harrison Avenue
Rockford, IL 61125

211-19th Street
Rock Island, IL 61201

Schaumburg Station
450 W. Schaumburg
Roselle, IL 60194

2105 E. Cook Street
Springfield, IL 62703

Edison Square Station
1520 Washington
Waukegan, IL 60085

1241 Central Avenue
Wilmette, IL 60091

Indiana
North Park Branch
4492-B 1st Avenue
Evansville, IN 47710

Fort Wayne
Postal Facility
1501 S. Clinton Street
Fort Wayne, IN 46802

5530 Sohl Street
Hammond, IN 46320

125 West South Street
Indianapolis, IN 46206

2719 South Webster
Kokomo, IN 46901

3450 State Road 26 E.
Lafayette, IN 47901

424 South Michigan
South Bend, IN 46624

Cross Roads Station
70 Rose Avenue
Terre Haute, IN 47803

Iowa
615 6th Avenue SE
Cedar Rapids, IA 52401

1165 Second Avenue
Des Moines, IA 50318

24 Johnson Street
Sioux City, IA 51100

Kansas
Indian Springs Station
4953 State Avenue
Kansas City, KS 66102

6029 Broadmoor
Shawnee Mission, KS
66202

43415 Kansas Avenue
Topeka, KS 66603

Downtown Station
330 West 2nd Street
Wichita, KS 67202

Kentucky
1088 Nadino Blvd.
Lexington, KY 40511

Okolona Branch
7400 Jefferson Blvd.
Louisville, KY 40219

St. Mathews Station
4600 Shelbyville Road
Louisville, KY 40207

Louisiana
1715 Odom Street
Alexandria, LA 71301

750 Florida Street
Baton Rouge, LA 70821

General Mail Facility
1105 Moss Street
Lafayette, LA 70501

3301 17th Street
Metairie, LA 70002

501 Sterlington Road
Monroe, LA 71201

701 Loyola Avenue
New Orleans, LA
70113

Vieux Carre Station
1022 Iberville Street
New Orleans, LA
70112

2400 Texas Avenue
Shreveport, LA 71102

Maine
40 Western Avenue
Augusta, ME 04330

202 Harlow Street
Bangor, ME 04401

125 Forest Avenue
Portland, ME 04101

Maryland
1 Church Circle
Annapolis, MD 21401

900 E. Fayette Street
Baltimore, MD 21233

Chevy Chase
Financial Unit
5910 Connecticut Ave.
Bethesda, MD 20815

215 Park Street
Cumberland, MD
21502

201 East Patrick Street
Frederick, MD 21701

6411 Baltimore Avenue
Riverdale, MD 20840

500 N. Washington St.
Rockville, MD 20850

U.S. Route 50
& Naylor Road
Salisbury, MD 21801

Silver Spring Centre
Finance Station
8455 Colesville Road
Silver Spring, MD
20911

Massachusetts
McCormick Station
Post Office &
Courthouse Bldg.
Boston, MA 02109

120 Commercial Street
Brockton, MA 02401

7 Bedford Street
Burlington, MA 01803

Center Station
100 Center Street
Chicopee, MA 01014

2 Government Center
Fall River, MA 02722

881 Main Street
Fitchburg, MA 01420

330 Cocituate Road
Framingham, MA
01701

431 Common Street
Lawrence, MA 01842

Post Office Square
Lowell, MA 01853

695 Pleasant Street
New Bedford, MA
02741

212 Fenn Street
Pittsfield, MA 01201

2 Margin Street
Salem, MA 01970

Main Street Station
1883 Main Street
Springfield, MA 01101

178 Avenue A
Turner Falls, MA
01376

462 Washington Street
Woburn, MA 01888

4 East Central Street
Worcester, MA 01603

Michigan
2075 W. Stadium Blvd.
Ann Arbor, MI 48106

90 South McCamly
Battle Creek, MI 49106

26200 Ford Road
Dearborn Heights, MI
48127

1401 West Fort Street
Detroit, MI 48233

250 East Boulevard Dr.
Flint, MI 48502

225 Michigan Avenue
Grand Rapids, MI
49501

200 South Otsego
Jackson, MI 49201

1121 Miller Road
Kalamazoo, MI 49001

General Mail Facility
4800 Collins Road
Lansing, MI 48924

735 West Huron Street
Pontiac, MI 48056

1300 Military Street
Port Huron, MI 48060

30550 Gratiot Street
Roseville, MI 48066

200 West 2nd Street
Royal Oak, MI 48068

1233 South Washington
Saginaw, MI 48605

6300 North Wayne
Road
Westland, MI 48185

Minnesota
2800 West Michigan
Duluth, MN 55806

100 South First Street
Minneapolis, MN
55401

Downtown Station
102 South Broadway
Rochester, MN 55904

The Pioneer
Postal Emporium
133 Endicott Arcade
St. Paul, MN 55101

Burnsville Branch
12212 12th Avenue
South Savage, MN
55378

Mississippi
2421-13th Street
Gulfport, MS 39501

La Fleur Station
1501 Jacksonian Plaza
Jackson, MS 39211

24

401 E. South Street
Jackson, MS 39201

500 West Miln Street
Tupelo, MS 38801

Missouri
920 Washington
Chillicothe, MO 64601

Columbia Mall Station
Columbia, MO 65203

315 Pershing Road
Kansas City, MO
64108

Northwest Plaza Station
500 Northwest Plaza
St. Ann, MO 63074

Pony Express Station
8th & Edmond
St. Joseph, MO 64503

Clayton Branch
7750 Maryland
St. Louis, MO 63105

Trading Post
1720 Market Street
St. Louis, MO 63155

500 W. Chestnut
Expwy.
Springfield, MO 65801

Montana
841 South 26th
Billings, MO 59101

215 First Ave. North
Great Falls, MT 59401

1100 West Kent
Missoula, MT 59801

Nebraska
204 W. South Front St.
Grand Island, NE
68801

700 R Street
Lincoln, NE 68501

300 East Third Street
North Platte, NE 69101

1124 Pacific
Omaha, NE 68108

Nevada
1001 Circus Circus Dr.
Las Vegas, NV 89114

200 Vassar Street
Reno, NV 89510

New Hampshire
55 Pleasant Street
Concord, NH 03301

50 South Main Street
Hanover, NH 03755

955 Goffs Falls Road
Manchester, NH 03103

80 Daniel Street
Portsmouth, NH 03801

New Jersey
1701 Pacific Avenue
Atlantic City, NJ 08401

Veterans Plaza
Bergenfield, NJ 07621

3 Miln Street
Cranford, NJ 07016

229 Main Street
Fort Lee, NJ 07024

Bellmawr Branch
Haag Ave. & Benigno
Gloucester, NJ 08031

Route 35 & Hazlet Ave.
Hazlet, NJ 07730

Borough Complex
East End & Van Sant
Ave.
Island Heights, NJ
08732

69 Montgomery Street
Jersey City, NJ 07305

160 Maplewood Avenue
Maplewood, NJ 07040

150 Ridgedale
Morristown, NJ 07960

Federal Square
Newark, NJ 07102

86 Bayard Street
New Brunswick, NJ
08906

Nutley Branch
372 Franklin Avenue
Nutley, NJ 07110

194 Ward Street
Paterson, NJ 07510

171 Broad Street
Red Bank, NJ 07701

680 Highway 130
Trenton, NJ 08650

Sheffield Station
150 Pompton Plains
Crossing
Wayne, NJ 07470

155 Clinton Road
West Caldwell, NJ
07006

41 Greenwood Ave.
Wykoff, NJ 07481

New Mexico
1135 Broadway NE
Albuquerque, NM
87101

200 E. Las Cruces Ave.
Las Cruces, NM 88001

415 N. Pennsylvania
Ave.
Roswell, NM 88201

New York
Empire State
Plaza Station
Rockefeller Plaza N.E.
Albany, NY 12220

General Mail Facility
30 Old Karner Road
Albany, NY 12212

115 Henry Street
Binghamton, NY 13902

Bronx General P.O.
149th Street &
Grand Concourse
Bronx, NY 10451

Parkchester Station
1449 West Avenue
Bronx, NY 10462

Riverdale Station
5951 Riverdale Avenue
Bronx, NY 10471

Throggs Neck Station
3630 East Tremont Ave.
Bronx, NY 10465

Wakefield Station
4165 White Plains Rd.
Bronx, NY 10466

Bayridge Station
5501 7th Avenue
Brooklyn, NY 11220

Brooklyn General P.O.
271 Cadman Plaza East
Brooklyn, NY 11201

Greenpoint Station
66 Meserole Avenue
Brooklyn, NY 11222

Homecrest Station
2002 Avenue U
Brooklyn, NY 11229

1200 William Street
Buffalo, NY 14240

1764 Route 9
Clifton Park, NY 12065

Baron deHirsch Road
Crempond, NY 10517

Downtown Station
255 Clemens Center
Pkwy.
Elmira, NY 14901

41-65 Main Street
Flushing, NY 11351

Broadway & Maple St.
Glenham, NY 12527

16 Hudson Avenue
Glens Falls, NY 12801

185 West John Street
Hicksville, NY 11802

88-40 164th Street
Jamaica, NY 11431

300 East 3rd Street
Jamestown, NY 14701

324 Broadway
Monticello, NY 12701

Ansonia Station
1980 Broadway
New York, NY 10023

Bowling Green Station
25 Broadway
New York, NY 10004

Church Street Station
90 Church Street
New York, NY 10007

Empire State Station
350 Fifth Avenue
New York, NY 10001

F.D.R. Station
909 Third Avenue
New York, NY 10022

Grand Central Station
45th St. & Lexington
Ave.
New York, NY 10017

Madison Square Station
149 East 23rd Street
New York, NY 10010

New York General P.O.
33rd St. and 8th Ave.
New York, NY 10001

Rockefeller Center
610 Fifth Avenue
New York, NY 10020

Times Square Station
340 West 42nd Street
New York, NY 10036

Main & Hunt Streets
Oneonta, NY 13820

Franklin & S. Main Sts.
Pearl River, NY 10965

10 Miller Street
Plattsburg, NY 12901

Branch Office
407 East Main Street
Port Jefferson, NY
11777

55 Mansion Street
Poughkeepsie, NY
12601

1335 Jefferson Road
Rochester, NY 14692

Ridgemont Branch
2899 Ridge Road West
Rochester, NY 14626

250 Merrick Road
Rockville Centre, NY
11570

29 Jay Street
Schenectady, NY 12305

*In addition to these Philatelic Centers, some larger Post Offices have
dedicated "Philatelic" Windows with many current stamps and products.*

25 Route 11
Smithtown, NY 11787

New Springville Station
2843 Richmond Avenue
Staten Island, NY
10314

5640 East Taft Road
Syracuse, NY 13220

100 Pitcher Street
Utica, NY 13503

108 Main Street
Warwick, NY 10990

100 Fisher Avenue
White Plains, NY
10602

78-81 Main Street
Yonkers, NY 10701

North Carolina
West Asheville Station
1300 Patton Avenue
Asheville, NC 28806

Eastway Station
3065 Eastway Drive
Charlotte, NC 28205

301 Green Street
Fayetteville, NC 28302

Four Seasons Station
Four Seasons Town
Centre
High Point Road
Greensboro, NC 27427

310 New Bern Avenue
Raleigh, NC 27611

North Dakota
220 East Rosser Ave.
Bismarck, ND 58501

675 2nd Avenue North
Fargo, ND 58102

Ohio
675 Wolf Ledges Pkwy.
Akron, OH 44309

2650 Cleveland Street
Canton, OH 44701

Fountain Square Station
5th & Walnut Street
Cincinnati, OH 45202

301 W. Prospect Ave.
Cleveland, OH 44101

850 Twin Rivers Drive
Columbus, OH 43216

1111 East 5th Street
Dayton, OH 45401

345 East Bridge Street
Elyria, OH 44035

105 Court Street
Hamilton, OH 45011

200 North Diamond St.
Mansfield, OH 44901

200 North 4th Street
Steubenville, OH 43952

435 S. St. Clair Street
Toledo, OH 43601

99 South Walnut Street
Youngstown, OH
44503

Oklahoma
208 First Street SW
Ardmore, OK 73401

101 East First
Edmond, OK 73034

115 West Broadway
Enid, OK 73701

102 South 5th
Lawton, OK 73501

525 West Okmulgee
Muskogee, OK 74401

129 West Gray
Norman, OK 73069

320 SW 5th Street
Oklahoma, City, OK
73125

116 East 9th Street
Shawnee, OK 74801

333 West 4th
Tulsa, OK 74101

12 South 5th
Yukon, OK 73099

Oregon
311 SW 2nd Street
Corvallis, OR 97333

520 Willamette Street
Eugene, OR 97401

751 NW Hoyt
Portland, OR 97208

1050 25th Street SW
Salem, OR 97301

Pennsylvania
442-456 Hamilton St.
Allentown, PA 18101

535 Wood Street
Bethlehem, PA 18016

115 Boylston Street
Bradford, PA 16701

229 Beaver Drive
Du Bois, PA 15801

Griswold Plaza
Erie, PA 16501

115 Buford Avenue
Gettysburg, PA 17325

238 S. Pennsylvania
Greensburg, PA 15601

10th and Markets Sts.
Harrisburg, PA 17105

Downtown Station
48-50 W. Chestnut St.
Lancaster, PA 17603

980 Wheeler Way
Langhorne, PA 19047

Lehigh Valley Branch
Airport Rd. & Route 22
Lehigh Valley, PA
18001

Monroeville Mall
Branch
348 Mall Circle Drive
Monroeville, PA 15146

1 W. Washington Street
Kennedy Square
New Castle, PA 16101

501 11th Street
New Kensington, PA
15068

28 East Airy Street
Norristown, PA 19401

B. Free Franklin Station
316 Market Street
Philadelphia, PA 19106

30th & Market Streets
Philadelphia, PA 19104

William Penn Annex
9th & Chestnut Streets
Philadelphia, PA 19107

Castle Shannon Branch
307 Castle Shannon
Blvd.
Pittsburgh, PA 15234

General Mail Facility
1001 California Avenue
Pittsburgh, PA 15290

Seventh Avenue
& Grant Street
Pittsburgh, PA 15219

McKnight Branch
McKnight & Seibert
Rds.
Pittsburgh, PA 15237

59 North 5th Street
Reading, PA 19603

North Washington Ave.
& Linden St.
Scranton, PA 18503

237 South Frazer Street
State College, PA
16801

7th & Ann Streets
Stroudsburg, PA 18360

300 South Main Street
Wilkes Barre, PA
18701

Center City Finance
Station
240 West Third Street
Williamsport, PA
17703

200 S. George Street
York, PA 17405

Puerto Rico
General Post Office
18 Roosevelt Avenue
Hate Rey
San Juan, PR 00918

Plaza Las Americas Sta.
San Juan, PR 00938

Rhode Island
320 Thames Street
Newport, RI 02840

40 Montgomery Street
Pawtucket, RI 02860

24 Corliss Street
Providence, RI 02904

South Carolina
4290 Daley Avenue
Charleston, SC 29402

1601 Assembly Street
Columbia, SC 29201

600 West Washington
Greenville, SC 29602

South Dakota
500 East Boulevard
Rapid City, SD 57701

320 S. 2nd Avenue
Sioux Falls, SD 57101

Tennessee
5424 Bell Forge Lane E.
Antioch, TN 37013

111 Sixth Street
Bristol, TN 37620

General Mail Facility
6050 Shallowford Road
Chattanooga, TN 37401

200 M.L. King Jr. Blvd.
Jackson, TN 38301

50 East Main Street
Johnson City, TN 37601

General Mail Facility
1237 E. Weisgarber Road
Knoxville, TN 37901

Colonial Finance Unit
4695 Southern Avenue
Memphis, TN 38124

Crosstown Finance Unit
1520 Union Avenue
Memphis, TN 38174

901 Broadway
Nashville, TN 37202

Texas
341 Pine Street
Abilene, TX 79604

2300 South Ross
Amarillo, TX 79105

300 East South Street
Arlington, TX 76010

Downtown Station
300 East 9th
Austin, TX 78701

General Mail Facility
8225 Cross Park Drive
Austin, TX 78710

300 Willow
Beaumont, TX 77704

1535 Los Ebanos
Brownsville, TX 78520

2121 E. Wm. J. Bryan
Pkwy.
Bryan, TX 77801

2201 Hilltop Drive
College Station, TX
77840

809 Nueces Bay
Corpus Christi, TX
78408

Air Mail Facility
2300 West 32nd Street
Dallas, TX 75261

400 North Ervay Street
Dallas, TX 75221

Olla Podrida
Finance Station
12215 Coit Road
Dallas, TX 75251

5300 East Paisano Dr.
El Paso, TX 79910

251 West Lancaster
Fort Worth, TX 76101

401 Franklin Avenue
Houston, TX 77201

Central Station2300
West Story RoadIrving,
TX 75038

300 North 10th
Killeen, TX 76541

411 "L" Avenue
Lubbock, TX 79408

601 East Pecan
McAllen, TX 78501

100 East Wall
Midland, TX 79702

433 Belle Grove
Richardson, TX 75080

1 North Bryant
San Angelo, TX 76902

Downtown Station
615 East Houston
San Antonio, TX 78205

10410 Perrin Beitel
Road
San Antonio, TX 78284

1411 Wunsche Loop
Spring, TX 77373

2211 North Robinson
Texarkana, TX 75501

221 West Ferguson
Tyler, TX 75702

800 Franklin
Waco, TX 76701

1000 Lamar Street
Wichita Falls, TX
76307

Utah
3680 Pacific Avenue
Ogden, UT 84401

95 West 100 South
Provo, UT 84601

1760 West 2100 South
Salt Lake City, UT
84119

Vermont
204 Main Street
Brattleboro, VT 05301

1 Elmwood Avenue
Burlington, VT 05401

151 West Street
Rutland, VT 05701

Sykes Avenue
White River Junction,
VT 05001

Virginia
1155 Seminole Trail
Charlottesville, VA
22906

1425 Battlefield Blvd. N.
Chesapeake, VA 23320

700 Main Street
Danville, VA 24541

Merrifield Branch
8409 Lee Highway
Fairfax, VA 22116

809 Aberdeen Road
Hampton, VA 23670

300 Odd Fellows Road
Lynchburg, VA 24506

Denbigh Station
14104 Warwick Blvd.
Newport News, VA
23602

600 Church Street
Norfolk, VA 23501

Thomas Corner Station
6274 East Virginia
Beach Boulevard
Norfolk, VA 23502

1801 Brook Road
Richmond, VA 23232

419 Rutherford Ave. NE
Roanoke, VA 24022

1430 North Augusta
Staunton, VA 24401

501 Viking Drive
Virginia Beach, VA
23450

Washington
11 3rd Street NW
Auburn, WA 98001

Crossroads Station
15800 NE 8th
Bellevue, WA 98008

315 Prospect Street
Bellingham, WA 98225

3102 Hoyt
Everett, WA 98201

3500 West Court
Pasco, WA 99301

424 East 1st Street
Port Angeles, WA
98362

301 Union Street
Seattle, WA 98101

West 904 Riverside
Spokane, WA 99210

1102 A Street
Tacoma, WA 98402

205 West Washington
Yakima, WA 98903

West Virginia
301 North Street
Bluefield, WV 24701

Lee & Dickinson St.
Charleston, WV 25301

500 West Pike Street
Clarksburg, WV 26301

1000 Virginia Ave. West
Huntington, WV 25704

217 King Street
Martinsburg, WV
25401

Wisconsin
126 N. Barstow Street
Eau Claire, WI 54703

325 East Walnut
Green Bay, WI 54301

425 State Street
La Crosse, WI 54601

3902 Milwaukee Street
Madison, WI 53707

345 West St. Paul Ave.
Milwaukee, WI 53203

1025 W. 20th Avenue
Oshkosh, WI 54901

235 Forrest Street
Wausau, WI 54401

Wyoming
150 East B Street
Casper, WY 82601

2120 Capitol Avenue
Cheyenne, WY 82001

FOREIGN CENTERS
Australia
Max Stern & Co.
Port Phillip Arcade
234 Flinders Street
Melbourne 3000

France
Theodore Champion
13 Rue Drouot
75009 Paris

**Federal Republic
of Germany**
Hermann W. Sieger
Venusbert 32-34
D-7073
Lorch/Wurttemberg

Great Britain
Harry Allen
Langwood House
Rickmansworth
Herts WD3 1EY

Japan
Japan Philatelic Co., Ltd.
Post Office Box 2
Suginami-Minami
Tokyo 168-91

Netherlands
J.A. Visser
Post Office Box 184
3300 Ad Dordrecht

Sweden
Bo Follin
Frimarkshuset AB
S-793 01 Leksand

Switzerland
De Rosa International
S.A.
Av Du Tribunal
Federal 34
Ch-1005 Lausanne

Your local Post Office may be able to direct you to the nearest "Philatelic" Window, Philatelic
Center or Postal Store (new, state-of-the-art facilities formerly called Store of the Future).   27

Elvis Mania!

**The King lives on in
1993 stamp release**

Elvis Presley
revolutionized American
music, becoming a
popular, controversial
symbol of the youth
culture that emerged
during the 1950s.

He shook up the establishment with his swiveling hips, seductive eyes, and music that blended country, pop, rhythm & blues (R & B), and gospel music into a completely new sound. The results were unlike anything that came before.

No commemorative stamp issued by the U.S. Postal Service has received as much attention as the 29-cent Elvis Presley stamp, which was issued Jan. 8, 1993. In fact, since Elvis's death in 1977, the Postal Service received more than 60,000 letters suggesting a commemorative stamp to honor Elvis.

Elvis's star power went to work for the Postal Service, inspiring a stamp that breaks all records.

The Popularity Continues

In celebration of Elvis's birthday, the United States Postal Service launched the Legends of American Music Stamp series on January 8, 1993. The first-day-issue Elvis stamp was released at 12:01 a.m. in Memphis, Tenn.

The excitement that preceded the offering as well as Elvis's popularity called for a special order: 500 million stamps were issued, triple the usual number printed. Elvis also appears in 72.5 million 20-stamp booklets, which feature six other Legends of American Music performers.

The popularity of the stamp has made waves across the country. Both Elvis fans and stamp collectors are truly "all shook up."

How was the stamp selected?

The image on the Elvis stamp represents a first-time event—it was selected by popular vote.

The Citizens' Stamp Advisory Committee, which reviews all stamp suggestions, evaluated more than 40 pieces of art by eight different illustrators, eventually narrowing the field to two stamps: a young, rocking Elvis as he looked in the 1950s, designed by Mark Stutzman of Mountain Lake Park, Maryland, and an older, sequined Elvis as he appeared in Las Vegas, designed by John Berkey of Excelsior, Minnesota.

The choice between the two images was put to the American public, in the first-ever stamp design poll, conducted during April 1992. Ballots with the two versions were distributed at post offices and in People magazine.

The Postal Service announced on June 4 that young Elvis stole the show with about 75 percent of the vote: 851,200 votes for the young rocker to 277,723 for the older Las Vegas showman.

An Elvis Chronology

January 8, 1935 — *Elvis Aaron Presley is born in Tupelo, Mississippi.*
1945 — *10-year-old Elvis sings "Old Shep" in a youth talent contest at the Mississippi-Alabama Fair and Dairy Show and wins second prize.*
1953 — *Elvis makes a demo acetate recording of "My Happiness" and "That's When Your Heartaches Begin" to give to his mother as a birthday present.*
1954 — *Sam Phillips, owner of Sun Studio, introduces Elvis to two local musicians. They record "That's all Right," the first of five singles Elvis released on the Sun label.*
August, 1955 — *Colonel Parker becomes Elvis' manager.*
November, 1955 — *Elvis signs his first contract with RCA Records.*
January, 1956 — *"Heartbreak Hotel" is released and sells more than one million copies.*
March, 1956 — *RCA releases "Elvis Presley," his first album, which goes to number one on Billboard's pop album chart for 10 weeks.*
June, 1956 – *Elvis appears on "The Milton Berle Show." His "bump-and-grind" performance of "Hound Dog" drives teens wild.*
September, 1956 — *Elvis makes the first of three appearances on Ed Sullivan's "Toast of the Town" show. During his third performance on the show, he is only shown on television from the waist up.*
November, 1956 — *"Love Me Tender," Elvis's first movie, premieres in New York City and is a smash hit.*
March, 1957 — *Elvis buys Graceland Mansion, in Memphis, for himself, his parents and his grandmother.*
December, 1957 — *Elvis receives a draft notice. He is inducted into the U.S. Army the following March.*
May, 1967 — *Elvis marries Priscilla Beaulieu in a private ceremony at the Aladdin Hotel in Las Vegas.*
February, 1968 — *Priscilla gives birth to Lisa Marie Presley.*
July, 1969 — *Elvis is booked for a four-week, 57-show Las Vegas engagement, which breaks Las Vegas attendance records.*
December, 1970 — *Elvis visits President Nixon in the White House.*
Late 1971 — *Elvis and Priscilla separate. They divorce in October, 1973, and continue to be close friends.*
October, 1973 — *Elvis is hospitalized for two weeks for recurring pneumonia and other ailments. He is hospitalized several times in the following years.*
August 16, 1977 — *Elvis dies in the early morning at Graceland.*

A Musical Melting Pot

**A**merican popular music is much like American culture: a melting pot of traditions, ethnic groups and ideas. The diverse heritage includes a wide variety of sounds including jazz, rhythm and blues (R&B), soul, country and western, pop, rock 'n' roll; the list goes on.

The Legends of American Music stamp series pays tribute to outstanding American musicians—people who created unique sounds and defined new directions in American music.

A 20-stamp booklet, issued in June 1993, honors such musical greats as Bill Haley, Buddy Holly, Clyde McPhatter, Elvis Presley (using the same image that appears on the commemorative), Otis Redding, Ritchie Valens, and Dinah Washington. Together they represent the sounds of soul, jazz, and rock 'n' roll.

Rebels with a Cause

In the early '50s, America had rebounded from World War II with new affluence and increased technology. American teenagers wanted energetic dance music to replace the lushly orchestrated music of the pre-war generation. In rock 'n' roll and rhythm and blues they found raucous, rebellious music with lyrics about important topics such as love and romance.

By the mid '60s, the music began to earn respect and moved beyond its roots in blues and country. A decade later, rock and soul had boomed. The influence of the rock 'n' roll revolution is now felt throughout American culture in movies, fashion, and politics.

F eatured Artists

Bill Haley

"Rock Around the Clock" made Bill Haley (1925-1981) and the Comets international stars in 1954, but the song was not an immediate success. It was used as the theme song for a movie about unruly students, called "The Blackboard Jungle," and became very popular. Bill Haley (born William John Clifton Haley) was the star of the show. The chubby, cowlicked Haley, an unlikely teen idol, was dethroned by Elvis in 1956.

Buddy Holly

By junior high school, Charles Hardin Holley (1936-1959) and his friends played "western and bop" at local dances. The tall, thin Texan with large black horn-rimmed glasses had a totally original sound and style and he wrote or co-wrote most of his biggest hits. Buddy Holly and The Crickets recorded a version of "That'll Be The

Day" which reached Number 3 on U.S. charts in 1957. The band toured Europe and Australia and had more hits including "Peggy Sue" and "Rave On."

Tragically, he died with Ritchie Valens and The Big Bopper in a plane crash in Iowa February 3, 1959. Holly's career only lasted a year and a half, but it was long enough to change the face of rock and roll.

Clyde McPhatter

Gospel music influenced Clyde McPhatter (1932-1972) early on. His father was a preacher in the Baptist church where McPhatter began singing. While he was still in school, he formed a gospel group, called the Mt. Lebanon Singers. Later he sang with The Dominoes. In 1953, McPhatter put together The Drifters. Their mixture of gospel and

pop, which became known as soul, was a big success. His hits include "Money Honey," "There Goes My Baby," and "Dance With Me."

Otis Redding

Otis Redding (1941-1967) had a short but powerful music career. His music was key to the development of soul music in the 1960s. Redding, who was known for his

plane crash December 10, 1967. His single "(Sittin' On) The Dock of the Bay" was recorded only three days before his death and it became his biggest hit.

Ritchie Valens

Rickard Stephen Valenzuela (1941-1959) brought Mexican and American sounds together to create his unique music. This musician was an up-and-coming star when he died in a plane crash with Buddy Holly and The Big Bopper. Valens's debut single was "Come On Let's Go," and he followed that up with the hit single, "Donna," in 1959. But on the flip

side of this single was the biggest hit of all: "La Bamba." This updated Spanish wedding song drove "Donna/La Bamba" to Number 2 on the charts.

Dinah Washington

Dinah Washington (1924-1963), whose real name was Ruth Lee Jones, started singing the blues early. When she was 15, she won an amateur singing contest. From 1943 to 1946, she sang in Lionel Hampton's band. Songs like "Evil Gal Blues" and her versions of "What a Difference a Day Makes" and "Stormy Weather" established her as a major rhythm and blues artist.

passionate stage acts, first performed as a teenager in his native Macon, Georgia. His classic soul ballads later scored hits on both U.S. rhythm and blues and pop charts. Redding was also a cult favorite in the United Kingdom. Redding died in a

Significant Stamp Details

1¢ Franklin Types I-V of 1851-57

5

Bust of **5**

Detail of **5, 18, 40** Type I
Has curved, unbroken lines outside labels. Scrollwork is substantially complete at top, forms little balls at bottom.

Detail of **5A** Type Ib
Lower scrollwork is incomplete, the little balls are not so clear.

Bust of **5**

Detail of **6, 19** Type Ia
Same as Type I at bottom but top ornaments and outer line partly cut away. Lower scrollwork is complete.

Bust of **5**

Detail of **7, 20** Type II
Lower scrollwork incomplete (lacks little balls and lower plume ornaments). Side ornaments are complete.

Bust of **5**

Detail of **8, 21** Type III
Outer lines broken in the middle. Side ornaments are substantially complete.

Detail of **8A, 22** Type IIIa
Outer lines broken top or bottom but not both.

Bust of **5**

Detail of **9, 23** Type IV
Similar to Type II, but outer lines recut top, bottom or both.

What does the color of the stamp signify?

In the 1940s, the United States Postal Service sought to create some uniformity among stamps. This was achieved through the printing process and ink selection. Different, distinctly colored inks were used to indicate different stamp prices. For example, stamps printed in green were worth 1 cent, red stamps were worth 2 cents, purple stamps were worth 3 cents, blue stamps were worth 5 cents and dark brown stamps were worth 10 cents (**#894-908**). There were some exceptions, however, and this stamp uniformity only lasted a few years.

Bust of 5

←

↓

Detail of 24 Type V
Similar to Type III of 1851-57 but with side ornaments partly cut away.

3¢ Washington Types I-IIa of 1851-57

10

Bust of 10

Detail of 10, 11, 25, 41 Type I
There is an outer frame line at top and bottom.

Bust of 10

↑

Detail of 26 Type II
The outer frame line has been removed at top and bottom. The side frame lines were recut so as to be continuous from the top to the bottom of the plate.

Bust of 10

Detail of 26a Type IIa
The side frame lines extend only to the bottom of the stamp design.

5¢ Jefferson Types I-II of 1851-57

12

Bust of 12

Detail of 12, 27-29 Type I
There are projections on all four sides.

Bust of 12

Detail of 30-30A Type II
The projections at top and bottom are partly cut away.

10¢ Washington Types I-V of 1851-57

15

Bust of 15

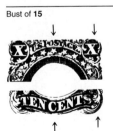

↓   ↓

↑   ↑

Detail of 13, 31, 43 Type I
The "shells" at the lower corners are practically complete. The outer line below the label is very nearly complete. The outer lines are broken above the middle of the top label and the "X" in each upper corner.

Bust of 15

↓

←

Detail of 14, 32 Type II
The design is complete at the top. The outer line at the bottom is broken in the middle. The shells are partly cut away.

Bust of 15

Detail of 15, 33 Type III
The outer lines are broken above the top label and the "X" numerals. The Outer line at the bottom and the shells are partly cut away, as in Type II.

Bust of 15

↓

←

Detail of 16, 34 Type IV
The outer lines have been recut at top or bottom or both. Types I, II, III and IV have complete ornaments at the sides of the stamps and three pearls at each outer edge of the bottom panel.

Bust of 15

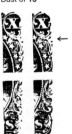

←

Detail of 35 Type V
(Two typical examples). Side ornaments slightly cut away. Outer lines complete at top except over right "X". Outer lines complete at bottom and shells nearly so.

1¢ Franklin of 1861-75

55

3¢ Washington of 1861-75

56

5¢ Jefferson of 1861-75

57

Detail of **55**

Detail of **56**

Detail of **57**

Detail of **63, 86, 92**
In 63, 86 and 92, a dash has been added under the tip of the ornament at right of the numeral in upper left corner.

Detail of **64-66, 74, 79, 82-83, 85, 85C, 88, 94**
In 64-66, 74, 79, 82-83, 85, 85C, 88 and 94, ornaments at corners have been enlarged and end in a small ball.

Detail of **67, 75, 80, 95**
In 67, 75, 80 and 95, a leaf has been added to the foliated ornaments at each corner.

How can a stamp get printed upside down?

When stamps were first issued in the mid-1800s, printing stamps in two colors required running the paper through the printing press twice. Because this process was done by hand, in a few rare instances, the paper would get turned around and the second color would print upside down or on the opposite side of the paper. One of the most valuable errors is the center-inverted 24-cent Curtiss Jenny **(#C3a)**. Today, multiple-colored stamps are printed in a single process.

10¢ Washington of 1861-75

58

Detail of **58, 62B**

Detail of **68, 85D, 89, 96**
In 68, 85D, 89 and 96, a heavy, curved line has been cut below the stars and an outer line added to the ornaments above them.

12¢ Washington of 1861-75

59

Detail of **59**

Detail of **69, 85E, 90, 97**
In 69, 85E, 90 and 97, ovals and scrolls have been added at the corners.

90¢ Washington of 1861-75

62

Detail of **62**

Detail of **72, 101**
In 72 and 101, parallel lines form an angle above the ribbon containing "U.S. Postage"; between these lines a row of dashes has been added, along with a point of color to the apex of the lower line.

15¢ Columbus Landing Types I-III of 1869-75

118

Vignette of **118**

Detail of **118** Type I
Picture unframed.

Vignette of **118**

Detail of **119** Type II
Picture framed.

Vignette of **118**

129 Type III
Same as Type I but without fringe of brown shading lines around central vignette.

134   135   136   137   138

Comparison of Issue of 1870-71: Printed by National Bank Note Company. Issued without secret marks (134-41, 145-52, 187) and **Issues of 1873-80: Printed by Continental and American Bank Note Companies.** Issued with secret marks (156-63, 167-74, 178, 180, 182-84, 186, 188-90, 192-99).

Detail of **134, 145**

Detail of **156, 167, 182, 192**
1¢. In the pearl at the left of the numeral "1" there is a small crescent.

Detail of **136, 147**

Detail of **158, 169, 184, 194**
3¢. The under part of the upper tail of the left ribbon is heavily shaded.

Detail of **138, 149**

Detail of **160, 171, 196**
7¢. Two small semicircles are drawn around the ends of the lines that outline the ball in the lower righthand corner.

Detail of **135, 146**

Detail of **157, 168, 178, 180, 183, 193**
2¢. Under the scroll at the left of "U.S." there is small diagonal line. This mark seldom shows clearly.

Detail of **137, 148**

Detail of **159, 170, 186, 195**
6¢. The first four vertical lines of the shading in the lower part of the left ribbon have been strengthened.

What are secret marks?

When stamps were first issued, printing companies would print stamps for certain periods, as specified by their contracts with the United States Postal Service. After their contracts expired, however, they had to relinquish the printing plates to new printers. When the new printing company received the plates, it would purposely insert secret marks to distinguish its stamps from the previous printer **(#134-138)**. Additionally, as time went on, pieces of the printing plate would wear down, crack or break after years of use. Stamps that exhibit "cracked plate" markings are more valuable than stamps without these markings.

139	140	141	143	206	207

Detail of **139, 150, 187**

Detail of **140, 151**

Detail of **141, 152**

Detail of **143, 154, 165, 176**

Detail of **161, 172, 188, 197**
10¢. There is a small semi-circle in the scroll at the right end of the upper label.

Detail of **162, 173, 198**
12¢. The balls of the figure "2" are crescent-shaped.

Detail of **163, 174, 189, 199**
15¢. In the lower part of the triangle in the upper left corner two lines have been made heavier, forming a "V". This mark can be found on some of the Continental and American (1879) printings, but not all stamps show it.

Detail of **190**
30¢. In the "S" of "CENTS," the vertical spike across the middle section of the letter has been broadened.

Detail of **206**
1¢. Upper vertical lines have been deepened, creating a solid effect in parts of background. Upper arabesques shaded.

Detail of **207**
3¢. Shading at sides of central oval is half its previous width. A short horizontal dash has been cut below the "TS" of "CENTS."

208	209

Detail of **208**
6¢. Has three vertical lines instead of four between the edge of the panel and the outside of the stamp.

Detail of **209**
10¢. Has four vertical lines instead of five between left side of oval and edge of the shield. Horizontal lines in lower part of background strengthened.

2¢ Washington Types of I-III of 1894-98

248

10¢ Webster Types I-II of 1898

282C

3¢ Washington Types I-IV of 1908-19

333

Triangle of **248-50, 265** Type I
Horizontal lines of uniform thickness run across the triangle.

←

Detail of **282C** Type I
The tips of the foliate ornaments do not impinge on the white curved line below "TEN CENTS."

Detail of **333, 345, 359, 376, 389, 394, 426, 445, 456, 464, 483, 493, 501-01b** Type I
Top line of toga rope is weak and rope shading lines are thin. Fifth line from left is missing. Line between lips is thin.

Triangle of **251, 266** Type II
Horizontal lines cross the triangle, but are thinner within than without.

Detail of **283** Type II
The lips of the ornaments break the curved line below the "E" of "TEN" and the "T" of "CENTS."

Detail of **484, 494, 502, 541** Type II
Top line of toga rope is strong and rope shading lines are heavy and complete. Line between lips is heavy.

Triangle of **252, 267, 279B-279Be** Type III
The horizontal lines do not cross the double frame lines of the triangle.

2¢ Washington of 1903

319

$1 Perry Types I-II of 1894

261

Detail of **319a, 319b, 319g** Die I

Detail of **259** Type III
Top row of toga rope is strong but fifth shading line is missing as in Type I. Toga button center shading line consists of two dashes, central dot. "P," "O" of "POSTAGE" are separated by line of color.

←

Detail of **261, 276** Type I
The circles enclosing $1 are broken.

Detail of **319c, 319f, 319h, 319i** Die II

←

Detail of **261A, 276A** Type II
The circles enclosing $1 are complete.

40

Detail of **530, 535** Type IV
*Toga rope shading lines are
complete. Second, fourth toga
button shading lines are
broken in middle; third line is
continuous with dot in center.
"P," "O" of "POSTAGE"
are joined.*

**2¢ Washington Types I-VII
of 1912-21**

406

Detail of **406-06a, 411, 413, 425-
25e, 442, 444, 449, 453, 461,
463-63a, 482, 499-99f**
Type I
*One shading line in first curve
of ribbon above left "2" and
one in second curve of ribbon
above right "2". Toga button
has only a faint outline. Top
line of toga rope, from button
to front of the throat, is very
faint. Shading lines of face end
in the front of the ear, with
little or no joining, to form
lock of hair.*

Detail of **482a, 500** Type Ia
*Similar to Type I but all lines
are stronger.*

Detail of **454, 487, 491, 539**
Type II
*Shading lines in ribbons as in
Type I. Toga button, rope and
rope shading lines are heavy.
Shading lines of face at lock of
hair end in strong vertical
curved line.*

Detail of **450, 455, 488, 492,
540, 546** Type III
*Two lines of shading in curves
of ribbons.*

Detail of **526, 532** Type IV
*Top line of toga rope is
broken. Toga button shading
lines form "DID". Line of
color in left "2" is very thin
and usually broken.*

Detail of **527, 533** Type V
*Top line of toga is complete.
Toga button has five vertical
shading lines. Line of color in
left "2" is very thin and
usually broken. Nose shading
dots are as shown.*

Detail of **528, 534** Type Va
*Same as Type V except third
row from bottom of nose
shading dots has four dots
instead of six. Overall height
of design is 1/3mm shorter
than Type V.*

Detail of **528A, 534A** Type VI
*Generally same as Type V
except line of color in left "2"
is very heavy.*

Detail of **528B, 534B** Type VII
*Line of color in left "2" is
continuous, clearly defined and
heavier than in Type V or Va
but not as heavy as Type VI.
An additional vertical row of
dots has been added to upper
lip. Numerous additional dots
appear in hair at top of head.*

**2¢ Washington Types I-II
of 1923-29**

599

Detail of **599, 634** Type I
*No heavy hair lines at top
center of head.*

Detail of **599A, 634A** Type II
*Three heavy hair lines at top
center of head.*

41

Explanation of Catalog Prices

The United States Postal Service sells only the commemoratives released during the past few years, current regular and special stamps, and current postal stationery.

Prices in this book are called "catalog prices" by stamp collectors. Collectors use catalog prices as guidelines when buying or trading stamps. It is important to remember the prices are simply guidelines to the stamp values. Stamp condition (see pp 10-11) is very important in determining the actual value of a stamp.

Condition Affects Value

The catalog prices are given for unused (mint) stamps and used (canceled) stamps, which have been hinged and are in Fine condition. Stamps in Superb condition that have never been hinged may cost more than the listed price. Stamps in less than Fine condition may cost less.

The prices for used stamps are based on a light cancellation; a heavy cancellation lessens a stamp's value. Canceled stamps may be worth more than uncanceled stamps. This happens if the cancellation is of a special type or for a significant date. Therefore, it is important to study an envelope before removing a stamp and discarding its "cover."

Prices are Estimated

Listed prices are estimates of how much you can expect to pay for a stamp from a dealer. **A 15-cent minimum valuation has been established which represents a fair-market price to have a dealer locate and provide a single stamp to a customer. Dealers may charge less per stamp to provide a group of such stamps, and may charge less for such a single stamp. Similarly, a $1.00 minimum has been established for First Day Covers (FDCs).** If you sell a stamp to a dealer, he or she may offer you much less than the catalog price. Dealers pay based on their interest in owning a particular stamp. If they already have a full supply, they may only buy additional stamps at a low price.

Sample Listing

			Un	U	PB/LP/PNC	#	FDC	Q
2636	29¢	Kentucky Statehood, June 1	.00	.00	0.00	( )	0.00	000,000,000

Scott Catalog Number (bold type indicates stamp is pictured)

Denomination

Description

First Day of Issue

Unused Catalog Price

Used Catalog Price

Plate Block Price, Line Pair Price or Plate Number Coil Price

# of stamps in Plate Block, Line Pair or Plate Number Coil

First Day Cover Price

Quantity Issued (where known)

2636

Understanding the Listings

- Prices in regular type for single unused and used stamps are taken from the *Scott 1994 Standard Postage Stamp Catalogue, Volume 1* ©1993, whose editors have based these prices on **actual retail values** as they found them in the marketplace. The Scott numbering system for stamps is used in this book. Prices quoted for unused and used stamps are for "Fine" condition, except where Fine is not available.

- Stamp values in *italic* generally refer to items difficult to value accurately.

- A dash (—) in a value column means the item is known to exist but information is insufficient for establishing a value.

- The stamp listings contain a number of additions designated "a," "b," "c," etc. These represent recognized variations of stamps as well as errors. These listings are as complete as space permits.

- Occasionally, a new stamp or major variation may be inserted by the catalog editors into a series or sequence where it was not originally anticipated. These additions are identified by capital letters "A," "B" and so forth. For example, a new stamp which logically belonged between 1044 and 1045 is designated 1044A, even though it is entirely different from 1044. The insertion was preferable to a complete renumbering of the series.

- Prices for Plate Blocks and First Day Covers are taken from *Scott's Specialized Catalogue of U.S. Stamps*, 1993 Edition, ©1992.

- Prices for American Commemorative Panels and Souvenir Pages are from the American Society of Philatelic Pages and Panels.

Sample Variation Listing

			Un	U	PB/LP/PNC	#	FDC	Q
2281	25¢	Honeybee, Sept. 2	.45	.15	3.75	(3)	1.00	000,000,000
a		Imperf. pair	*45.00*					
b		Black omitted	*100.00*					
d		Pair, imperf. between	—					

Scott Catalog Number (bold type indicates stamp is pictured)

Denomination

Description

First Day of Issue

Unused Catalog Price

Used Catalog Price

Plate Block Price, Line Pair Price or Plate Number Coil Price

# of stamps in Plate Block, Line Pair or Plate Number Coil

First Day Cover Price

Quantity Issued (where known)

2281

43

Commemorative and Definitive Stamps

1847-1861

1 2 3

4

5 11

12 14 17

	Issues of 1847, Thin, Bluish Wove Paper, July 1, Imperf., Unwmkd.		
		Un	**U**
1	5¢ Benjamin Franklin	4,500.00	425.00
b	5¢ orange brown	5,000.00	525.00
c	5¢ red orange	*10,000.00*	*3,500.00*
	Pen cancel	—	225.00
	Double transfer of top, or top and bottom, or bottom and lower left frame lines		525.00
	Double transfer of top, bottom and left frame lines and numerals		900.00
2	10¢ George Washington	*20,000.00*	900.00
	Pen cancel	—	450.00
	Vertical line through second "F" of "OFFICE," or with "stick pin" in tie, or with "harelip," or double transfer in lower right "X," or in "POST OFFICE," or of left and bottom frame lines	—	1,250.00

Issues of 1875, Reproductions of 1 and 2, Bluish Paper, Without Gum

		Un	U
3	5¢ Franklin	750.00	—
4	10¢ Washington	925.00	—

5¢. On the original, the left side of the white shirt frill touches the oval on a level with the top of the "F" of "Five." On the reproduction, it touches the oval about on a level with the top of the figure "5."

10¢. On the reproduction, line of coat at left points to right of "X" and line of coat at right points to center of "S" of CENTS. On the original, line of coat points to "I" of TEN and between "T" and "S" of CENTS.

On the reproduction, the eyes have a sleepy look, the line of the mouth is straighter and in the curl of hair near the left cheek is a strong black dot, while the original has only a faint one.

Issues of 1851-57, Imperf.

		Un	U
5	1¢ Franklin, type I	*200,000.00*	*17,500.00*
5A	1¢ blue, type Ib	*8,500.00*	*2,500.00*
	#6-9: Franklin (5), 1851		
6	1¢ dark blue, type Ia	*22,500.00*	*6,500.00*
7	1¢ blue, type II	575.00	110.00
	Cracked plate	700.00	250.00
8	1¢ blue, type III	*6,500.00*	1,500.00
8A	1¢ pale blue, type IIIA	*2,500.00*	600.00
9	1¢ blue, type IV	425.00	90.00
	Triple transfer, one inverted	500.00	125.00

#10-11, #25-26a all had plates on which at least four outer frame lines (and usually much more) were recut, adding to their value.

	Issues of 1851-57 (continued), Imperf.		
		Un	U
10	3¢ orange brown Washington, type I (11)	1,250.00	40.00
	3¢ copper brown	1,300.00	60.00
	On part-India paper		250.00
11	3¢ Washington, type I	130.00	7.00
	3¢ deep claret	185.00	13.50
	Double transfer, "GENTS" for "CENTS"	200.00	25.00
12	5¢ Jefferson, type I	*8,500.00*	875.00
13	10¢ green Washington, type I (14)	*9,000.00*	575.00
14	10¢ green, type II	2,000.00	190.00
15	10¢ Washington, type III	2,000.00	190.00
16	10¢ green, type IV (14)	*12,500.00*	1,100.00
17	12¢ Washington	2,500.00	225.00

Issues of 1857-61, Perf. 15½ (Issued in 1857 except #18, 27, 28A, 29, 30, 30A, 35, 36b, 37, 38, 39)

	#18-24: Franklin (5)		
18	1¢ blue, type I	800.00	325.00
19	1¢ blue, type Ia	11,500.00	*2,750.00*
20	1¢ blue, type II	450.00	150.00
21	1¢ blue, type III	5,000.00	1,250.00
22	1¢ blue, type IIIa	800.00	275.00
23	1¢ blue, type IV	2,750.00	325.00
24	1¢ blue, type V	120.00	25.00
	"Curl" on shoulder	150.00	37.50
	"Earring" below ear	200.00	52.50
	Long double "curl" in hair	185.00	42.50
b	Laid paper	—	—
	#25-26a: Washington (11)		
25	3¢ rose, type I	900.00	30.00
	Cracked plate	1,000.00	100.00
26	3¢ dull red, type II	45.00	3.25
	3¢ brownish carmine	50.00	3.75
	3¢ claret	60.00	3.50
	Left or right frame line double	65.00	8.75
	Cracked plate	*425.00*	125.00
26a	3¢ dull red, type IIa	110.00	20.00
	Double transfer	175.00	30.00
	Left frame line double	—	45.00

	Issues of 1857-61 (continued), Perf. 15½	Un	U
	#27-29: Jefferson (12)		
27	5¢ brick red, type I	9,000.00	675.00
28	5¢ red brown, type I	1,350.00	250.00
b	5¢ brt. red brn., type I	1,850.00	400.00
28A	5¢ Indian red, type I	12,000.00	1,750.00
29	5¢ brown, type I	850.00	200.00
	Defective transfer	—	—
30	5¢ orange brown, type II	750.00	1000.00
30A	5¢ brown, type II (30)	475.00	185.00
b	Printed on both sides	3,750.00	3,000.00
	#31-35: Washington (15)		
31	10¢ grn., type I	6,750.00	500.00
32	10¢ grn., type II	2,500.00	165.00
33	10¢ grn., type III	2,500.00	165.00
	"Curl" on forehead or in left "X"		225.00
34	10¢ grn., type IV	17,500.00	1,400.00
35	10¢ grn., type V	200.00	50.00
	Small "curl" on forehead	235.00	60.00
	"Curl" in "e" or "t" of "Cents"	250.00	70.00
	Plate I—Outer frame lines complete.		
36	12¢ blk. Washington (17), plate I	375.00	85.00
	Triple transfer	500.00	—
36b	12¢ black, plate III	350.00	110.00
	Vertical line through rosette	450.00	145.00
37	24¢ gray lilac	675.00	200.00
a	24¢ gray	675.00	200.00
b	24¢ red lilac	1,000.00	

	Issues of 1857-61 (continued), Perf. 15½	Un	U
38	30¢ orange Franklin	750.00	300.00
	Recut at bottom	900.00	400.00
39	90¢ blue Washington	1,150.00	5,000.00
	Double transfer at top or bottom	1,250.00	—
	90¢ Same, with pen cancel		900.00

Note: Beware of forged cancellations of #39. Genuine cancellations are rare.

Issues of 1875, Government Reprints, White Paper, Without Gum, Perf. 12

		Un	U
40	1¢ bright blue Franklin (5)	425.00	
41	3¢ scarlet Wash. (11)	2,000.00	
42	5¢ orange brown Jefferson (30)	850.00	
43	10¢ blue green Washington (14)	1,750.00	
44	12¢ greenish black Washington (17)	2,000.00	
45	24¢ blackish violet Washington (37)	2,000.00	
46	30¢ yellow orange Franklin (38)	2,000.00	
47	90¢ deep blue Washington (39)	3,250.00	
48-54	Not assigned		

Issue of 1861, Thin, Semi-Transparent Paper

		Un	U
	Former #55-62 are now considered essays.		
62B	10¢ dark green Washington (58)	5,000.00	450.00
	Double transfer	6,500.00	525.00

Who wrote the Declaration of Independence?

Thomas Jefferson (1743-1826) is best known as the author of the Declaration of Independence. This document, a declaration of freedom from British rule, was adopted July 4, 1776. This date is also considered the birthday of the United States. Jefferson's talents and interests covered an amazing range. He became one of the leading architects of his time and designed the Virginia Capitol, the University of Virginia and his own home, Monticello. Jefferson served two terms as President of the United States from 1801 to 1809. **(#30)**

30   37   38   39

55   56   57   58

59   60   61   62

47

67   73   77

Protect wildlife! Read the article about Duck Stamps and learn how buying these stamps helps to save waterfowl habitat.

Please detach at perforation.

U.S. MAIL

*Penalty for private
use to avoid payment
of postage: $300*

**United States Postal Service
Kansas City MO 64144-9997**

Official Business

U.S. Postal Service Stamp Guide Survey
c/o Mobium Corporation for Design
and Communication
414 North Orleans Suite 610
Chicago IL 60610-4487

You asked for it!

The U.S. Postal Service received over three thousand responses to the reply card inserted in last year's Guide. We listened to your comments and suggestions when planning and creating this year's book. Here are some of **your** *ideas that we added to the 1994 Guide:*

- **Expanded stamp listings**
- **Dozens of new illustrations**
- **More stamp background than ever**
- **Updated stamp prices**
- **New Duck Stamps section**
- **User-friendly subject index**
- **Improved binding**

Please answer these questions and return this postage-paid reply card so we can continue to provide a book that suits **your** *collecting needs.*

1. What do you like most about this book?

_____

_____

_____

2. What do you like least about this book?

_____

_____

_____

3. How could this book be improved to help you?

_____

_____

_____

_____

4. Which newly added feature is most useful to you?

_____

_____

_____

Please answer yes or no to the following statements by making an X in the appropriate box. Please use the lines below for any additional comments you have.

The improved stamp listings are useful.	❑ Yes ❑ No
The improved stamp listings are complete.	❑ Yes ❑ No
I like the overall design of this year's book.	❑ Yes ❑ No
The new binding is helpful.	❑ Yes ❑ No
I enjoy reading the additional stamp articles.	❑ Yes ❑ No
The improved subject index is easier to use.	❑ Yes ❑ No

Comments:

_____

_____

_____

_____

_____

_____

_____

_____

Issues of 1861-62, Perf. 12	Un	U
63	1¢ blue Franklin (55)	140.00	15.00
a	1¢ ultramarine	250.00	40.00
b	1¢ dark blue	350.00	25.00
	Double transfer	—	22.50
	Dot in "U"	150.00	17.50
c	Laid paper	—	—
d	Vert. pair, imperf. horiz.		—
e	Printed on both sides	—	2,500.00
64	3¢ pink Washington (56)	4,500.00	350.00
a	3¢ pigeon blood pink	—	1,750.00
b	3¢ rose pink	300.00	45.00
65	3¢ rose Washington (56)	70.00	1.00
b	Laid paper	—	—
d	Vertical pair, imperf. horizontally	1,200.00	750.00
e	Printed on both sides	1,650.00	1,000.00
f	Double impression	—	1,200.00
	Cracked plate	—	—
	Double transfer	85.00	2.50
66	3¢ lake Washington (56)	1,650.00	
	Double transfer	2,000.00	
67	5¢ buff Jefferson (57)	6,000.00	425.00
68	10¢ yellow green Washington (58)	275.00	30.00
	10¢ deep yellow green on thin paper	350.00	40.00
a	10¢ dark green	290.00	31.00
b	Vert. pair, imperf. horiz.	—	3,500.00
	Double transfer	325.00	40.00
69	12¢ blk. Washington (59)	550.00	55.00
	12¢ intense black	575.00	60.00
	Double transfer of top or bottom frame line	575.00	65.00
	Double transfer of top and bottom frame lines	600.00	70.00
70	24¢ red lilac Washington (60)	700.00	80.00
a	24¢ brown lilac	600.00	67.50
b	24¢ steel blue	4,000.00	300.00
c	24¢ violet	6,500.00	550.00
d	24¢ grayish lilac	1,400.00	350.00
	Scratch under "A" of "POSTAGE"		—
71	30¢ orange Franklin (61)	625.00	70.00
	Printed on both sides		—
72	90¢ bl. Washington (62)	1,450.00	250.00
b	90¢ dark blue	1,600.00	275.00
73	2¢ blk. Andrew Jackson	175.00	22.50
	Double transfer	200.00	25.00
	Major double transfer of top left corner and "POSTAGE"		6,000.00
	Cracked plate	—	—

Issues of 1861-66, Perf. 12	Un	U
	#74 was not regularly issued.		
74	3¢ scarlet Washington (56)	6,500.00	
75	5¢ red brown Jefferson (57)	1,450.00	225.00
76	5¢ brown Jefferson (57)	375.00	60.00
a	5¢ dark brown	425.00	72.50
	Double transfer of top or bottom frame line	425.00	72.50
77	15¢ blk. Abraham Lincoln	575.00	70.00
	Double transfer	600.00	75.00
78	24¢ lilac Washington (60)	300.00	50.00
c	24¢ black violet	17,500.00	1,100.00
	Scratch under "A" of "POSTAGE"	—	—

Grills on U.S. Stamps

Between 1867 and 1870, postage stamps were embossed with pyramid-shaped grills that absorbed cancellation ink to prevent reuse of canceled stamps.

Issues of 1867, With Grills	Un	U
	Grills A, B, C: Points Up		
	A. Grill Covers Entire Stamp		
79	3¢ rose Washington (56)	2,000.00	475.00
b	Printed on both sides		—
80	5¢ brown Jefferson (57)	—	—
a	5¢ dark brown		
81	30¢ orange Franklin (61)		
	B. Grill about 18 x 15mm		
82	3¢ rose Washington (56)		45,000.00
	C. Grill about 13 x 16mm		
83	3¢ rose Washington (56)	2,250.00	425.00
	Double grill	4,000.00	1,500.00
	Grills, D, Z, E, F: Points Down		
	D. Grill about 12 x 14mm		
84	2¢ black Jackson (73)	4,500.00	1,100.00
85	3¢ rose Washington (56)	1,900.00	450.00
	Split grill		500.00
	Z. Grill about 11 x 14mm		
85A	1¢ blue Franklin (55)		—
85B	2¢ black Jackson (73)	1,750.00	400.00
	Double transfer	1,850.00	425.00
85C	3¢ rose Washington (56)	5,000.00	950.00
	Double grill	6,000.00	
85D	10¢ grn. Washington (58)		25,000.00
85E	12¢ blk. Washington (59)	2,500.00	575.00
	Double transfer of top frame line		625.00
85F	15¢ black Lincoln (77)		100,000.00
	E. Grill about 11 x 13mm		
86	1¢ blue Franklin (55)	1,000.00	250.00
	Double grill	—	375.00
	Split grill	1,050.00	275.00

	Issues of 1867 (continued), With Grills, Perf. 12	Un	U
87	2¢ black Jackson (73)	450.00	70.00
	2¢ intense black	475.00	75.00
	Double grill	—	—
	Double transfer	475.00	75.00
88	3¢ rose Washington (56)	350.00	10.00
a	3¢ lake red	400.00	12.50
	Double grill	—	—
	Very thin paper	375.00	11.00
89	10¢ grn. Washington (58)	1,750.00	175.00
	Double grill	2,500.00	300.00
90	12¢ blk. Washington (59)	2,000.00	200.00
	Double transfer of top or bottom frame line	2,100.00	220.00
91	15¢ black Lincoln (77)	5,000.00	450.00
	Double grill	—	700.00
	F. Grill about 9 x 13mm		
92	1¢ blue Franklin (55)	450.00	100.00
	Double transfer	475.00	120.00
	Double grill	—	200.00
93	2¢ black Jackson (73)	175.00	25.00
	Double grill	—	100.00
	Very thin paper	190.00	30.00
94	3¢ red Washington (56)	125.00	2.50
c	Vertical pair, imperf. horizontally	1,000.00	
d	Printed on both sides	1,100.00	
	Double grill	—	—
	End roller grill		200.00
	Quadruple split grill	275.00	75.00
95	5¢ brown Jefferson (57)	1,500.00	225.00
a	5¢ dark brown	1,600.00	250.00
	Double transfer of top frame line	—	—
	Double grill	—	—
96	10¢ yellow green Washington (58)	900.00	110.00
	Double transfer	—	—
	Quadruple split grill		350.00
97	12¢ blk. Washington (59)	900.00	125.00
	Double transfer of top or bottom frame line	950.00	135.00
	Triple grill	—	
98	15¢ black Lincoln (77)	900.00	135.00
	Double transfer of upper right corner	—	—
	Double grill	—	250.00
	Quadruple split grill	1,750.00	350.00
99	24¢ gray lilac Washington (60)	1,700.00	425.00
100	30¢ orange Franklin (61)	2,500.00	375.00
	Double grill	2,400.00	700.00
101	90¢ bl. Washington (62)	5,000.00	750.00
	Double grill	7,000.00	

	Issues of 1875, Reissue of 1861-66 Issue, Without Grill, Perf. 12	Un	U
102	1¢ blue Franklin (55)	500.00	800.00
103	2¢ black Jackson (73)	2,250.00	4,000.00
104	3¢ brown red Washington (56)	2,750.00	3,500.00
105	5¢ brown Jefferson (57)	1,600.00	2,250.00
106	10¢ grn. Washington (58)	1,850.00	3,750.00
107	12¢ blk. Washington (59)	2,750.00	4,500.00
108	15¢ black Lincoln (77)	2,750.00	4,750.00
109	24¢ deep violet Washington (60)	3,750.00	6,000.00
110	30¢ brownish orange Franklin (61)	4,250.00	6,000.00
111	90¢ bl. Washington (62)	5,250.00	17,500.00
	Issues of 1869, With Grill		
	G. Grill about 9½ x 9mm		
112	1¢ Franklin, Mar. 27	275.00	65.00
b	Without grill	750.00	
	Double grill	450.00	150.00
113	2¢ br. Post Rider, Mar. 27	200.00	25.00
	Split grill	225.00	35.00
	Double transfer		30.00
114	3¢ Locomotive, Mar. 27	175.00	7.00
a	Without grill	600.00	—
d	Double impression	—	—
	Triple grill	—	—
	Sextuple grill	2,000.00	
	Gray paper	—	—
115	6¢ Washington	825.00	95.00
	Quadruple split grill	—	400.00
116	10¢ Shield and Eagle	900.00	85.00
	End roller grill	—	—
117	12¢ S.S. Adriatic, Apr. 5	850.00	95.00
	Split grill	850.00	100.00
118	15¢ Columbus Landing, type I, Apr. 2	2,250.00	325.00
119	15¢ type II (118)	1000.00	150.00
b	Center inverted	175,000.00	14,000.00
c	Center double, one inverted		—
120	24¢ Declaration of Independence, Apr. 7	2,400.00	500.00
b	Center inverted	150,000.00	15,000.00
121	30¢ Shield, Eagle and Flags, May 15	2,400.00	250.00
b	Flags inverted	165,000.00	55,000.00
	Double grill	—	500.00
122	90¢ Lincoln	5,000.00	1,150.00
	Split grill	—	—
	Issues of 1875, Reissue of 1869 Issue, Without Grill, Hard, White Paper		
123	1¢ buff (112)	325.00	225.00
124	2¢ brown (113)	375.00	325.00
125	3¢ blue (114)	3,000.00	10,000.00
126	6¢ blue (115)	850.00	550.00

112

113

114

115

116

117

118

120

121

122

134 135 136 137

138 139 140 141

142 143 144

156 157 158 159

160 161 162 163

179

Issues of 1875 (continued), Perf. 12	Un	U
127 10¢ yellow (116)	1,400.00	1,200.00
128 12¢ green (117)	1,500.00	1,200.00
129 15¢ brown and blue, type III (118)	1,300.00	550.00
a Imperf. horizontally	1,600.00	—
130 24¢ grn. & violet (120)	1,250.00	550.00
131 30¢ bl. & carmine (121)	1,750.00	1,000.00
132 90¢ car. & black (122)	4,500.00	4,750.00
Issue of 1880, Reissue of 1869 Issue, Soft, Porous Paper		
133 1¢ buff (112)	200.00	175.00
a 1¢ brown orange, issued without gum	175.00	150.00
Issues of 1870-71, With Grill, White Wove Paper, No Secret Marks		
H. Grill about 10 x 12mm		
134 1¢ Franklin, April 1870	800.00	60.00
End roller grill		300.00
135 2¢ Jackson, April 1870	475.00	37.50
136 3¢ Washington	365.00	10.00
Cracked plate	—	50.00
137 6¢ Lincoln, April 1870	1,850.00	300.00
Double grill	—	500.00
138 7¢ Edwin M. Stanton	1,350.00	275.00
139 10¢ Jefferson	1,600.00	450.00
140 12¢ Henry Clay	13,000.00	1,750.00
141 15¢ Daniel Webster	2,750.00	750.00
142 24¢ Gen. Winfield Scott	—	11,500.00
143 30¢ Alexander Hamilton	5,250.00	950.00
144 90¢ Commodore Perry	6,750.00	800.00
Split grill		825.00
Without Grill, White Wove Paper, No Secret Marks		
145 1¢ ultra. Franklin (134)	200.00	7.50
146 2¢ red brn. Jackson (135)	125.00	5.00
147 3¢ grn. Washington (136)	150.00	.50
148 6¢ carmine Lincoln (137)	290.00	12.00
6¢ violet carmine	290.00	15.00
149 7¢ verm. Stanton (138)	375.00	55.00
150 10¢ brown Jefferson (139)	290.00	12.00
151 12¢ dull violet Clay (140)	625.00	65.00
152 15¢ brt. or. Webster (141)	600.00	62.50
153 24¢ purple Scott (142)	700.00	85.00
154 30¢ black Hamilton (143)	1,200.00	100.00
155 90¢ carmine Perry (144)	1,600.00	185.00
Issues of 1873, Without Grill, White Wove Paper, Thin to Thick, Secret Marks		
156 1¢ ultra. Franklin	75.00	1.75
Paper with silk fibers	—	15.00
f Imperf. pair	—	500.00
157 2¢ br. Jackson	210.00	10.00
Double paper	275.00	20.00
c With grill	1,100.00	600.00

Issues of 1873 (continued), Perf. 12	Un	U
158 3¢ gr. Washington	65.00	.15
3¢ olive green	75.00	2.50
Cracked plate	—	27.50
159 6¢ dull pk. Lincoln	235.00	10.00
b With grill	1,000.00	
160 7¢ or. verm. Stanton	465.00	57.50
Ribbed paper	—	70.00
161 10¢ br. Jefferson	285.00	11.50
162 12¢ bl. vio. Clay	775.00	67.50
163 15¢ yel. or. Webster	700.00	62.50
a With grill	3,000.00	
164 24¢ pur. Scott		
165 30¢ gray blk. Hamilton	800.00	65.00
166 90¢ rose carm. Perry	1,600.00	185.00
Issues of 1875, Special Printing, Hard, White Wove Paper, Without Gum, Secret Marks		
Although perforated, these stamps were usually cut apart with scissors. As a result, the perforations are often much mutilated and the design is frequently damaged.		
167 1¢ ultra. Franklin (156)	7,500.00	
168 2¢ dk. br. Jackson (157)	3,500.00	
169 3¢ blue green Washington (158)	9,500.00	—
170 6¢ dull rose Lincoln (159)	8,500.00	
171 7¢ reddish vermilion Stanton (160)	2,250.00	
172 10¢ pale brown Jefferson (161)	8,250.00	
173 12¢ dark vio. Clay (162)	3,000.00	
174 15¢ bright orange Webster (163)	8,250.00	
175 24¢ dull pur. Scott (142)	1,850.00	—
176 30¢ greenish black Hamilton (143)	7,500.00	
177 90¢ vio. car. Perry (144)	7,500.00	
Yellowish Wove Paper		
178 2¢ verm. Jackson (157)	190.00	5.00
c With grill	300.00	
179 5¢ Zachary Taylor, June	235.00	9.00
Cracked plate	—	100.00
Double paper	250.00	
c With grill	400.00	
Paper with silk fibers	—	15.00
Special Printing, Hard, White Wove Paper, Without Gum		
180 2¢ carmine vermilion Jackson (157)	17,500.00	
181 5¢ br. bl. Taylor (179)	32,500.00	
Issues of 1879, Soft, Porous Paper, Thin to Thick		
182 1¢ dark ultramarine Franklin (156)	160.00	1.25
183 2¢ verm. Jackson (157)	70.00	1.25
a Double impression	—	500.00

Issues of 1879 (continued), Perf. 12	Un	U
184 3¢ grn. Washington (158)	55.00	.15
Double transfer	—	4.00
Short transfer	—	5.00
185 5¢ blue Taylor (179)	300.00	8.00
186 6¢ pink Lincoln (159)	550.00	13.00
187 10¢ brown Jefferson (139) (no secret mark)	875.00	15.00
188 10¢ brown Jefferson (161) (with secret mark)	600.00	16.00
10¢ black brown	625.00	22.50
Double transfer		30.00
189 15¢ red or. Webster (163)	200.00	15.00
190 30¢ full blk. Hamilton (143)	575.00	35.00
191 90¢ carmine Perry (144)	1,200.00	155.00
Issues of 1880, Special Printing, Soft, Porous Paper, Without Gum		
192 1¢ dark ultramarine Franklin (156)	10,000.00	
193 2¢ blk. br. Jackson (157)	6,500.00	
194 3¢ blue green Washington (158)	15,000.00	
195 6¢ dull rose Lincoln (159)	11,000.00	
196 7¢ scarlet vermilion Stanton (160)	2,250.00	
197 10¢ deep brown Jefferson (161)	10,000.00	
198 12¢ blk. pur. Clay (162)	4,500.00	
199 15¢ or. Webster (163)	9,750.00	
200 24¢ dk. vio. Scott (142)	3,500.00	
201 30¢ greenish black Hamilton (143)	8,500.00	
202 90¢ dull carmine Perry (144)	9,000.00	
203 2¢ scarlet vermilion Jackson (157)	18,000.00	
204 5¢ dp. bl. Taylor (179)	30,000.00	
Issues of 1882		
205 5¢ Garfield, Apr. 10	135.00	4.50
Special Printing, Soft, Porous Paper, Without Gum		
205C 5¢ gray brown Garfield (205)	20,000.00	
Issues of 1881-82, Designs of 1873 Re-engraved		
206 1¢ Franklin, Aug. 1881	40.00	.40
Double transfer	52.50	4.00
207 3¢ Washington, July 16, 1881	45.00	.15
Double transfer	—	7.50
Cracked plate	—	
208 6¢ Lincoln, June 1882	250.00	45.00
a 6¢ brown red	225.00	55.00
209 10¢ Jefferson, Apr. 1882	90.00	2.50
10¢ pur. or olive brown	100.00	2.75
b 10¢ black brown	140.00	10.00

Issues of 1883, Perf. 12	Un	U
210 2¢ Washington, Oct. 1	37.50	.15
Double transfer	37.50	1.25
211 4¢ Jackson, Oct. 1	160.00	8.00
Cracked plate	—	
Special Printing, Soft, Porous Paper		
211B 2¢ pale red brown Washington (210)	600.00	—
c Horizontal pair, imperf. between	2,500.00	
211D 4¢ deep blue green Jackson (211) no gum	15,000.00	
Issues of 1887		
212 1¢ Franklin, June	65.00	.65
Double transfer	—	
213 2¢ green Washington (210), Sept. 10	25.00	.15
b Printed on both sides	—	
Double transfer	—	3.00
214 3¢ vermilion Washington (207), Oct. 3	50.00	37.50
Issues of 1888		
215 4¢ carmine Jackson (211), Nov.	160.00	11.00
216 5¢ indigo Garfield (205), Feb.	160.00	6.50
217 30¢ orange brown Hamilton (165), Jan.	360.00	75.00
218 90¢ pur. Perry (166), Feb.	750.00	130.00
Issues of 1890-93		
219 1¢ Franklin, Feb. 22, 1890	18.50	.15
Double transfer	—	—
219D 2¢ lake Washington (220), Feb. 22, 1890	150.00	.45
Double transfer	—	—
220 2¢ Washington, 1890	15.00	.15
a Cap on left "2"	35.00	1.00
c Cap on both "2s"	125.00	8.00
Double transfer	—	3.00
221 3¢ Jackson, Feb. 22, 1890	50.00	4.50
222 4¢ Lincoln, June 2, 1890	50.00	1.50
Double transfer	65.00	—
223 5¢ Grant, June 2, 1890	50.00	1.50
Double transfer	65.00	1.75
224 6¢ Garfield, Feb. 22, 1890	55.00	15.00
225 8¢ Sherman, Mar. 21, 1893	40.00	8.50
226 10¢ Webster, Feb. 22, 1890	95.00	1.75
Double transfer	—	—
227 15¢ Clay, Feb. 22, 1890	150.00	15.00
Double transfer	—	—
Triple transfer	—	—
228 30¢ Jefferson, Feb. 22, 1890	225.00	20.00
Double transfer	—	—
229 90¢ Perry, Feb. 22, 1890	350.00	95.00
Short transfer at bottom	—	—

205   206   207   208

209   210   211   212

219   220   221   222

223   224   225   226

227   228   229

55

230

231

232

233

234

235

236

237

238

239

240

241

242

243

244

245

Issues of 1893, Perf. 12	Un	U	PB	#	FDC	Q
Columbian Exposition Issue, Printed by The American Bank Note Co., Jan. 2 (8¢ March)						
230	1¢ Columbus in Sight of Land	21.00	.25	300.00	(6)	*3,500.00*	449,195,550
	Double transfer	24.00	.50				
	Cracked plate	80.00					
231	2¢ Landing of Columbus	19.00	.15	250.00	(6)	*2,600.00*	1,464,588,750
	Double transfer	22.50	.25				
	Triple transfer	57.50	—				
	Quadruple transfer	85.00					
	Broken hat on third figure left of Columbus	50.00	.20				
	Broken frame line	20.00	.15				
	Recut frame lines	20.00	—				
	Cracked plate	80.00	—				
232	3¢ *Santa Maria,* Flagship of Columbus	50.00	12.50	650.00	(6)	*6,000.00*	11,501,250
	Double transfer	67.50	—				
233	4¢ ultramarine Fleet of Columbus	70.00	5.50	1000.00	(6)	*6000.00*	19,181,550
a	4¢ blue (error)	*10,000.00*	*4,000.00*	*45,000.00*	(4)		
	Double transfer	100.00	—				
234	5¢ Columbus Soliciting Aid from Isabella	75.00	6.50	1,250.00	(6)	*6,250.00*	35,248,250
	Double transfer	120.00	—				
235	6¢ Columbus Welcomed at Barcelona	70.00	18.00			*6,750.00*	4,707,550
a	6¢ red violet	70.00	18.00	1,100.00	(6)		
	Double transfer	90.00	25.00				
236	8¢ Columbus Restored to Favor	60.00	8.00	725.00	(6)		10,656,650
	Double transfer	70.00	—				
237	10¢ Columbus Presenting Natives	115.00	5.50	2,750.00	(6)	*7,500.00*	16,516,950
	Double transfer	150.00	10.00				
	Triple transfer	—					
238	15¢ Columbus Announcing His Discovery	190.00	50.00	*4,500.00*	(6)		1,576,950
	Double transfer	—	—				
239	30¢ Columbus at La Rábida	260.00	70.00	*7,000.00*	(6)		617,250
240	50¢ Recall of Columbus	450.00	120.00	*10,500.00*	(6)		243,750
	Double transfer	—	—				
	Triple transfer	—	—				
241	$1 Isabella Pledging Her Jewels	1,350.00	525.00	*35,000.00*	(6)		55,050
	Double transfer	—	—				
242	$2 Columbus in Chains	1,400.00	450.00	*40,000.00*	(6)	*18,000.00*	45,550
243	$3 Columbus Describing His Third Voyage	2,400.00	800.00	*60,000.00*	(6)		27,650
a	$3 olive green	2,400.00	800.00				
244	$4 Isabella and Columbus	2,900.00	1,000.00	*165,000.00*	(6)		26,350
a	$4 rose carmine	2,900.00	1,000.00				
245	$5 Portrait of Columbus	3,250.00	1,200.00	*150,000.00*	(6)		27,350

		Un	U	PB	#

Bureau Issues Starting in 1894, the Bureau of Engraving and Printing in Washington has produced all U.S. postage stamps except #909-21, 1335, 1355, 1410-18, 1789, 1804, 1825, 1833, 2023, 2038, 2065-66, 2073, 2080, 2087, 2091, 2093, 2102, 2110, 2137-41, 2153, 2159-64, 2167, 2203-04, 2210-11, 2220-23, 2240-43, 2250, 2283, 2337-39, 2343-44, 2347, 2369, 2371-75, 2377, 2386-89, 2395-98, 2403-04, 2411, 2416-18, 2420, 2426, 2439-41, 2445-49, 2481-82, 2489, 2494, 2496-2500, 2506-7, 2512-13, 2515, 2517, 2520-22, 2523A, 2524, 2527-28, 2531A, 2532-33, 2535, 2537-38, 2540-41, 2545-50, 2552-57, C121, C127-30.

#	Description	Un	U	PB	#
246	1¢ Franklin, Oct.	16.00	2.00	200.00	(6)
	Double transfer	20.00	3.00		
247	1¢ blue Franklin (246)	40.00	.85	400.00	(6)
	Double transfer	—	2.50		
248	2¢ pink Washington, type I, Oct.	12.50	1.50	145.00	(6)
	Double transfer	—	—		
249	2¢ carmine lake, type I (248)	77.50	1.00	850.00	(6)
	Double transfer	—	1.50		
250	2¢ carmine, type I (248)	15.00	.25	200.00	(6)
a	Vertical pair, imperf. horizontally	1,500.00			
b	Horizontal pair, imperf. between	1,500.00			
	Double transfer	—	1.10		
251	2¢ carmine, type II (248)	125.00	1.50	1,450.00	(6)
252	2¢ carmine, type III (248)	70.00	2.00	950.00	(6)
b	Horizontal pair, imperf. between	1,500.00			
253	3¢ Jackson, Sept.	52.50	4.25	700.00	(6)
254	4¢ Lincoln, Sept.	60.00	2.00	850.00	(6)
255	5¢ Grant, Sept.	50.00	2.50	575.00	(6)
c	Vertical pair, imperf. horiz.	1,000.00			
	Worn plate, diagonal lines missing in oval background	57.50	3.00		
	Double transfer	67.50	3.00		
256	6¢ Garfield, July	90.00	12.00	1,500.00	(6)
a	Vertical pair, imperf. horizontally	850.00			
257	8¢ Sherman, Mar.	80.00	8.00	800.00	(6)
258	10¢ Webster, Sept.	115.00	5.00	1,600.00	(6)
	Double transfer	150.00	6.00		
259	15¢ Clay, Oct.	185.00	30.00	2,750.00	(6)

246   248   253

254   255   256

257   258   259

59

260

261

262

263

Watermark 191

All your stamps will be easy to find when you use our newly expanded Subject Index! The type is larger for easy reading, and the index is organized in a more user-friendly manner.

	Issues of 1894 (continued), Unwmkd., Perf. 12	Un	U	PB	#
260	50¢ Jefferson, Nov.	250.00	60.00	4,250.00	(6)
261	$1 Perry, type I, Nov.	500.00	160.00	11,000.00	(6)
261A	$1 black Perry, type II (261), Nov.	1,300.00	350.00	18,500.00	(6)
262	$2 James Madison, Dec.	1,700.00	400.00	26,000.00	(6)
263	$5 John Marshall, Dec.	2,250.00	750.00	10,000.00	(4)
	Issues of 1895, Wmkd. (191)				
264	1¢ blue Franklin (246), Apr.	3.50	.15	130.00	(6)
265	2¢ carmine Washington, type I (248), May	18.00	.40	225.00	(6)
	Double transfer	27.50	3.00		
266	2¢ carmine, type II (248)	15.00	1.75	200.00	(6)
267	2¢ carmine, type III (248)	3.00	.15	90.00	(6)
	Triple transfer	—			
	Triangle at right without shading	17.50	5.00		
268	3¢ purple Jackson (253), Oct.	22.50	.65	375.00	(6)
	Double transfer	32.50	2.25		
269	4¢ dark brown Lincoln (254), June	24.00	.75	400.00	(6)
	Double transfer	25.00	2.25		
270	5¢ chocolate Grant (255), June 11	22.50	1.20	400.00	(6)
	Double transfer	32.50	2.50		
	Worn plate, diagonal lines missing in oval background	25.00	1.60		
271	6¢ dull brown Garfield (256), Aug.	42.50	2.50	1,100.00	(6)
	Very thin paper	47.50	2.50		
a	Wmkd. USIR	2,250.00	350.00		
272	8¢ violet brown Sherman (257), July	35.00	.65	475.00	(6)
a	Wmkd. USIR	1,750.00	110.00	5,500.00	(3)
	Double transfer	50.00	2.00		
273	10¢ dark green Webster (258), June	45.00	.80	800.00	(6)
	Double transfer	65.00	2.75		
274	15¢ dark blue Clay (259), Sept.	125.00	5.50	2,100.00	(6)
275	50¢ orange Jefferson (260), Nov.	175.00	14.00	4,000.00	(6)
a	50¢ red orange	195.00	16.00		
276	$1 black Perry, type I (261), Aug.	425.00	45.00	7,500.00	(6)
276A	$1 black Perry, type II (261)	875.00	95.00	15,000.00	(6)
277	$2 bright blue Madison (262), Aug.	675.00	225.00	14,000.00	(6)
a	$2 dark blue	650.00	235.00		
278	$5 dark green Marshall (263), Aug.	1,350.00	300.00	50,000.00	(6)

Who is known as "the Great Chief Justice"?

John Marshall (1755-1835), the fourth Chief Justice of the United States, established the Supreme Court as a vital part of the federal government. Known as "the Great Chief Justice," Marshall made a tremendous impact on the United States judicial system. He is credited with having raised the Supreme Court to a level equal to the executive and legislative branches of the government. **(#263)**

	Issues of 1898-1900, Wmkd. (191), Perf. 12 (279Be issued in 1900, rest in 1898)	Un	U	PB	#	FDC	Q
279	1¢ dp. grn. Franklin (246), Jan.	6.00	.15	110.00	(6)		
	Double transfer	9.00	.75				
279B	2¢ red Washington, type III (248)	5.50	.15	120.00	(6)		
c	2¢ rose carmine, type III	185.00	25.00	1,750.00	(6)		
d	2¢ orange red, type III	6.50	.15	120.00	(6)		
e	Booklet pane of 6, Apr. 16, 1900	350.00	200.00				
f	2¢ deep red, type III	12.50	.75				
280	4¢ rose brn. Lincoln (254), Oct.	20.00	.45	400.00	(6)		
a	4¢ lilac brown	20.00	.45				
b	4¢ orange brown	20.00	.45				
	Extra frame line at top	32.50	3.50				
281	5¢ dark blue Grant (255), Mar.	22.50	.40	425.00	(6)		
	Double transfer	32.50	1.75				
	Worn plate, diagonal lines missing in oval background	26.00	.55				
282	6¢ lake Garfield (256), Dec.	32.50	1.40	650.00	(6)		
a	6¢ purple lake	35.00	1.65	750.00	(6)		
	Double transfer	42.50	2.50				
282C	10¢ brown Webster (258), type I, Nov.	125.00	1.20	1,600.00	(6)		
	Double transfer	150.00	3.00				
283	10¢ orange brown Webster (258), type II	75.00	1.00	950.00	(6)		
284	15¢ olive grn. Clay (259), Nov.	100.00	4.50	1,600.00	(6)		
	Issues of 1898, Trans-Mississippi Exposition Issue, June 17						
285	1¢ Marquette on the Mississippi	21.00	4.00	250.00	(6)	5,500.00	70,993,400
	Double transfer	30.00	5.25				
286	2¢ Farming in the West	19.00	1.00	210.00	(6)	5,000.00	159,720,800
	Double transfer	27.50	1.75				
	Worn plate	20.00	1.25				
287	4¢ Indian Hunting Buffalo	110.00	16.00	1,150.00	(6)		4,924,500
288	5¢ Fremont on the Rocky Mountains	95.00	14.00	1,000.00	(6)	6,250.00	7,694,180
289	8¢ Troops Guarding Train	140.00	30.00	2,250.00	(6)	9,250.00	2,927,200
a	Vertical pair, imperf. horizontally	13,500.00		55,000.00	(4)		
290	10¢ Hardships of Emigration	135.00	18.00	2,500.00	(6)		4,629,760
291	50¢ Western Mining Prospector	400.00	150.00	13,000.00	(6)	11,000.00	530,400
292	$1 Western Cattle in Storm	1,050.00	400.00	37,500.00	(6)	15,000.00	56,900
293	$2 Mississippi River Bridge	1,700.00	700.00	90,000.00	(6)		56,200
	Issues of 1901, Pan-American Exposition Issue, May 1						
294	1¢ Great Lakes Steamer	16.00	2.50	210.00	(6)	3,750.00	91,401,500
a	Center inverted	9,000.00	5,500.00	40,000.00	(3)		
295	2¢ An Early Locomotive	15.00	.75	210.00	(6)	3,250.00	209,759,700
a	Center inverted	30,000.00	13,500.00	210,000.00	(4)		
296	4¢ Automobile	75.00	12.50	2,250.00	(6)	4,250.00	5,737,100
a	Center inverted	12,500.00		55,000.00	(4)		
297	5¢ Bridge at Niagara Falls	90.00	11.00	2,600.00	(6)	4,500.00	7,201,300
298	8¢ Canal Locks at Sault Ste. Marie	100.00	45.00	4,250.00	(6)		4,921,700
299	10¢ American Line Steamship	160.00	20.00	6,500.00	(6)		5,043,700

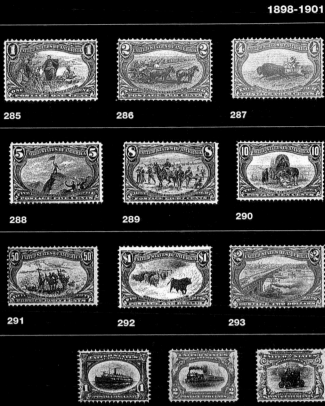

285   286   287

288   289   290

291   292   293

294   295   296

297   298   299

300 301 302 303
304 305 306 307
308 309 310 311
312 313 319

Issues of 1902-03, Wmkd. (191), Perf. 12 (All issued in 1903 except #300b, 306, 308)		Un	U	PB/LP	#	FDC
300	1¢ Franklin, Feb.	6.00	.15	130.00	(6)	
b	Booklet pane of 6, Mar. 6, 1907	*450.00*	*250.00*			
	Double transfer	10.00	1.00			
	Worn plate	7.50	.25			
	Cracked plate	—	—			
301	2¢ Washington, Jan. 17	8.00	.15	130.00	(6)	*2,750.00*
c	Booklet pane of 6, Jan. 24	*400.00*	*250.00*			
	Double transfer	14.00	.90			
	Cracked plate	—				
302	3¢ Jackson, Feb.	30.00	2.00	535.00	(6)	
	Double transfer	52.50	3.00			
	Cracked plate	—				
303	4¢ Grant, Feb.	30.00	.90	535.00	(6)	
	Double transfer	47.50	2.50			
304	5¢ Lincoln, Jan.	35.00	1.10	600.00	(6)	
305	6¢ Garfield, Feb.	40.00	2.00	625.00	(6)	
	6¢ brownish lake	47.50	2.00			
	Double transfer	60.00	2.50			
306	8¢ M. Washington, Dec. 1902	27.50	1.50	450.00	(6)	
	8¢ lavender	35.00	1.75			
307	10¢ Webster, Feb.	30.00	.70	700.00	(6)	
308	13¢ B. Harrison, Nov. 18, 1902	27.50	5.00	425.00	(6)	
309	15¢ Clay, May 27	90.00	3.75	2,000.00	(6)	
	Double transfer	135.00	7.50			
310	50¢ Jefferson, Mar. 23	285.00	17.50	4,750.00	(6)	
011	$1 David G. Farragut, June 5	450.00	45.00	10,000.00	(6)	
312	$2 Madison, June 5	675.00	140.00	17,500.00	(6)	
313	$5 Marshall, June 5	2,000.00	450.00	45,000.00	(6)	
	For listings of #312 and 313 with perf. 10, see #479 and 480.					
	Issues of 1906-08, Imperf. (All issued in 1908 except #314)					
314	1¢ bl. grn. Franklin (300), Oct. 2, 1906	20.00	15.00	150.00	(6)	
314A	4¢ brown Grant (303), Apr.	*18,500.00*	*11,000.00*			
	#314A was issued imperforate, but all copies were privately perforated at the sides.					
315	5¢ blue Lincoln (304), May 12	300.00	*350.00*	2,900.00	(6)	
	Coil Stamps, Perf. 12 Horizontally					
316	1¢ bl. grn. pair Franklin (300), Feb. 18	*50,000.00*	—	*100,000.00*	(2)	
317	5¢ blue pair Lincoln (304), Feb. 24	*6,000.00*	—	*9,000.00*	(2)	
	Coil Stamp, Perf. 12 Vertically					
318	1¢ bl. grn. pair Franklin (300), July 31	*5,000.00*	—	*7,500.00*	(2)	
	Issue of 1903, Perf. 12					
319	2¢ Washington, Nov. 12	4.00	.15	67.50	(6)	
a	2¢ lake, die I	—	—			
b	2¢ carmine rose, die I	6.00	.20	125.00	(6)	
c	2¢ scarlet, die I	4.00	.15	60.00	(6)	
d	Vertical pair, imperf. horizontally	*2,000.00*				
f	2¢ lake, die II	5.00	.20			
g	Booklet pane of 6, carm., die I, Dec. 3	90.00	50.00			
h	Booklet pane of 6, carm., die II	150.00				
i	2¢ carmine, die II	17.50	—			
q	Booklet pane of 6, lake, die II	125.00				

	Issues of 1906, Washington (319), Imperf.	Un	U	PB/LP	#	FDC	Q
320	2¢ carmine, Oct. 2	17.50	11.00	200.00	(6)		
a	2¢ lake, die II	50.00	35.00	625.00	(6)		
b	2¢ scarlet	16.00	12.00	175.00	(6)		
	Double transfer	24.00	15.00				
	Issues of 1908, Coil Stamp (319), Perf. 12 Horizontally						
321	2¢ carmine pair, Feb. 18	55,000.00	—				
	Coil Stamp, Perf. 12 Vertically						
322	2¢ carmine pair, July 31	6,000.00	—	8,000.00	(2)		
	Issues of 1904, Louisiana Purchase Exposition Issue, Apr. 30, Perf. 12						
323	1¢ Robert R. Livingston	19.50	3.00	200.00	(6)	3,000.00	79,779,200
	Diagonal line through left "1"	35.00	10.00				
324	2¢ Thomas Jefferson	17.00	1.00	200.00	(6)	3,250.00	192,732,400
325	3¢ James Monroe	65.00	24.00	750.00	(6)	3,750.00	4,542,600
326	5¢ William McKinley	67.50	15.00	800.00	(6)	5,500.00	6,926,700
327	10¢ Map of Louisiana Purchase	130.00	21.00	1,600.00	(6)	8,000.00	4,011,200
	Issues of 1907, Jamestown Exposition Issue, Apr. 26, Wmkd. (191), Perf. 12						
328	1¢ Captain John Smith	13.00	2.00	175.00	(6)	3,750.00	77,728,794
	Double transfer	16.00	3.00				
329	2¢ Founding of Jamestown, 1607	17.00	1.75	250.00	(6)	5,500.00	149,497,994
330	5¢ Pocahontas	72.50	16.00	1,600.00	(6)		7,980,594

Whose name meant "playful one"?

The name Pocahontas (1595?-1617) meant "playful one." The daughter of the American Indian chief Powhatan, Pocahontas worked to maintain friendly relations between the Indians and early English colonists in America. Captain John Smith, leader of the settlers in Jamestown, Virginia, claimed that Pocahontas saved his life when her father was about to kill him with a stone war club. In 1614, Pocahontas married English colonist John Rolfe.

(#330)

323   **324**   **325**

326   **327**

328   **329**   **330**

Have you noticed? We've improved the binding on your book so that it will stay open and lay flat. This new binding, called "Flex Binding," will make your guide a more convenient tool.

331   332   333

334   335   336

337   338   339

340   341   342

Issues of 1908-09, Wmkd. (191) Perf. 126 (All issued in 1908 except #336, 338-42, 345-47)				
	Un	U	PB/LP	#
331 1¢ Franklin, Dec.	4.75	.15	45.00	(6)
a Booklet pane of 6, Dec. 2	165.00	*35.00*		
Double transfer	6.75	.60		
332 2¢ Washington, Nov.	4.50	.15	42.50	(6)
a Booklet pane of 6, Nov. 16	100.00	*35.00*		
Double transfer	9.00	—		
Cracked plate	—	—		
333 3¢ Washington, type I, Dec.	21.00	1.75	200.00	(6)
334 4¢ Washington, Dec.	25.00	.55	250.00	(6)
Double transfer	40.00	—		
335 5¢ Washington, Dec.	32.50	1.50	345.00	(6)
336 0¢ Washington, Jan. 1909	40.00	3.50	550.00	(6)
337 8¢ Washington, Dec.	30.00	1.75	300.00	(6)
Double transfer	40.00	—		
338 10¢ Washington, Jan. 1909	47.50	1.00	650.00	(6)
a "China Clay" paper	—			
Very thin paper	—			
339 13¢ Washington, Jan. 1909	27.50	14.00	300.00	(6)
Line through "TAG" of "POSTAGE"	47.50	—		
340 15¢ Washington, Jan. 1909	42.50	3.75	400.00	(6)
a "China Clay" paper	—			
341 50¢ Washington, Jan. 13, 1909	190.00	10.00	*6,000.00*	(6)
342 $1 Washington, Jan. 29, 1909	350.00	50.00	*10,000.00*	(6)
Imperf.				
343 1¢ green Franklin (331), Dec.	5.50	3.00	47.50	(6)
Double transfer	11.50	5.50		
344 2¢ carmine Washington (332), Dec. 10	7.50	2.00	90.00	(6)
Double transfer	12.50	3.50		
Double transfer, design of 1¢	*1,250.00*			
#345-47: Washington (333-35)				
345 3¢ deep violet, type I, Mar. 3, 1909	14.00	15.00	180.00	(6)
Double transfer	22.50	—		
346 4¢ orange brown, Feb. 25, 1909	24.00	17.50	210.00	(6)
Double transfer	42.50	—		
347 5¢ blue, Feb. 25, 1909	42.50	30.00	350.00	(6)
Cracked plate	—			
Issues of 1908-10, Coil Stamps, Perf. 12 Horizontally				
#350-51, 354-56: Washington (Designs of 334-35, 338)				
348 1¢ green Franklin (331), Dec. 29, 1908	21.00	10.00	150.00	(2)
349 2¢ carmine Washington (332), Jan. 1909	37.50	6.00	265.00	(2)
Double transfer, design of 1¢	—	*1,750.00*		
350 4¢ orange brown, Aug. 15, 1910	80.00	60.00	575.00	(2)
351 5¢ blue, Jan. 1909	90.00	90.00	575.00	(2)
Issues of 1909, Coil Stamps, Perf. 12 Vertically				
352 1¢ green Franklin (331), Jan.	40.00	25.00	275.00	(2)
Double transfer	—	—		

	Issues of 1909 (continued), Coil Stamps, Perf. 12 Vertically	Un	U	PB/LP	#		
353	2¢ carmine Washington (332), Jan. 12	40.00	6.00	275.00	(2)		
354	4¢ orange brown, Feb. 23	100.00	45.00	700.00	(2)		
355	5¢ blue, Feb. 23	110.00	65.00	725.00	(2)		
356	10¢ yellow, Jan. 7	1,500.00	750.00	7,000.00	(2)		
	Issues of 1909, Bluish Paper, Perf. 12, #359-66: Washington (Designs of 333-40)						
357	1¢ green Franklin (331), Feb. 16	80.00	65.00	875.00	(6)		
358	2¢ carmine Washington (332), Feb. 16	75.00	55.00	850.00	(6)		
	Double transfer	—					
359	3¢ deep violet, type I	1,400.00	*1,300.00*	*15,000.00*	(6)		
360	4¢ orange brown	*13,500.00*		*75,000.00*	(3)		
361	5¢ blue	3,250.00	*3,500.00*	*30,000.00*	(6)		
362	6¢ red orange	1,000.00	850.00	*13,000.00*	(6)		
363	8¢ olive green	*13,500.00*		*75,000.00*	(3)		
364	10¢ yellow	1,100.00	1,000.00	*13,500.00*	(6)		
365	13¢ blue green	2,250.00	*1,250.00*	*18,500.00*	(6)		
366	15¢ pale ultramarine	1,000.00	800.00	*10,000.00*	(6)		
	Lincoln Memorial Issue, Feb. 12, Wmkd. (191)						
367	2¢ Bust of Abraham Lincoln	4.25	1.40	100.00	(6)	*350.00*	148,387,191
	Double transfer	6.75	2.50				
	Imperf.						
368	2¢ carmine (367)	20.00	16.00	175.00	(6) *7,000.00*		1,273,900
	Double transfer	40.00	24.00				
	Bluish Paper						
369	2¢ carmine (367)	170.00	175.00	*2,400.00*	(6)		637,000
	Alaska-Yukon Pacific Exposition Issue, June 1						
370	2¢ Willam H. Seward	7.50	1.25	175.00	(6) *1,800.00*		152,887,311
	Double transfer	10.00	4.00				
	Imperf.						
371	2¢ carmine (370)	27.50	20.00	200.00	(6)		525,400
	Double transfer	40.00	25.00				
	Hudson-Fulton Celebration Issue, Sept. 25, Wmkd. (191)						
372	2¢ *Half Moon & Clermont*	10.00	3.25	250.00	(6)	*800.00*	72,634,631
	Double transfer	14.00	4.25				
	Imperf.						
373	2¢ carmine (372)	32.50	22.50	235.00	(6)	—	216,480
	Double transfer	45.00	25.00				
	Issues of 1910-11, Wmkd. (190) #376-82: Washington (Designs of 333-38, 340)						
374	1¢ green Franklin (331), Nov. 23, 1910	5.00	.15	65.00	(6)		
a	Booklet pane of 6, Oct. 7, 1910	110.00	*30.00*				
	Double transfer	12.50	—				
	Cracked plate	—	—				
375	2¢ carmine Washington (332), Nov. 23, 1910	5.00	.15	70.00	(6)		
	2¢ lake	*150.00*					
a	Booklet pane of 6, Nov. 30, 1910	95.00	*25.00*				
	Cracked plate	—	—				
	Double transfer	10.00	—				
	Double transfer, design of 1¢	—	*1,000.00*				
376	3¢ dp. vio., type I, Jan. 16, 1911	11.50	1.00	100.00	(6)		

367

370

372

Watermark 190

We eliminated stamp listings on black pages. This will help you read your stamp listings more quickly and easily.

397

398

399

400

Protect wildlife! Read the article about Duck Stamps and learn how buying these stamps helps to save waterfowl habitat.

	Issues of 1910-11 (continued), Wmkd. (190), Perf. 12	Un	U	PB/LP	#	FDC	Q
377	4¢ brown, Jan. 20, 1911	20.00	.30	130.00	(6)		
	Double transfer	—	—				
378	5¢ blue, Jan. 25, 1911	17.50	.30	160.00	(6)		
	Double transfer	—	—				
379	6¢ red orange, Jan. 25, 1911	25.00	.40	325.00	(6)		
380	8¢ olive green, Feb. 8, 1911	75.00	8.50	775.00	(6)		
381	10¢ yellow, Jan. 24, 1911	70.00	2.50	775.00	(6)		
382	15¢ pale ultramarine, Mar. 1, 1911	190.00	11.50	1,750.00	(6)		
	Issues of 1910, Jan. 3, Imperf.						
383	1¢ green Franklin (331)	2.25	2.00	37.50	(6)		
	Double transfer	5.75	—				
384	2¢ carmine Washington (332)	3.50	1.75	115.00	(6)		
	Dbl. transfer, design of 1¢	*1,250.00*					
	Double transfer	7.00	—				
	Cracked plate	17.50	—				
	Issues of 1910, Nov.1, Coil Stamps, Perf. 12 Horizontally						
385	1¢ green Franklin (331)	18.00	10.00	200.00	(2)		
386	2¢ carmine Washington (332)	32.50	12.50	375.00	(2)		
	Issues of 1910-11, Coil Stamps, Wmkd. (190), Perf. 12 Vertically						
387	1¢ green Franklin (331), Nov. 1, 1910	60.00	30.00	235.00	(2)		
388	2¢ carmine Washington (332), Nov. 1, 1910	550.00	200.00	3,250.00	(2)		
389	3¢ deep violet Washington, type I (333), Jan. 24, 1911	*15,000.00*	*7,000.00*				
	Issues of 1910-13, Coil Stamps, Perf. 8¹/₂ Horizontally						
390	1¢ green Franklin (331), Dec. 12, 1910	3.00	4.00	20.00	(2)		
	Double transfer	—	—				
391	2¢ carmine Washington (332), Dec. 23, 1910	20.00	6.75	115.00	(2)		
	Coil Stamps, Perf. 8¹/₂ Vertically #394-96: Washington (Designs of 333-35)						
392	1¢ green Franklin (331), Dec.12, 1910	12.00	14.00	85.00	(2)		
	Double transfer	—	—				
393	2¢ carmine Washington (332), Dec. 16, 1910	24.00	5.50	140.00	(2)		
394	3¢ deep violet, type I, Sept. 18, 1911	32.50	40.00	210.00	(2)		
395	4¢ brown, Apr. 15, 1912	32.50	30.00	210.00	(2)		
396	5¢ blue, Mar. 1913	32.50	30.00	210.00	(2)		
	Issues of 1913, Panama Pacific Exposition Issue, Wmkd. (190), Perf. 12						
397	1¢ Vasco Nunez de Balboa, Jan. 1	11.00	.85	110.00	(6)	*3,500.00*	167,398,463*
	Double transfer	17.50	2.00				
398	2¢ Pedro Miguel Locks, Panama Canal, Jan.	12.50	.30	210.00	(6)		251,856,543*
	2¢ carmine lake	*400.00*					
	Double transfer	35.00	2.00				
399	5¢ Golden Gate, Jan. 1	52.50	6.50	1,500.00	(6)	*4,000.00*	14,544,363*
400	10¢ Discovery of San Francisco Bay, Jan. 1	95.00	14.00	2,000.00	(6)	—	8,484,182*
400A	10¢ orange (400), Aug.	175.00	10.50	*7,750.00*	(6)		
	*Includes perf. 10 printing quantities.						

	Issues of 1914-15, Perf. 10	Un	U	PB/LP	#
401	1¢ green (397), Dec. 1914	16.00	4.00	225.00	(6)
402	2¢ carmine (398), Jan. 1915	55.00	1.00	1,150.00	(6)
403	5¢ blue (399), Feb. 1915	120.00	11.00	3,250.00	(6)
404	10¢ orange (400), July 1915	825.00	42.50	10,000.00	(6)
	Issues of 1912-14, Wmkd. (190), Perf. 12				
405	1¢ green, Feb. 1912	4.00	.15	67.50	(6)
a	Vertical pair, imperf. horizontally	650.00	—		
b	Booklet pane of 6, Feb. 8, 1912	50.00	7.50		
	Cracked plate	12.00	—		
	Double transfer	5.75	—		
406	2¢ carmine, type I, Feb. 1912	3.75	.15	85.00	(6)
	2¢ lake	200.00	—		
a	Booklet pane of 6, Feb. 8, 1912	60.00	17.50		
b	Double impression	—			
	Double transfer	6.50	—		
407	7¢ black, Apr. 1914	60.00	8.00	900.00	(6)
	Imperf. #408-13: Washington (Designs of 405-6)				
408	1¢ green, Mar. 1912	.90	.50	15.00	(6)
	Double transfer	2.50	1.00		
	Cracked plate	—	—		
409	2¢ carmine, type I, Feb. 1912	1.00	.50	30.00	(6)
	Cracked plate	15.00	—		
	Coil Stamps, Perf. 8¹/₂ Horizontally				
410	1¢ green, Mar. 1912	4.50	3.00	25.00	(2)
	Double transfer	—	—		
411	2¢ carmine, type I, Mar. 1912	6.00	2.50	30.00	(2)
	Double transfer	9.00	—		
	Coil Stamps, Perf. 8¹/₂ Vertically				
412	1¢ green, Mar. 18, 1912	15.00	3.75	65.00	(2)
413	2¢ carmine, type I, Mar. 1912	24.00	.75	130.00	(2)
	Double transfer	40.00	—		
	Perf. 12				
414	8¢ Franklin, Feb. 1912	27.50	.85	325.00	(6)
415	9¢ Franklin, Apr. 1914	35.00	9.50	500.00	(6)
416	10¢ Franklin, Jan. 1912	30.00	.25	365.00	(6)
417	12¢ Franklin, Apr. 1914	30.00	3.00	350.00	(6)
	Double transfer	40.00	—		
	Triple transfer	55.00	—		
418	15¢ Franklin, Feb. 1912	55.00	2.00	475.00	(6)
	Double transfer	—	—		

405   406   407

414   415   416

417   418

We eliminated stamp listings on black pages. This will help you read your stamp listings more quickly and easily.

419   **420**   **421**

423   **434**

*Protect wildlife! Read the article about Duck Stamps
and learn how buying these stamps helps to save
waterfowl habitat.*

	Issues of 1912-14 (continued), Perf. 12	Un	U	PB	#
419	20¢ Franklin, Apr. 1914	125.00	9.00	1,300.00	(6)
420	30¢ Franklin, Apr. 1914	90.00	10.00	1,150.00	(6)
421	50¢ Franklin, Aug. 1914	325.00	10.00	5,750.00	(6)
	Wmkd. (191)				
422	50¢ Franklin (421), Feb. 12, 1912	175.00	9.50	3,750.00	(6)
423	$1 Franklin, Feb. 12, 1912	400.00	40.00	*8,000.00*	(6)
	Double transfer	450.00	—		
	Issues of 1914-15, Wmkd. (190), Perf.10 #424-30: Wash. (Designs of 405-06, 333-36, 407)				
424	1¢ green, Sept. 5, 1914	1.60	.15	35.00	(6)
	Cracked plate	—	—		
	Double transfer	4.25	—		
	Experimental precancel, New Orleans		—		
a	Perf. 12 x 10	*600.00*	*500.00*		
b	Perf. 10 x 12		250.00		
c	Vertical pair, imperf. horizontally	425.00	250.00		
d	Booklet pane of 6	3.50	.75		
e	Vertical pair, imperf. between and at top	—			
425	2¢ rose red, type I, Sept. 5, 1914	1.50	.15	22.50	(6)
	Cracked plate	9.00	—		
	Double transfer	—	—		
c	Perf. 10 x 12		—		
d	Perf. 12 x 10	—	600.00		
e	Booklet pane of 6, Jan. 6, 1914	12.50	*3.00*		
426	3¢ deep violet, type I, Sept. 18, 1914	10.00	.90	150.00	(6)
427	4¢ brown, Sept. 7, 1914	26.00	.30	475.00	(6)
	Double transfer	40.00	—		
428	5¢ blue, Sept. 14, 1914	22.50	.30	325.00	(6)
a	Perf. 12 x 10		*1,000.00*		
429	6¢ red orange, Sept. 28, 1914	35.00	.90	475.00	(6)
430	7¢ black, Sept. 10, 1914	65.00	2.50	875.00	(6)
	#431-33, 435, 437-40: Franklin (414-21, 423)				
431	8¢ pale olive green, Sept. 26, 1914	27.50	1.10	475.00	(6)
	Double impression	—			
432	9¢ salmon red, Oct. 6, 1914	37.50	5.00	650.00	(6)
433	10¢ orange yellow, Sept. 9, 1914	35.00	.20	650.00	(6)
434	11¢ Franklin, Aug. 11, 1915	16.00	5.50	225.00	(6)
435	12¢ claret brown, Sept. 10, 1914	18.00	2.75	260.00	(6)
a	12¢ copper red	19.00	2.75	290.00	(6)
	Double transfer	27.50	—		
	Triple transfer	32.50	—		
436	Not assigned				
437	15¢ gray, Sept. 16, 1914	87.50	4.50	825.00	(6)
438	20¢ ultramarine, Sept. 19, 1914	165.00	2.50	2,750.00	(6)
439	30¢ orange red, Sept. 19, 1914	190.00	10.00	3,500.00	(6)
440	50¢ violet, Dec. 10, 1915	475.00	10.00	13,500.00	(6)

	Issues of 1914, Coil Stamps, Perf. 10 Horizontally #441-59: Wash. (Designs of 405-06, 333-35; Flat Press, 18½-19 x 22mm)	Un	U	PB	#
441	1¢ green, Nov. 14	.55	.80	4.25	(2)
442	2¢ carmine, type I, July 22	6.00	4.50	35.00	(2)
	Coil Stamps, Perf. 10 Vertically				
443	1¢ green, May 29	15.00	4.00	80.00	(2)
444	2¢ carmine, type I, Apr. 25	21.00	1.00	120.00	(2)
445	3¢ violet, type I, Dec. 18	175.00	100.00	875.00	(2)
446	4¢ brown, Oct. 2	90.00	24.00	450.00	(2)
447	5¢ blue, July 30	30.00	17.50	165.00	(2)
	Issues of 1915-16, Coil Stamps, Perf. 10 Horizontally (Rotary Press, Designs 18½–19 x 22½mm)				
448	1¢ green, Dec. 12, 1915	4.25	2.25	25.00	(2)
449	2¢ red, type I, Dec. 5, 1915	1,750.00	225.00	8,500.00	(2)
450	2¢ carmine, type III, Feb. 1916	7.00	2.25	35.00	(2)
451	Not assigned				
	Issues of 1914-16, Coil Stamps, Perf. 10 Vertically (Rotary Press, Designs 19½–20 x 22mm)				
452	1¢ green, Nov. 11, 1914	7.50	1.40	50.00	(2)
453	2¢ carmine rose, type I, July 3, 1914	90.00	3.25	425.00	(2)
	Cracked plate	—	—		
454	2¢ red, type II, June 1915	72.50	7.50	350.00	(2)
455	2¢ carmine, type III, Dec. 1915	7.00	.75	37.50	(2)
456	3¢ violet, type I, Feb. 2, 1916	190.00	75.00	825.00	(2)
457	4¢ brown, Feb. 18, 1916	19.00	15.00	100.00	(2)
	Cracked plate	35.00	—		
458	5¢ blue, Mar. 9, 1916	22.50	15.00	125.00	(2)
	Issue of 1914, Horizontal Coil Stamp, Imperf.				
459	2¢ carmine, type I, June 30	375.00	*750.00*	1,250.00	(2)
	Issues of 1915, Wmkd. (191), Perf. 10				
460	$1 violet black Franklin (423), Feb. 8	600.00	55.00	*10,000.00*	(6)
	Double transfer	650.00	—		
	Perf. 11				
461	2¢ pale carmine red Washington (406), type I, June 17	75.00	*150.00*	*1,000.00*	(6)
	Privately perforated copies of #409 have been made to resemble #461.				
	From 1916 to date, all postage stamps except #519 and 832b are on unwatermarked paper.				
	Issues of 1916-17, Unwmkd., Perf. 10 #462-69: Wash. (Designs of 405-06, 333-36, 407)				
462	1¢ green, Sept. 27, 1916	5.00	.15	125.00	(6)
	Experimental precancel, Springfield, MA, or New Orleans, LA		10.00		
a	Booklet pane of 6, Oct. 15, 1916	7.50	*1.00*		
463	2¢ carmine, type I, Sept. 25, 1916	3.25	.15	115.00	(6)
	Experimental precancel, Springfield, MA		22.50		
a	Booklet pane of 6, Oct. 8, 1916	85.00	*20.00*		
	Double transfer	5.75	—		
464	3¢ violet, type I, Nov. 11, 1916	57.50	8.00	1,200.00	(6)
	Double transfer in "CENTS"	*75.00*	—		
465	4¢ orange brown, Oct. 7, 1916	32.50	1.00	600.00	(6)
466	5¢ blue, Oct. 17, 1916	57.50	1.00	825.00	(6)
	Experimental precancel, Springfield, MA		150.00		
467	5¢ carmine (error in plate of 2¢)	475.00	525.00		
468	6¢ red orange, Oct. 10, 1916	70.00	5.00	1,100.00	(6)
	Experimental precancel, Springfield, MA		175.00		
469	7¢ black, Oct. 10, 1916	92.50	7.50	1,300.00	(6)
	Experimental precancel, Springfield, MA		175.00		

	Issues of 1916-17 (continued), Perf. 10	Un	U	PB/LP	#	FDC
	#470-78: Franklin (Designs of 414-16, 434, 417-21, 423)					
470	8¢ olive green, Nov. 13, 1916	42.50	3.75	500.00	(6)	
	Experimental precancel, Springfield, MA		165.00			
471	9¢ salmon red, Nov. 16, 1916	45.00	9.50	650.00	(6)	
472	10¢ orange yellow, Oct. 17, 1916	85.00	.75	1,200.00	(6)	
473	11¢ dark green, Nov. 16, 1916	25.00	11.00	300.00	(6)	
	Experimental precancel, Springfield, MA		*650.00*			
474	12¢ claret brown, Oct. 10, 1916	40.00	3.50	575.00	(6)	
	Double transfer	50.00	5.25			
	Triple transfer	65.00	8.50			
475	15¢ gray, Nov. 16, 1916	135.00	7.00	2,500.00	(6)	
476	20¢ light ultramarine, Dec. 5, 1916	200.00	7.50	3,250.00	(6)	
476A	30¢ orange red	*3,500.00*	—			
477	50¢ light violet, Mar. 2, 1917	875.00	40.00	*40,000.00*	(6)	
478	$1 violet black, Dec. 22, 1916	600.00	11.00	*13,000.00*	(6)	
	Double transfer	700.00	15.00			
479	$2 dark blue Madison (312), Mar. 22, 1917	290.00	30.00	4,000.00	(6)	
480	$5 light green Marshall (313), Mar. 22, 1917	225.00	32.50	2,750.00	(6)	
	Issues of 1916-17, Imperf.					
	#481-96: Washington (Designs of 405-06, 333-35)					
481	1¢ green, Nov. 1916	.65	.45	9.75	(6)	
	Double transfer	2.50	1.25			
482	2¢ carmine, type I, Dec. 8, 1916	1.25	1.00	20.00	(6)	
482A	2¢ deep rose, type Ia		*7,500.00*			
483	3¢ violet, type I, Oct. 13, 1917	9.50	6.50	110.00	(6)	
	Double transfer	16.00	—			
484	3¢ violet, type II	7.00	3.00	87.50	(6)	
	Double transfer	12.50	—			
485	5¢ carmine (error in plate of 2¢), Mar. 1917	*7,500.00*				
	Issues of 1916-22, Coil Stamps, Perf. 10 Horizontally					
486	1¢ green, Jan. 1918	.65	.20	3.00	(2)	
	Double transfer	2.25	—			
487	2¢ carmine, type II, Nov. 15, 1916	12.00	2.50	80.00	(2)	
488	2¢ carmine, type III, 1919	2.00	1.35	12.00	(2)	
	Cracked plate	12.00	7.50			
489	3¢ violet, type I, Oct. 10, 1917	4.00	1.00	22.50	(2)	
	Coil Stamps, Perf. 10 Vertically					
490	1¢ green, Nov. 17, 1916	.40	.15	2.50	(2)	
	Cracked plate (horizontal)	7.50	—			
	Cracked plate (vertical) retouched	9.00	—			
	Rosette crack	*35.00*	—			
491	2¢ carmine, type II, Nov. 17, 1916	1,500.00	450.00	7,250.00	(2)	
492	2¢ carmine, type III	6.50	.15	35.00	(2)	
493	3¢ violet, type I, July 23, 1917	13.50	2.00	90.00	(2)	
494	3¢ violet, type II, Feb. 4, 1918	7.50	1.00	50.00	(2)	
495	4¢ orange brown, Apr. 15, 1917	8.00	3.00	55.00	(2)	
	Cracked plate	25.00	—			
496	5¢ blue, Jan. 15, 1919	2.75	.90	20.00	(2)	
497	10¢ orange yellow Franklin (416), Jan. 31, 1922	16.00	9.00	100.00	(2)	*2,000.00*

	Issues of 1917-19, **Perf. 11** #498-507: Washington (Designs of 405-06, 333-36, 407)	Un	U	PB	#
498	1¢ green, Mar. 1917	.30	.15	13.00	(6)
a	Vertical pair, imperf. horizontally	175.00			
b	Horizontal pair, imperf. between	75.00			
d	Double impression	150.00			
e	Booklet pane of 6, Apr. 6, 1917	2.00	.35		
f	Booklet pane of 30, Sept. 1917	600.00			
g	Perf. 10 top or bottom	500.00	—		
	Cracked plate	7.50	—		
499	2¢ rose, type I, Mar. 1917	.35	.15	14.00	(6)
a	Vertical pair, imperf. horizontally	150.00			
b	Horizontal pair, imperf. vertically	200.00	100.00		
e	Booklet pane of 6, Mar. 31, 1917	3.00	.50		
f	Booklet pane of 30, Sept. 1917	11,500.00			
g	Double impression	125.00	—		
	Double transfer	6.00	—		
500	2¢ deep rose, type Ia	200.00	110.00	1,650.00	(6)
	Pair, types I and Ia	1,000.00			
501	3¢ light violet, type I, Mar. 1917	8.00	.15	80.00	(6)
b	Booklet pane of 6, Oct. 17, 1917	50.00	15.00		
d	Double impression	200.00			
502	3¢ dark violet, type II	11.00	.15	120.00	(6)
b	Booklet pane of 6	42.50	10.00		
c	Vertical pair, imperf. horizontally	250.00	125.00		
e	Perf. 10, top or bottom	425.00	—		
503	4¢ brown, Mar. 1917	7.50	.15	110.00	(6)
504	5¢ blue, Mar. 1917	6.50	.15	110.00	(6)
	Double transfer	10.00	—		
505	5¢ rose (error in plate of 2¢)	350.00	400.00		
506	6¢ red orange, Mar. 1917	10.00	.20	135.00	(6)
507	7¢ black, Mar. 1917	20.00	.85	200.00	(6)
	#508-12, 514-18: Franklin (Designs of 414-16, 434, 417-21, 423)				
508	8¢ olive bister, Mar. 1917	9.00	.40	130.00	(6)
c	Perf. 10 top or bottom		500.00		
509	9¢ salmon red, Mar. 1917	11.00	1.40	125.00	(6)
510	10¢ orange yellow, Mar. 1917	13.00	.15	160.00	(6)
511	11¢ light green, May 1917	7.00	2.00	115.00	(6)
	Double transfer	12.50	3.00		
512	12¢ claret brown, May 1917	7.00	.30	105.00	(6)
a	12¢ brown carmine	7.50	.35		
b	Perf. 10, top or bottom	—	450.00		
513	13¢ apple green, Jan. 10, 1919	8.50	4.75	115.00	(6)
	13¢ deep apple green	9.75	5.25		
514	15¢ gray, May 1917	30.00	.80	425.00	(6)
515	20¢ light ultramarine, May 1917	37.50	.20	475.00	(6)
	20¢ deep ultramarine	39.00	.16		
b	Vertical pair, imperf. between	325.00			
516	30¢ orange red, May 1917	30.00	.60	475.00	(6)
a	Perf. 10 top or bottom	850.00	—		
517	50¢ red violet, May 1917	60.00	.45	1,500.00	(6)
c	Perf. 10, top or bottom		700.00		
518	$1 violet brown, May 1917	45.00	1.20	1,200.00	(6)
b	$1 deep brown	1,000.00	450.00		

513

*Become a stamp-collecting expert. Learn all you
need to know in the improved "Words and Phrases"
section. Definitions of key philatelic terms are
thoroughly explained there.*

523

524

537

You asked for it! This edition contains more stamp trivia than ever before. We added twice as many stamp stories, and now there are two feature articles.

	Issue of 1917, Wmkd. (191), Perf. 11	Un	U	PB	#	FDC	Q
519	2¢ carm. Washington (332), Oct. 10	225.00	*450.00*	2,000.00	(6)		
	Privately perforated copies of #344 have been made to resemble #519.						
520-22	Not assigned						
	Issues of 1918, Unwmkd.						
523	$2 Franklin, Aug. 19	600.00	200.00	*12,500.00*	(8)		
524	$5 Franklin, Aug. 19	200.00	27.50	*4,000.00*	(8)		
	Issues of 1918-20 #525-35: Washington (Designs of 405-06, 333)						
525	1¢ gray green, Dec. 1918	1.50	.35	15.00	(6)		
	1¢ Emerald	2.00	.85				
a	1¢ dark green	1.65	.75				
	Double impression	15.00	15.00				
526	2¢ carmine, type IV, Mar. 15, 1920	21.00	2.75	160.00	(6)	*800.00*	
	Gash on forehead	27.50	—				
	Malformed "2" at left	26.00	5.25				
527	2¢ carmine, type V	11.50	.60	85.00	(6)		
a	Double impression	55.00	10.00				
	Line through "2" and "EN"	18.50	—				
528	2¢ carmine, type Va	6.00	.15	42.50	(6)		
	Double impression	25.00					
528A	2¢ carmine, type VI	37.50	1.00	235.00	(6)		
d	Double impression	150.00	—				
528B	2¢ carmine, type VII	14.00	.30	100.00	(6)		
e	Double impression	55.00					
	Retouched on check	—	—				
529	3¢ violet, type III, Mar. 1918	2.25	.15	40.00	(6)		
a	Double impression	30.00	—				
b	Printed on both sides	*350.00*					
530	3¢ purple, type IV	1.00	.15	10.00	(6)		
a	Double impression	20.00	6.00				
b	Printed on both sides	250.00					
	"Blister" under "U.S."	4.00	—				
	Recut under "U.S."	4.00	—				
	Imperf.						
531	1¢ green, Jan. 1919	7.00	7.00	60.00	(6)		
532	2¢ carmine rose, type IV	35.00	25.00	225.00	(6)		
533	2¢ carmine, type V	175.00	65.00	1,300.00	(6)		
534	2¢ carmine, type Va	9.00	6.00	75.00	(6)		
534A	2¢ carmine, type VI	32.50	20.00	250.00	(6)		
534B	2¢ carmine, type VII	1,250.00	600.00	10,000.00	(6)		
535	3¢ violet, type IV, 1918	7.00	4.50	50.00	(6)		
a	Double impression	100.00	—				
	Issues of 1919, Perf. 12¹/₂						
536	1¢ gray green Washington (405), Aug.	11.00	14.00	120.00	(6)		
a	Horizontal pair, imperf. vertically	*500.00*					
	Perf. 11						
537	3¢ Allied Victory, Mar. 3	7.50	2.75	85.00	(6)		99,585,200
a	deep red violet	*350.00*	50.00	2,250.00	(6)		
c	red violet	30.00	7.50				
	Double transfer	—	—				

	Issues of 1919 (continued), Perf. 11 x 10	Un	U	PB	#	FDC	Q
	#538-46: Washington (Designs of 405-06, 333; 19¹/₂–20 x 22-22¹/₄ mm)						
538	1¢ green, June	7.50	6.00	72.50	(4)		
a	Vertical pair, imperf. horizontally	50.00	*100.00*	750.00	(4)		
	Double transfer	15.00	—				
539	2¢ carmine rose, type II	2,750.00	*2,000.00*	11,500.00	(4)		
540	2¢ carmine rose, type III, June 14	7.50	6.00	75.00	(4)		
	Double transfer	20.00	—				
a	Vertical pair,imperf. horizontally	50.00	*100.00*				
b	Horizontal pair, imperf. vertically	*550.00*					
541	3¢ violet, type II, June	22.50	20.00	265.00	(4)		
	Issue of 1920, Perf. 10 x 11 (Design 19 x 22¹/₂–22³/₄mm)						
542	1¢ green, May 26	6.50	.65	100.00	(6)	950.00	
	Issues of 1921, Perf. 10 (Design 19 x 22¹/₂mm)						
543	1¢ green, May	.35	.15	1.40	(4)		
a	Horizontal pair, imperf. between	*550.00*					
	Double transfer		—				
	Triple transfer	—	—				
	Issue of 1922, Perf. 11 (Design 19 x 22¹/₂mm)						
544	1¢ green	*12,500.00*	*2,750.00*				
	Issues of 1921 (Designs 19¹/₂–20 x 22mm)						
545	1¢ green, May	95.00	110.00	750.00	(4)		
546	2¢ carmine rose, type III, May	60.00	*110.00*	525.00	(4)		
a	Perf. 10 at left	—					
	Recut in hair	85.00	*150.00*				
	Issues of 1920, Perf. 11						
547	$2 Franklin, Nov. 1	175.00	32.50	4,000.00	(8)		
	Pilgrim Tercentenary Issue, Dec. 21						
548	1¢ The Mayflower	3.50	1.65	40.00	(6)	*800.00*	137,978,207
	Double transfer	—	—				
549	2¢ Landing of the Pilgrims	5.50	1.25	50.00	(6)	*650.00*	196,037,327
550	5¢ Signing of the Compact	35.00	10.00	400.00	(6)	—	11,321,607
	Issues of 1922-25, Perf. 11 (See also #581-91, 594-606, 622-23, 631-42, 658-79, 684-87, 692-701, 723)						
551	¹/₂¢ Nathan Hale, Apr. 4, 1925	.15	.15	4.25	(6)	15.00 (4)	
	"Cap" on fraction bar	.45	.15				
552	1¢ Franklin, Jan. 17, 1923	1.25	.15	17.50	(6)	20.00 (2)	
a	Booklet pane of 6, Aug. 11, 1923	4.50	*.50*				
	Double transfer	3.50	—				
553	1¹/₂¢ Harding, Mar. 19, 1925	2.25	.15	25.00	(6)	25.00 (2)	
554	2¢ Washington, Jan. 15, 1923	1.25	.15	17.50	(6)	35.00	
a	Horizontal pair, imperf. vertically	175.00					
b	Vertical pair, imperf. horizontally	*500.00*					
c	Booklet pane of 6, Feb. 10, 1923	6.00	*1.00*				
	Double transfer	2.25	.60				
555	3¢ Lincoln, Feb. 12, 1923	15.00	.85	125.00	(6)	27.50	
556	4¢ M. Washington, Jan. 15, 1923	15.00	.20	125.00	(6)	50.00	
b	Perf. 10, top or bottom	*425.00*	—				
557	5¢ T. Roosevelt, Oct. 27, 1922	15.00	.15	150.00	(6)	*125.00*	
a	Imperf. pair	*1,250.00*					
c	Perf. 10, top or bottom	—	*500.00*				
558	6¢ Garfield, Nov. 20, 1922	27.50	.75	325.00	(6)	225.00	
	Double transfer	40.00	2.00				
	Same, recut	40.00	2.00				

547

548   549

550

551   552   553

554   555   556

557   558

85

559

560

561

562

563

564

565

566

567

568

569

570

571

572

573

	Issues of 1922-25 (continued), Perf. 11	Un	U	PB	#	FDC
559	7¢ McKinley, May 1, 1923	7.00	.45	50.00	(6)	140.00
	Double transfer	—	—			
560	8¢ Grant, May 1, 1923	37.50	.35	500.00	(6)	175.00
	Double transfer	—	—			
561	9¢ Jefferson, Jan. 15, 1923	12.00	.90	115.00	(6)	175.00
	Double transfer	—	—			
562	10¢ Monroe, Jan. 15, 1923	16.00	.15	150.00	(6)	160.00
a	Vertical pair, imperf. horizontally	1,250.00				
b	Imperf. pair	1,500.00				
c	Perf. 10 at top or bottom		750.00			
563	11¢ Hayes, Oct. 4, 1922	1.25	.25	22.50	(6)	600.00
564	12¢ Cleveland, Mar. 20, 1923	5.50	.15	62.50	(6)	175.00
a	Horizontal pair, imperf. vertically	1,000.00				
b	Imperf. pair	—				
565	14¢ American Indian, May 1, 1923	3.50	.65	45.00	(6)	375.00
	Double transfer	—	—			
566	15¢ Statue of Liberty, Nov. 11, 1922	19.00	.15	225.00	(6)	500.00
567	20¢ Golden Gate, May 1, 1923	19.00	.15	165.00	(6)	500.00
a	Horizontal pair, imperf. vertically	1,500.00				
568	25¢ Niagara Falls, Nov. 11, 1922	17.00	.38	175.00	(6)	675.00
b	Vertical pair, imperf. horizontally	850.00				
c	Perf. 10 at one side	—				
569	30¢ Buffalo, Mar. 20, 1923	30.00	.30	235.00	(6)	825.00
	Double transfer	37.50	1.50			
570	50¢ Arlington Amphitheater, Nov. 11, 1922	50.00	.15	600.00	(6)	1,200.00
571	$1 Lincoln Memorial, Feb. 12, 1923	40.00	.35	425.00	(6)	5,500.00
	Double transfer	80.00	1.50			
572	$2 U.S. Capitol, Mar. 20, 1923	87.50	8.00	800.00	(6)	11,000.00
573	$5 Head of Freedom, Capitol Dome, Mar. 20, 1923	175.00	12.50	3,000.00	(8)	16,000.00
574	Not assigned					
	Issues of 1923-25, Imperf.					
575	1¢ green Franklin (552), Mar. 20, 1923	7.00	3.50	70.00	(6)	
576	1½¢ yel. brn. Harding (553), Apr. 4, 1925	1.50	1.00	17.00	(6)	45.00
577	2¢ carmine Washington (554)	1.50	1.25	25.00	(6)	
	Issues of 1923, Perf. 11 x 10					
578	1¢ green Franklin (552)	70.00	110.00	600.00	(4)	
579	2¢ carmine Washington (554)	60.00	110.00	450.00	(4)	
	Recut in eye	70.00	125.00			
	Issues of 1923-26, Perf. 10 (See also #551-73, 622-23, 631-42, 658-79, 684-87, 692-701, 723)					
580	Not assigned					
581	1¢ green Franklin (552), Apr. 21, 1923	7.00	.55	75.00	(4)	2,000.00
582	1½¢ brn. Harding (553), Mar. 19, 1925	3.50	.45	27.50	(4)	40.00
	Pair with full horiz. gutter between	135.00				
583	2¢ carm. Wash. (554), Apr. 14, 1924	1.75	.15	17.00	(4)	
a	Booklet pane of 6, Aug. 27, 1926	75.00	25.00			1,500.00
584	3¢ violet Lincoln (555), Aug. 1, 1925	19.00	1.75	160.00	(4)	55.00
585	4¢ yellow brown Martha Washington (556), Mar. 1925	11.50	.30	140.00	(4)	55.00
586	5¢ blue T. Roosevelt (557), Dec. 1924	12.00	.18	135.00	(4)	57.50
587	6¢ red orange Garfield (558), Mar. 1925	5.50	.25	60.00	(4)	60.00
588	7¢ black McKinley (559), May 29, 1926	8.00	4.25	67.50	(4)	70.00

	Issues of 1923-26 (continued), Perf. 11 x 10	Un	U	PB/LP	#	FDC	Q
589	8¢ olive grn. Grant (560), May 29, 1926	17.50	2.75	150.00	(4)	72.50	
590	9¢ rose Jefferson (561), May 29, 1926	3.75	1.90	30.00	(4)	72.50	
591	10¢ orange Monroe (562), June 8, 1925	47.50	.15	350.00	(4)	95.00	
592-93	Not assigned						
	Perf. 11						
594	1¢ green Franklin (552), design 19³/₄ x 22¹/₄mm	10,000.00	4,000.00				
595	2¢ carmine Washington (554), design 19³/₄ x 22¹/₄mm	200.00	225.00	900.00	(4)		
596	1¢ green Franklin (552), design 19¹/₄ x 22³/₄mm		22,500.00				
	Issues of 1923-29, Coil Stamps, Perf. 10 Vertically						
597	1¢ green Franklin (552), July 18, 1923	.25	.15	1.65	(2)	*550.00*	
	Gripper cracks or double transfer	2.25	1.00				
598	1¹/₂¢ brown Harding (553), Mar. 19, 1925	.60	.15	2.85	(2)	50.00	
599	2¢ carmine Washington (554), type I, Jan. 1923	.30	.15	1.65	(2)	*600.00*	
	Double transfer	1.65	1.00				
	Gripper cracks	2.00	2.00				
599A	2¢ carmine Washington (554), type II, Mar. 1929	100.00	9.50	550.00	(2)		
600	3¢ violet Lincoln (555), May 10, 1924	5.50	.15	18.50	(2)	60.00	
601	4¢ yellow brown M. Washington (556), Aug. 5, 1923	2.75	.30	17.50	(2)		
602	5¢ dark blue T. Roosevelt (557), Mar. 5, 1924	1.25	.15	7.25	(2)	82.50	
603	10¢ orange Monroe (562), Dec. 1, 1924	2.75	.15	17.50	(2)	100.00	
	Coil Stamps, Perf. 10 Horizontally						
604	1¢ yel. grn. Franklin (552), July 19, 1924	.20	.15	2.15	(2)	90.00	
605	1¹/₂¢ yel. brn. Harding (553), May 9, 1925	.25	.15	1.65	(2)	70.00	
606	2¢ carmine Washington (554), Dec. 31, 1923	.25	.15	1.25	(2)	100.00	
607-09	Not assigned						
	Issues of 1923, Harding Memorial Issue, Perf. 11						
610	2¢ blk. Harding, Sept. 1	.55	.15	18.00	(6)	30.00	1,459,487,085
a	Horizontal pair, imperf. vertically	*1,100.00*					
	Double transfer	1.75	.50				
	Imperf.						
611	2¢ blk. Harding (610), Nov. 15	6.50	4.25	85.00	(6)	90.00	770,000
	Perf. 10						
612	2¢ blk. Harding (610), Sept. 12	12.00	1.50	225.00	(4)	100.00	99,950,300
	Perf. 11						
613	2¢ black Harding (610)		15,000.00				
	Issues of 1924, Huguenot-Walloon Tercentary Issue, May 1						
614	1¢ Ship *Nieu Nederland*	2.50	3.00	30.00	(6)	30.00	51,378,023
615	2¢ Walloons' Landing at Fort Orange (Albany)	5.00	2.00	60.00	(6)	32.50	77,753,423
	Double transfer	12.50	3.50				
616	5¢ Huguenot Monument to Jan Ribault at Mayport, Florida	25.00	11.00	300.00	(6)	50.00	5,659,023
	Issues of 1925, Lexington-Concord Issue, Apr. 4						
617	1¢ Washington at Cambridge	2.50	2.25	40.00	(6)	27.50	15,615,000
618	2¢ "The Birth of Liberty," by Henry Sandham	5.00	3.75	67.50	(6)	30.00	26,596,600

610

614

615

616

617

618

*You asked for it! This edition contains more stamp
trivia than ever before. We added twice as many
stamp stories, and now there are two feature articles.*

619

620   **621**

622   **623**

627   **629**

628

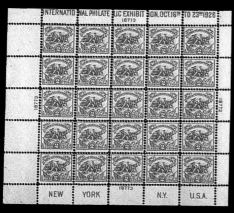

630

	Issues of 1925 (continued), Perf. 11	Un	U	PB	#	FDC	Q
	Norse-American Issue, May 18						
619	5¢ "The Minute Man," by Daniel Chester French	24.00	12.50	275.00	(6)	65.00	5,348,800
	Line over head	50.00	18.50				
620	2¢ Sloop *Restaurationen*	3.50	2.75	200.00	(8)	20.00	9,104,983
621	5¢ Viking Ship	14.00	10.50	650.00	(8)	30.00	1,900,983
	Issues of 1925-26 (See also #551-79, 581-91, 594-606, 631-42, 658-79, 684-87, 692-701, 723)						
622	13¢ B. Harrison, Jan. 11, 1926	12.00	.40	150.00	(6)	20.00	
623	17¢ Wilson, Dec. 28, 1925	13.00	.20	165.00	(6)	25.00	
624-26	Not assigned						
	Issues of 1926						
627	2¢ Independence Sesquicentennial Exposition, May 10	2.75	.40	35.00	(6)	10.00	307,731,900
628	5¢ John Ericsson Memorial, May 29	5.50	2.75	75.00	(6)	22.50	20,280,500
629	2¢ Battle of White Plains, Oct. 18	1.75	1.50	35.00	(6)	6.25	40,639,485
a	Vertical pair, imperf. between	1,250.00					
	International Philatelic Exhibition Souvenir Sheet, Oct. 18						
630	2¢ Battle of White Plains, sheet of 25 with selvage inscription (629)	350.00	375.00			1,400.00	107,398
	Dot over first "S" of "States"	350.00	375.00				
	Imperf. (See also #551-79, 581-91, 594-606, 622-23, 658-79, 684-87, 692-701, 723)						
631	1¹/₂¢ yellow brown Harding (553), Aug. 27	1.75	1.60	42.50	(4)	30.00	
	Issues of 1926-34, Perf. 11 x 10¹/₂ (See also #551-73, 575-79, 581-91, 594-606, 622-23, 631-42, 684-87, 692-701, 723)						
632	1¢ green Franklin (552), June 10, 1927	.15	.15	1.65	(4)	45.00	
a	Booklet pane of 6, Nov. 2, 1927	4.50	.25			3,000.00	
b	Vertical pair, imperf. between	200.00	125.00				
	Pair with full vertical gutter between	150.00	—				
	Cracked plate	—	—				
633	1¹/₂¢ yellow brown Harding (553), May 17, 1927	1.00	.15	50.00	(4)	45.00	
634	2¢ carmine Washington (554), type I, Dec. 10, 1926	.15	.15	1.00	(4)	47.50	
	Pair with full vertical gutter between	200.00					
b	2¢ carmine lake, type I	3.00	1.00	30.00			
c	Horizontal pair, imperf. between	2,000.00					
d	Booklet pane of 6, Feb. 25, 1927	1.75	.15				
634A	2¢ carmine Washington (554), type II, Dec. 1928	300.00	12.50	1,550.00	(4)		
	Pair with full vertical or horizontal gutter between	1,000.00					
635	3¢ violet Lincoln (555), Feb. 3, 1927	.35	.15	5.00	(4)	47.50	
a	3¢ bright violet Lincoln, Feb. 7, 1934	.25	.15	3.25	(4)	25.00	
	Gripper cracks	3.25	2.00				
636	4¢ yellow brown Martha Washington (556), May 17, 1927	2.00	.15	60.00	(4)	50.00	
	Pair with full vertical gutter between	200.00					
637	5¢ dark blue Theodore Roosevelt (557), Mar. 24, 1927	1.90	.15	12.00	(4)	50.00	
	Pair with full vertical gutter between	275.00					
638	6¢ red orange Garfield (558), July 27, 1927	2.00	.15	12.00	(4)	57.50	
	Pair with full vert. gutter between	200.00					

	Issues of 1926-34 (continued), Perf. 11 x 10½	Un	U	PB/LB	#	FDC	Q
639	7¢ black McKinley (559), Mar. 24, 1927	2.00	.15	21.00	(4)	57.50	
a	Vertical pair, imperf. between	150.00	80.00				
640	8¢ olive green Grant (560), June 10, 1927	2.00	.15	12.00	(4)	62.50	
641	9¢ orange red Jefferson (561), 1931	2.00	.15	12.00	(4)	72.50	
642	10¢ orange Monroe (562), Feb. 3, 1927	3.25	.15	23.50	(4)	90.00	
	Double transfer	—	—				
	Issues of 1927, Perf. 11						
643	2¢ Vermont Sesquicentennial, Aug. 3	1.25	.75	35.00	(6)	5.00	39,974,900
644	2¢ Burgoyne Campaign, Aug. 3	3.00	1.90	35.00	(6)	12.50	25,628,450
	Issues of 1928						
645	2¢ Valley Forge, May 26	.90	.35	22.50	(6)	4.00	101,330,328
	Perf. 11 x 10½						
646	2¢ Battle of Monmouth/ Molly Pitcher, Oct. 20	.95	.95	25.00	(4)	15.00	9,779,896
	Wide spacing, vertical pair	20.00	—				
	Hawaii Sesquicentennial Issue, Aug. 13						
647	2¢ Washington (554)	3.75	3.75	90.00	(4)	15.00	5,519,897
	Wide spacing, vertical pair	75.00					
648	5¢ Theodore Roosevelt (557)	11.00	11.00	225.00	(4)	22.50	1,459,897
	Aeronautics Conference Issue, Dec. 12, Perf. 11						
649	2¢ Wright Airplane	1.00	.75	11.50	(6)	7.00	51,342,273
650	5¢ Globe and Airplane	4.50	3.00	50.00	(6)	10.00	10,319,700
	Plate flaw, "prairie dog"	27.50	12.50				
	Issues of 1929						
651	2¢ George Rogers Clark, Feb. 25	.55	.40	8.50	(6)	6.00	16,684,674
	Double transfer	4.00	2.00				
652	Not assigned						
	Perf. 11 x 10½						
653	½¢ olive brown Nathan Hale (551), May 25	.15	.15	1.00	(4)	25.00	
	Electric Light's Golden Jubilee Issue, June 5, Perf. 11						
654	2¢ Thomas Edison's First Lamp	.60	.60	25.00	(6)	10.00	31,679,200
	Perf. 11 x 10½						
655	2¢ carmine rose (654), June 11	.55	.15	30.00	(4)	80.00	210,119,474
	Coil Stamp, Perf. 10 Vertically						
656	2¢ carmine rose (654), June 11	11.50	1.25	50.00	(2)	90.00	133,530,000
	Perf. 11						
657	2¢ Sullivan Expedition, June 17	.60	.50	24.00	(6)	4.00	51,451,880
	2¢ lake	50.00	—				

643   **644**   **645**

        646   **647**

                648

        649   **650**

                651

        654   **657**

658

669

680

681

682

683

684

685

	Issues of 1929 (continued), Perf. 11 x 10½	Un	U	PB/LP	#	FDC	Q
	#658-68 overprinted "Kans.," May 1, Perf. 11 x 10½ (See also #551-73, 575-79, 581-91, 594-606, 622-23, 631-42, 684-87, 692-701, 723)						
658	1¢ Franklin	1.50	1.35	25.00	(4)	35.00	13,390,000
a	Vertical pair, one without overprint	300.00					
659	1½¢ brown Harding (553)	2.25	1.90	35.00	(4)	35.00	8,240,000
	Wide spacing, pair	65.00					
660	2¢ carmine Washington (554)	2.75	.75	30.00	(4)	35.00	87,410,000
661	3¢ violet Lincoln (555)	12.50	10.00	115.00	(4)	37.50	2,540,000
662	4¢ yellow brown Martha Washington (556)	12.50	6.00	120.00	(4)	40.00	2,290,000
663	5¢ deep blue T. Roosevelt (557)	9.00	6.50	92.50	(4)	40.00	2,700,000
664	6¢ red orange Garfield (558)	19.00	12.00	275.00	(4)	50.00	1,450,000
665	7¢ black McKinley (559)	18.00	18.00	350.00	(4)	50.00	1,320,000
666	8¢ olive green Grant (560)	60.00	50.00	525.00	(4)	95.00	1,530,000
667	9¢ light rose Jefferson (561)	9.00	7.50	110.00	(4)	95.00	1,130,000
668	10¢ orange yel. Monroe (562)	15.00	8.00	200.00	(4)	100.00	2,860,000
	#669-79 overprinted "Nebr.," May 1						
669	1¢ Franklin	2.25	1.50	30.00	(4)	35.00	8,220,000
a	Vertical pair, one without overprint	275.00					
670	1½¢ brown Harding (553)	2.00	1.65	32.50	(4)	35.00	8,990,000
671	2¢ carmine Washington (554)	2.00	.85	25.00	(4)	35.00	73,220,000
672	3¢ violet Lincoln (555)	8.50	7.50	87.50	(4)	40.00	2,110,000
673	4¢ yellow brown Martha Washington (556)	13.00	9.50	140.00	(4)	47.50	1,600,000
	Wide spacing, pair	110.00					
674	5¢ deep blue T. Roosevelt (557)	11.00	9.50	150.00	(4)	47.50	1,860,000
675	6¢ red orange Garfield (558)	27.50	15.00	300.00	(4)	70.00	980,000
676	7¢ black McKinley (559)	15.00	11.50	180.00	(4)	75.00	850,000
677	8¢ olive green Grant (560)	20.00	16.00	275.00	(4)	75.00	1,480,000
678	9¢ light rose Jefferson (561)	24.00	18.00	350.00	(4)	85.00	530,000
679	10¢ orange yel. Monroe (562)	70.00	14.00	750.00	(4)	95.00	1,890,000
	Warning: Excellent forgeries of the Kansas and Nebraska overprints exist.						
	Perf. 11						
680	2¢ Battle of Fallen Timbers, Sept. 14	.65	.65	21.00	(6)	3.50	29,338,274
681	2¢ Ohio River Canalization, Oct. 19	.50	.50	16.00	(6)	3.50	32,680,900
	Issues of 1930						
682	2¢ Mass. Bay Colony, Apr. 8	.50	.38	20.00	(6)	3.50	74,000,774
683	2¢ Carolina-Charleston, Apr. 10	1.00	.90	35.00	(6)	3.50	25,215,574
	Perf. 11 x 10½						
684	1½¢ Warren G. Harding, Dec. 1	.25	.15	1.25	(4)	4.50	
	Pair with full horizontal gutter between	175.00					
	Pair with full vert. gutter between	—					
685	4¢ William H. Taft, June 4	.75	.15	9.00	(4)	6.00	
	Gouge on right "4"	2.00	.60				
	Recut right "4"	2.00	.65				
	Pair with full horizontal gutter between	—					
	Coil Stamps, Perf. 10 Vertically						
686	1½¢ brn. Harding (684), Dec. 1	1.50	.15	4.50	(2)	5.00	
687	4¢ brown Taft (685), Sept. 18	2.75	.38	9.00	(2)	20.00	

	Issues of 1930 (continued), Perf. 11	Un	U	PB	#	FDC	Q
688	2¢ Battle of Braddock's Field, July 9	.85	.75	28.50	(6)	4.00	25,609,470
689	2¢ General von Steuben, Sept. 17	.45	.45	17.00	(6)	4.00	66,487,000
a	Imperf. pair	*2,500.00*		*12,000.00*	(6)		
	Issues of 1931						
690	2¢ General Pulaski, Jan. 16	.20	.15	10.00	(6)	4.00	96,559,400
691	Not assigned						
	Perf. 11 x 10¹/₂ (See also #551-73, 575-79, 581-91, 594-606, 622-23, 631-42, 658-79, 684-87, 723)						
692	11¢ light bl. Hayes (563), Sept. 4	2.00	.15	10.50	(4)	100.00	
	Retouched forehead	6.50	1.00				
693	12¢ brown violet Cleveland (564), Aug. 25	4.00	.15	17.50	(4)	100.00	
694	13¢ yellow green Harrison (622), Sept. 4	1.75	.15	10.00	(4)	100.00	
695	14¢ dark blue American Indian (565), Sept. 8	2.75	.22	12.50	(4)	100.00	
696	15¢ gray Statue of Liberty (566), Aug. 27	6.50	.15	30.00	(4)	125.00	
	Perf. 10¹/₂ x 11						
697	17¢ black Wilson (623), July 25	3.50	.15	16.50	(4)	400.00	
698	20¢ carmine rose Golden Gate (567), Sept. 8	7.75	.15	35.00	(4)	325.00	
	Double transfer	20.00	—				
699	25¢ blue green Niagara Falls (568), July 25	7.25	.15	34.00	(4)	450.00	
700	30¢ brown Buffalo (569), Sept. 8	11.50	.15	57.50	(4)	325.00	
	Cracked plate	22.50	.85				
701	50¢ lilac Arlington Amphitheater (570), Sept. 4	35.00	.15	170.00	(4)	450.00	
	Perf. 11						
702	2¢ Red Cross, May 21	.15	.15	1.60	(4)	3.00	99,074,600
	Red cross omitted	—					
703	2¢ Yorktown, Oct. 19	.35	.25	2.25	(4)	3.50	25,006,400
a	2¢ lake and black	4.00	.65				
b	2¢ dark lake and black	*300.00*		*1,750.00*	(4)		
c	Pair, imperf. vertically	*4,000.00*					
	Issues of 1932, Washington Bicentennial Issue, Jan. 1, Perf. 11 x 10¹/₂						
704	¹/₂¢ Portrait by Charles W. Peale	.15	.15	3.00	(4)	5.00 (4)	87,969,700
	Broken circle	.60	.15				
705	1¢ Bust by Jean Antoine Houdon	.15	.15	4.00	(4)	4.00 (2)	1,265,555,100
706	1¹/₂¢ Portrait by Charles W. Peale	.32	.15	13.00	(4)	4.00 (2)	304,926,800
707	2¢ Portrait by Gilbert Stuart	.15	.15	1.50	(4)	4.00	4,222,198,300
	Gripper cracks	1.50	.50				
708	3¢ Portrait by Charles W. Peale	.40	.15	10.50	(4)	4.00	456,198,500
709	4¢ Portrait by Charles P. Polk	.22	.15	4.25	(4)	4.00	151,201,300
	Broken bottom frame line	1.50	.50				
710	5¢ Portrait by Charles W. Peale	1.40	.15	14.50	(4)	4.00	170,565,100
	Cracked plate	5.00	1.00				
711	6¢ Portrait by John Trumbull	2.75	.15	50.00	(4)	4.00	111,739,400
712	7¢ Portrait by John Trumbull	.22	.15	4.25	(4)	4.00	83,257,400
713	8¢ Portrait by Charles B.J.F. Saint Memin	2.50	.50	50.00	(4)	4.50	96,506,100
	Pair, full vert. gutter between	—					
714	9¢ Portrait by W. Williams	2.00	.15	30.00	(4)	4.50	75,709,200
715	10¢ Portrait by Gilbert Stuart	8.50	.15	95.00	(4)	4.50	147,216,000

688

689

690

702

703

704

705

706

707

708

709

710

711

712

713

714

715

716

717

718

719

720

724

725

726

727

728

729

730

731

732

734

733

	Issues of 1932 (continued), Perf. 11	Un	U	PB/LP	#	FDC	Q
	Olympic Winter Games Issue, Jan. 25						
716	2¢ Ski Jumper	.35	.16	10.00	(6)	6.00	51,102,800
	Recut	3.50	1.50				
	Colored "snowball"	25.00	5.00				
	Perf. 11 x 10½						
717	2¢ Arbor Day, Apr. 22	.15	.15	6.50	(4)	4.00	100,869,300
	Olympic Summer Games Issue, June 15						
718	3¢ Runner at Starting Mark	1.25	.15	9.50	(4)	6.00	168,885,300
	Gripper cracks	4.00	.75				
719	5¢ Myron's Discobolus	2.00	.20	18.00	(4)	8.00	53,376,100
	Gripper cracks	4.00	1.00				
720	3¢ Washington, June 16	.15	.15	1.20	(4)	7.50	
	Pair with full vertical or horizontal gutter between	200.00					
b	Booklet pane of 6, July 25	27.50	5.00			100.00	
c	Vertical pair, imperf. between	300.00					
	Recut lines on nose	2.00	.75				
	Coil Stamp, Perf. 10 Vertically						
721	3¢ deep violet (720), June 24	2.25	.15	8.25	(2)	15.00	
	Recut lines around eyes	—	—				
	Coil Stamp, Perf. 10 Horizontally						
722	3¢ deep violet (720), Oct. 12	1.25	.30	5.00	(2)	15.00	
	Coil Stamp, Perf. 10 Vertically (See also #551-73, 575-79, 581-91, 594-606, 622-23, 631-42, 684-87, 692-701)						
723	6¢ deep orange Garfield (558), Aug. 18	8.50	.25	42.50	(2)	15.00	
	Perf. 11						
724	3¢ William Penn, Oct. 24	.25	.15	8.00	(6)	0.25	49,949,000
a	Vertical pair, imperf. horizontally	—					
725	3¢ Daniel Webster, Oct. 24	.30	.24	16.50	(6)	3.25	49,538,500
	Issues of 1933						
726	3¢ Georgia Settlement, Feb. 12	.25	.18	10.00	(6)	3.25	61,719,200
	Perf. 10½ x 11						
727	3¢ Peace of 1783, Apr. 19	.15	.15	4.00	(4)	3.50	73,382,400
	Century of Progress Issue, May 25						
728	1¢ Restoration of Fort Dearborn	.15	.15	2.00	(4)	3.00	348,266,800
	Gripper cracks	2.00	—				
729	3¢ Federal Building at Chicago	.15	.15	2.00	(4)	3.00	480,239,300
	American Philatelic Society Issue Souvenir Sheets, Aug. 25, Without Gum, Imperf.						
730	1¢ sheet of 25 (728)	24.00	24.00			100.00	456,704
a	Single stamp from sheet	.65	.35			3.25 (3)	11,417,600
731	3¢ sheet of 25 (729)	22.50	22.50			100.00	441,172
a	Single stamp from sheet	.50	.35			3.25	11,029,300
	Perf. 10½ x 11						
732	3¢ NRA, Aug. 15	.15	.15	1.50	(4)	3.25	1,978,707,300
	Gripper cracks	1.50	—				
	Recut at right	2.00					
	Perf. 11						
733	3¢ Byrd Antarctic Expedition II, Oct. 9	.40	.48	15.00	(6)	7.00	5,735,944
	Double transfer	2.50	1.00				
734	5¢ Kosciuszko, Oct. 13	.50	.22	27.50	(6)	4.50	45,137,700
a	Horizontal pair, imperf. vertically	2,000.00					

	Issues of 1934, Imperf.	Un	U	PB	#	FDC	Q
	National Stamp Exhibition Issue Souvenir Sheet, Feb. 10, Without Gum						
735	3¢ sheet of 6 (733)	12.50	10.00			40.00	811,404
a	Single stamp from sheet	2.00	1.65			5.00	4,868,424
	Perf. 11						
736	3¢ Maryland Tercentary, Mar. 23	.15	.15	7.50	(6)	1.60	46,258,300
	Double transfer	—	—				
	Mothers of America Issue, May 2, Perf. 11 x 10½						
737	3¢ Portrait of his Mother, by James A. McNeill Whistler	.15	.15	1.00	(4)	1.60	193,239,100
	Perf. 11						
738	3¢ deep violet (737)	.15	.15	4.25	(6)	1.60	15,432,200
739	3¢ Wisconsin Tercentary, July 7	.15	.15	3.00	(6)	1.10	64,525,400
a	Vertical pair, imperf. horizontally	250.00					
b	Horizontal pair, imperf. vertically	325.00					
	National Parks Issue, Unwmkd.						
740	1¢ El Capitan, Yosemite (California), July 16	.15	.15	1.00	(6)	2.25	84,896,350
	Recut	1.50	.50				
a	Vertical pair, imperf. horizontally, with gum	450.00					
741	2¢ Grand Canyon (Ariz.), July 24	.15	.15	1.25	(6)	2.25	74,400,200
a	Vertical pair, imperf. horizontally, with gum	300.00					
b	Horizontal pair, imperf. vertically, with gum	300.00					
	Double transfer	1.25	—				
742	3¢ Mirror Lake, Mt. Rainier (Washington), Aug. 3	.15	.15	1.75	(6)	2.50	95,089,000
a	Vertical pair, imperf. horizontally, with gum	350.00					
743	4¢ Cliff Palace, Mesa Verde (Colorado), Sept. 25	.35	.32	7.00	(6)	2.25	19,178,650
a	Vertical pair, imperf. horizontally, with gum	500.00					
744	5¢ Old Faithful, Yellowstone (Wyoming), July 30	.60	.55	8.75	(6)	2.25	30,980,100
a	Horizontal pair, imperf. vertically, with gum	400.00					
745	6¢ Crater Lake (Oregon), Sept. 5	1.00	.75	15.00	(6)	3.00	16,923,350
746	7¢ Great Head, Acadia Park (Maine), Oct. 2	.55	.65	10.00	(6)	3.00	15,988,250
a	Horizontal pair, imperf. vertically, with gum	550.00					
747	8¢ Great White Throne, Zion Park (Utah), Sept. 18	1.40	1.65	15.00	(6)	3.25	15,288,700
748	9¢ Mt. Rockwell and Two Medicine Lake, Glacier National Park (Montana), Aug. 27	1.50	.55	15.00	(6)	3.50	17,472,600
749	10¢ Great Smoky Mountains (North Carolina), Oct. 8	2.75	.90	25.00	(6)	6.00	18,874,300
	American Philatelic Society Issue Souvenir Sheet, Aug. 28, Imperf.						
750	3¢ sheet of 6 (742)	27.50	25.00			40.00	511,391
a	Single stamp from sheet	3.25	3.00			3.25	3,068,346
	Trans-Mississippi Philatelic Exposition Issue Souvenir Sheet, Oct. 10						
751	1¢ sheet of 6 (740)	12.00	12.00			35.00	793,551
a	Single stamp from sheet	1.35	1.50			3.25 (3)	4,761,306

735

736

737

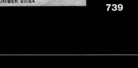

739

740

741

742

744

743

745

746

747

748

749

750

751

101

Examples of Special Printing Position Blocks

Gutter Block 752

Cross-Gutter Block 768

Line Block 756

Centerline Block 754

Arrow Block 763

	Issues of 1935, Special Printing (#752-71), March 15, Without Gum, Perf. 10½ x 11	Un	U	PB	#	FDC	Q
752	3¢ violet Peace of 1783 (727)	.15	.15	11.00	(4)	5.00	3,274,556
	Perf. 11						
753	3¢ blue Byrd Expedition II (733)	.40	.40	15.00	(6)	6.00	2,040,760
	Imperf.						
754	3¢ dp. vio. Whistler's Mother (737)	.50	.50	16.50	(6)	6.00	2,389,288
755	3¢ deep violet Wisconsin (739)	.50	.50	16.50	(6)	6.00	2,294,948
756	1¢ green Yosemite (740)	.20	.20	3.65	(6)	6.00	3,217,636
757	2¢ red Grand Canyon (741)	.22	.22	4.50	(6)	6.00	2,746,640
	Double transfer	—					
758	3¢ deep violet Mt. Rainier (742)	.45	.40	12.50	(6)	6.00	2,168,088
759	4¢ brown Mesa Verde (743)	.90	.90	16.50	(6)	6.50	1,822,684
760	5¢ blue Yellowstone (744)	1.40	1.25	18.50	(6)	6.50	1,724,576
	Double transfer	—					
761	6¢ dark blue Crater Lake (745)	2.25	2.00	30.00	(6)	6.50	1,647,696
762	7¢ black Acadia (746)	1.40	1.25	25.00	(6)	6.50	1,682,948
	Double transfer	—					
763	8¢ sage green Zion (747)	1.50	1.40	30.00	(6)	7.50	1,638,644
764	9¢ red orange Glacier (748)	1.75	1.50	32.50	(6)	7.50	1,625,224
765	10¢ gray black Smoky Mts. (749)	3.50	3.00	41.50	(6)	7.50	1,644,900
766	1¢ yellow grn. (728), pane of 25	24.00	24.00			250.00	98,712
a	Single stamp from pane	.65	.35			5.50	2,467,800
767	3¢ violet (729), pane of 25	22.50	22.50			250.00	85,914
a	Single stamp from pane	.50	.35			5.50	(3)	2,147,850
768	3¢ dark blue (733), pane of 6	18.00	12.50			250.00	267,200
a	Single stamp from pane	2.50	2.00			6.50	1,603,200
769	1¢ green (740), pane of 6	12.00	9.00			250.00	279,960
a	Single stamp from pane	1.75	1.50			4.00	1,679,760
770	3¢ deep violet (742), pane of 6	27.50	22.50			250.00	215,920
a	Single stamp from pane	3.00	3.00			5.00	1,295,520
771	16¢ dark blue Great Seal of U.S.	2.00	2.00	43.50	(6)	12.50	1,370,560
	For perforate variety, see #CE2.						

A number of position pieces can be collected from the panes or sheets of the 1935 Special Printing issues, including horizontal and vertical gutter (#752, 766-70) or line (#753-65, 771) blocks of four (HG/L and VG/L), arrow-and-guideline blocks of four (AGL) and crossed-gutter or centerline blocks of four (CG/L). Pairs sell for half the price of blocks of four.

	HG/L	VG/L	AGL	CG/L		HG/L	VG/L	AGL	CG/L
752	9.00	15.00		35.00	762	6.00	6.00	6.50	10.00
753	3.50	37.50	40.00	42.50	763	6.50	6.50	7.00	11.00
754	2.10	2.10	2.25	5.00	764	7.50	7.50	8.00	21.00
755	2.10	2.10	2.25	5.00	765	14.50	14.50	15.00	21.50
756	.90	.90	1.00	2.35	766	8.50	9.75		11.50
757	.95	.95	1.00	2.75	767	7.50	8.75		11.50
758	1.95	1.95	2.00	4.00	768	12.00	13.00		15.00
759	3.75	3.75	4.00	5.50	769	11.00	11.00		12.00
760	6.50	6.50	7.00	11.00	770	20.00	20.00		21.50
761	9.25	9.25	9.50	14.50	771	8.75	8.75	10.00	36.50

	Issues of 1935 (continued), Perf. 11 x 10½	Un	U	PB	#	FDC	Q
	Beginning with #772, unused values are for never-hinged stamps.						
772	3¢ Connecticut Settlement, Apr. 26	.15	.15	1.40	(4)	8.00	70,726,800
	Defect in cent design	1.00	.25				
773	3¢ California Pacific International Exposition, May 29	.15	.15	1.40	(4)	8.00	100,839,600
	Pair with full vertical gutter between	—					
	Perf. 11						
774	3¢ Boulder Dam, Sept. 30	.15	.15	1.85	(6)	10.00	73,610,650
	Perf. 11 x 10½						
775	3¢ Michigan Statehood, Nov. 1	.15	.15	1.40	(4)	8.00	75,823,900
	Issues of 1936						
776	3¢ Republic of Texas Independence, Mar. 2	.15	.15	1.40	(4)	17.50	124,324,500
	Perf. 10½ x 11						
777	3¢ Rhode Island Settlement, May 4	.15	.15	1.40	(4)	8.00	67,127,650
	Pair with full gutter between	200.00					
	Third International Philatelic Exhibition Issue Souvenir Sheet, May 9, Imperf.						
778	Sheet of 4 different stamps (#772, 773, 775 and 776)	1.75	1.75			13.00	2,809,039
a-d	Single stamp from sheet	.40	.30				2,809,039
779-81	Not assigned						
	Perf. 11 x 10½						
782	3¢ Arkansas Statehood, June 15	.15	.15	1.40	(4)	8.00	72,992,650
783	3¢ Oregon Territory, July 14	.15	.15	1.40	(4)	8.50	74,407,450
	Double transfer	1.00	.50				
784	3¢ Susan B. Anthony, Aug. 26	.15	.15	.75	(4)	5.00	269,522,200
	Period missing after "B"	.75	.25				

What does the word "Alamo" mean?

"Remember the Alamo" is a phrase associated with Texas' independence from Mexico. The Alamo was originally an 18th-century Franciscan mission in San Antonio, Texas. Even though a famous battle was fought there, the word "Alamo" stands for something more peaceful. *Alamo* is the Spanish word for cottonwood. The grove of cottonwoods that surrounded the structure gave the mission its name.

During the famous battle that was fought there, a small group of Texan volunteers occupied the Alamo. The Mexican Army stormed through, and the Texans suffered heavy losses. The Alamo was recaptured by the Texans shortly afterward, and Texas achieved independence. **(#776)**

772

773

774

775

776

777

778

782

783

784

785

786

787

788

789

790

791

792

793

794

795

796

798

799

800

801

802

Issues of 1936-37, Perf. 11 x 10½	Un	U	PB	#	FDC	Q
Army Issue						
785 1¢ George Washington, Nathanael Green and Mount Vernon, Dec. 15, 1936	.15	.15	.85	(4)	5.00	105,196,150
Pair with full vertical gutter between	—					
786 2¢ Andrew Jackson, Winfield Scott and The Hermitage, Jan. 15, 1937	.15	.15	.85	(4)	5.00	93,848,500
787 3¢ Generals Sherman, Grant and Sheridan, Feb. 18, 1937	.15	.15	1.10	(4)	5.00	87,741,150
788 4¢ Generals Robert E. Lee and "Stonewall" Jackson and Stratford Hall, Mar. 23, 1937	.30	.15	8.00	(4)	5.50	35,794,150
789 5¢ U.S. Military Academy at West Point, May 26, 1937	.60	.15	8.50	(4)	5.50	36,839,250
Navy Issue						
790 1¢ John Paul Jones, John Barry, *Bon Homme Richard* and *Lexington,* Dec. 15, 1936	.15	.15	.85	(4)	5.00	104,773,450
791 2¢ Stephen Decatur, Thomas Macdonough and *Saratoga,* Jan. 15, 1937	.15	.15	.80	(4)	5.00	92,054,550
792 3¢ David G. Farragut and David D. Porter, *Hartford* and *Powhatan*, Feb. 18, 1937	.15	.15	1.00	(4)	5.00	93,291,650
793 4¢ Admirals William T. Sampson, George Dewey and Winfield S. Schley, Mar. 23, 1937	.30	.15	8.00	(4)	5.50	34,552,950
794 5¢ Seal of U.S. Naval Academy and Naval Cadets, May 26, 1937	.60	.15	8.50	(4)	5.50	36,010,050
Issues of 1937						
795 3¢ Northwest Territory Ordinance, July 13	.15	.15	1.10	(4)	6.00	84,825,250
Perf. 11						
796 5¢ Virginia Dare, Aug. 18	.20	.18	7.00	(6)	7.00	25,040,400
Society of Philatelic Americans Issue Souvenir Sheet, Aug. 26, Imperf.						
797 10¢ blue green (749)	.60	.40			6.00	5,277,445
Perf. 11 x 10½						
798 3¢ Constitution Sesquicentennial, Sept. 17	.15	.15	1.00	(4)	6.50	99,882,300
Territorial Issues, Perf. 10½ x 11						
799 3¢ Hawaii, Oct. 18	.15	.15	1.25	(4)	7.00	78,454,450
Perf. 11 x 10½						
800 3¢ Alaska, Nov. 12	.15	.15	1.25	(4)	7.00	77,004,200
Pair with full gutter between	—					
801 3¢ Puerto Rico, Nov. 25	.15	.15	1.25	(4)	7.00	81,292,450
802 3¢ Virgin Islands, Dec. 15	.15	.15	1.25	(4)	7.00	76,474,550
Pair with full vertical gutter between	275.00					

Minimum value listed for a stamp is 15 cents; for a First Day Cover (FDC), $1.00. This minimum represents a fair-market price for having a dealer locate and provide a single stamp or cover from his or her stock. Dealers may charge less per stamp or cover for a group of such stamps or covers, or less for a single stamp or cover.

	Issues of 1938-54, Perf. 11 x 10¹/₂	Un	U	PB	#	FDC
	Presidential Issue (#804b, 806b, 807a issued in 1939, 832b in 1951, 832c in 1954, rest in 1938; see also 839-51)					
803	¹/₂¢ Benjamin Franklin, May 19	.15	.15	.35	(4)	1.75
804	1¢ George Washington, Apr. 25	.15	.15	.35	(4)	2.00
b	Booklet pane of 6, Jan. 27, 1939	1.50	.20			15.00
	Pair with full vertical gutter between	125.00	—			
805	1¹/₂¢ Martha Washington, May 5	.15	.15	.30	(4)	2.00
b	Horizontal pair, imperf. between	150.00	25.00			
	Pair with full horizontal gutter between	150.00				
806	2¢ John Adams, June 3	.15	.15	.35	(4)	2.00
b	Booklet pane of 6, Jan. 27, 1939	3.25	.50			15.00
	Recut at top of head	3.00	1.50			
807	3¢ Thomas Jefferson, June 16	.15	.15	.35	(4)	2.00
a	Booklet pane of 6, Jan. 27, 1939	6.50	.50			18.00
b	Horizontal pair, imperf. between	650.00	—			
c	Imperf. pair	2,500.00				
808	4¢ James Madison, July 1	.80	.15	4.00	(4)	2.00
809	4¹/₂¢ The White House, July 11	.15	.15	1.60	(4)	2.00
810	5¢ James Monroe, July 21	.22	.15	1.25	(4)	2.00
811	6¢ John Quincy Adams, July 28	.25	.15	1.75	(4)	2.00
812	7¢ Andrew Jackson, Aug. 4	.28	.15	1.75	(4)	2.00
813	8¢ Martin Van Buren, Aug. 11	.30	.15	1.75	(4)	2.00
814	9¢ William H. Harrison, Aug. 18	.38	.15	1.90	(4)	3.00
	Pair with full vertical gutter between	—				
815	10¢ John Tyler, Sept. 2	.28	.15	1.40	(4)	3.00
816	11¢ James K. Polk, Sept. 8	.65	.15	3.25	(4)	3.00
817	12¢ Zachary Taylor, Sept. 14	1.10	.15	4.50	(4)	3.00
818	13¢ Millard Fillmore, Sept. 22	1.50	.15	6.75	(4)	3.00
819	14¢ Franklin Pierce, Oct. 6	.90	.15	4.50	(4)	3.00
820	15¢ James Buchanan, Oct. 13	.50	.15	2.50	(4)	3.00
821	16¢ Abraham Lincoln, Oct. 20	.90	.25	4.50	(4)	5.00
822	17¢ Andrew Johnson, Oct. 27	.85	.15	4.25	(4)	5.00
823	18¢ Ulysses S. Grant, Nov. 3	1.50	.15	7.50	(4)	5.00
824	19¢ Rutherford B. Hayes, Nov. 10	1.25	.35	6.25	(4)	5.00
825	20¢ James A. Garfield, Nov. 10	.70	.15	3.50	(4)	5.00
826	21¢ Chester A. Arthur, Nov. 22	1.50	.15	7.50	(4)	5.00
827	22¢ Grover Cleveland, Nov. 22	1.25	.40	9.50	(4)	5.00
828	24¢ Benjamin Harrison, Dec. 2	3.50	.18	18.75	(4)	5.00
829	25¢ William McKinley, Dec. 2	.80	.15	4.00	(4)	6.00
830	30¢ Theodore Roosevelt, Dec. 8	4.25	.15	24.00	(4)	7.50
831	50¢ William Howard Taft, Dec. 8	7.00	.15	37.50	(4)	10.00

803 804 805 806 807

808 809 810 811 812

813 814 815 816 817

818 819 820 821 822

823 824 825 826 827

828 829 830 831

832 833 834

835 836 837 838

855

852 853 854

856 858

857

	Issues of 1938-54, Perf. 11	Un	U	PB/LP	#	FDC	Q
832	$1 Woodrow Wilson, Aug. 29	7.00	.15	35.00	(4)	45.00	
a	Vertical pair, imperf. horizontally	1,750.00					
	Wmkd. USIR						
b	$1 purple and black, 1951	300.00	70.00	1,850.00	(4)		
	Unwmkd.						
c	$1 red violet and black, Aug. 31, 1954	6.00	.15	30.00	(4)	25.00	
d	As "c," vert. pair, imperf. horiz.	1,000.00					
e	Vertical pair, imperf. between	2,500.00					
f	As "c," vert. pair, imperf. between	7,000.00					
833	$2 Warren G. Harding, Sept. 29	21.00	3.75	110.00	(4)	90.00	
834	$5 Calvin Coolidge, Nov. 17	95.00	3.00	425.00	(4)	140.00	
a	$5 red, brown and black	2,000.00	1,250.00				
	Issues of 1938, Perf. 11 x 10¹/₂						
835	3¢ Constitution Ratification, June 21	.22	.15	3.50	(4)	6.50	73,043,650
	Perf. 11						
836	3¢ Swedish-Finnish Tercentary, June 27	.15	.15	2.75	(6)	6.00	58,564,368
	Perf. 11 x 10¹/₂						
837	3¢ Northwest Territory Sesquicentennial, July 15	.15	.15	8.00	(4)	6.00	65,939,500
838	3¢ Iowa Territorial Centennial, Aug. 24	.15	.15	4.50	(4)	6.00	47,064,300
	Pair with full vertical gutter between	—					
	Issues of 1939, Coil Stamps, Jan. 20, Perf. 10 Vertically						
839	1¢ green Washington (804)	.20	.15	.90	(2)	5.00	
840	1¹/₂¢ bister brn. Martha Washington (805)	.24	.15	.95	(2)	5.00	
841	2¢ rose carmine, John Adams (806)	.24	.15	1.25	(2)	5.00	
842	3¢ deep violet Jefferson (807)	.42	.15	1.50	(2)	5.00	
	Gripper cracks	—					
	Thin, translucent paper	2.00	—				
843	4¢ red violet Madison (808)	6.75	.35	22.50	(2)	5.00	
844	4¹/₂¢ dark gray White House (809)	.50	.35	3.25	(2)	5.00	
845	5¢ bright blue Monroe (810)	4.50	.30	20.00	(2)	5.00	
846	6¢ red orange John Quincy Adams (811)	1.10	.15	7.00	(2)	7.00	
847	10¢ brown red Tyler (815)	10.00	.40	35.00	(2)	9.00	
	Coil Stamps, Jan. 27, Perf. 10 Horizontally						
848	1¢ green Washington (804)	.55	.15	2.00	(2)	5.00	
849	1¹/₂¢ bister brn. Martha Washington (805)	1.10	.30	3.00	(2)	5.00	
850	2¢ rose carmine John Adams (806)	2.00	.40	6.00	(2)	5.00	
851	3¢ deep violet Jefferson (807)	1.90	.35	5.00	(2)	6.00	
	Perf. 10¹/₂ x 11						
852	3¢ Golden Gate Exposition, Feb. 18	.15	.15	1.40	(4)	6.00	114,439,600
853	3¢ New York World's Fair, Apr. 1	.15	.15	1.90	(4)	8.00	101,699,550
	Perf. 11						
854	3¢ Washington's Inauguration, Apr. 30	.40	.15	3.50	(6)	6.00	72,764,550
	Perf. 11 x 10¹/₂						
855	3¢ Baseball, June 12	1.10	.15	6.75	(4)	25.00	81,269,600
	Perf. 11						
856	3¢ Panama Canal, Aug. 15	.18	.15	3.00	(6)	5.00	67,813,350
	Perf. 10¹/₂ x 11						
857	3¢ Printing, Sept. 25	.15	.15	1.00	(4)	5.00	71,394,750
	Perf. 11 x 10¹/₂						
858	3¢ 50th Anniversary of Statehood (Montana, North Dakota, South Dakota, Washington), Nov. 2	.15	.15	1.25	(4)	5.00	66,835,000

	Issues of 1940, Perf. 10½ x 11	Un	U	PB	#	FDC	Q
	Famous Americans Issue						
	Authors						
859	1¢ Washington Irving, Jan. 29	.15	.15	.90	(4)	1.50	56,348,320
860	2¢ James Fenimore Cooper, Jan. 29	.15	.15	.90	(4)	1.50	53,177,110
861	3¢ Ralph Waldo Emerson, Feb. 5	.15	.15	1.25	(4)	1.50	53,260,270
862	5¢ Louisa May Alcott, Feb. 5	.28	.20	8.50	(4)	2.25	22,104,950
863	10¢ Samuel L. Clemens (Mark Twain), Feb. 13	1.50	1.35	35.00	(4)	3.75	13,201,270
	Poets						
864	1¢ Henry W. Longfellow, Feb. 16	.15	.15	1.65	(4)	1.50	51,603,580
865	2¢ John Greenleaf Whittier, Feb. 16	.15	.15	1.75	(4)	1.50	52,100,510
866	3¢ James Russell Lowell, Feb. 20	.15	.15	2.00	(4)	1.50	51,666,580
867	5¢ Walt Whitman, Feb. 20	.32	.18	9.00	(4)	4.00	22,207,780
868	10¢ James Whitcomb Riley, Feb. 24	1.65	1.40	35.00	(4)	6.00	11,835,530
	Educators						
869	1¢ Horace Mann, Mar. 14	.15	.15	1.90	(4)	1.50	52,471,160
870	2¢ Mark Hopkins, Mar. 14	.15	.15	1.00	(4)	1.50	52,366,440
871	3¢ Charles W. Eliot, Mar. 28	.15	.15	2.00	(4)	1.50	51,636,270
872	5¢ Frances E. Willard, Mar. 28	.38	.25	9.50	(4)	4.00	20,729,030
873	10¢ Booker T. Washington, Apr. 7	1.10	1.25	25.00	(4)	6.00	14,125,580
	Scientists						
874	1¢ John James Audubon, Apr. 8	.15	.15	.90	(4)	1.50	59,409,000
875	2¢ Dr. Crawford W. Long, Apr. 8	.15	.15	.75	(4)	1.50	57,888,600
876	3¢ Luther Burbank, Apr. 17	.15	.15	1.00	(4)	2.00	58,273,180
877	5¢ Dr. Walter Reed, Apr. 17	.25	.15	5.75	(4)	2.50	23,779,000
878	10¢ Jane Addams, Apr. 26	1.00	.95	22.50	(4)	5.00	15,112,580
	Composers						
879	1¢ Stephen Collins Foster, May 3	.15	.15	.90	(4)	1.50	57,322,790
880	2¢ John Philip Sousa, May 3	.15	.15	.90	(4)	1.50	58,281,580
881	3¢ Victor Herbert, May 13	.15	.15	1.10	(4)	1.50	56,398,790
882	5¢ Edward A. MacDowell, May 13	.40	.22	8.75	(4)	2.50	21,147,000
883	10¢ Ethelbert Nevin, June 10	3.50	1.35	32.50	(4)	5.00	13,328,000
	Artists						
884	1¢ Gilbert Charles Stuart, Sept. 5	.15	.15	1.00	(4)	1.50	54,389,510
885	2¢ James A. McNeill Whistler, Sept. 5	.15	.15	.90	(4)	1.50	53,636,580
886	3¢ Augustus Saint-Gaudens, Sept. 16	.15	.15	.90	(4)	1.50	55,313,230
887	5¢ Daniel Chester French, Sept. 16	.48	.22	8.00	(4)	1.75	21,720,580
888	10¢ Frederic Remington, Sept. 30	1.75	1.40	30.00	(4)	5.00	13,600,580
	Inventors						
889	1¢ Eli Whitney, Oct. 7	.15	.15	1.75	(4)	1.50	47,599,580
890	2¢ Samuel F.B. Morse, Oct. 7	.15	.15	.90	(4)	1.50	53,766,510
891	3¢ Cyrus Hall McCormick, Oct. 14	.25	.15	1.65	(4)	1.50	54,193,580
892	5¢ Elias Howe, Oct. 14	1.00	.32	13.00	(4)	3.00	20,264,580
893	10¢ Alexander Graham Bell, Oct. 28	10.00	2.25	70.00	(4)	7.50	13,726,580

Minimum value listed for a stamp is 15 cents; for a First Day Cover (FDC), $1.00. This minimum represents a fair-market price for having a dealer locate and provide a single stamp or cover from his or her stock. Dealers may charge less per stamp or cover for a group of such stamps or covers, or less for a single stamp or cover.

859 860 861 862 863

864 865 866 867 868

869 870 871 872 873

874 875 876 877 878

879 880 881 882 883

884 885 886 887 888

889 890 891 892 893

113

894

895

896

897

898

899

900

901

902

903

904

905

906

907

908

	Issues of 1940 (continued), Perf. 11 x 10½	Un	U	PB	#	FDC	Q
894	3¢ Pony Express, Apr. 3	.25	.15	3.00	(4)	5.00	46,497,400
	Perf. 10½ x 11						
895	3¢ Pan American Union, Apr. 14	.20	.15	2.75	(4)	4.50	47,700,000
	Perf. 11 x 10½						
896	3¢ Idaho Statehood, July 3	.15	.15	1.75	(4)	4.50	50,618,150
	Perf. 10½ x 11						
897	3¢ Wyoming Statehood, July 10	.15	.15	1.50	(4)	4.50	50,034,400
	Perf. 11 x 10½						
898	3¢ Coronado Expedition, Sept. 7	.15	.15	1.50	(4)	4.50	60,943,700
	National Defense Issue, Oct. 16						
899	1¢ Statue of Liberty	.15	.15	.45	(4)	4.25	
a	Vertical pair, imperf. between	500.00	—				
b	Horizontal pair, imperf. between	40.00	—				
	Pair with full vertical gutter between	200.00					
	Cracked plate	3.00					
	Gripper cracks	3.00					
900	2¢ 90mm Anti-aircraft Gun	.15	.15	.50	(4)	4.25	
a	Horizontal pair, imperf. between	40.00	—				
	Pair with full vertical gutter between	275.00					
901	3¢ Torch of Enlightenment	.15	.15	.60	(4)	4.25	
a	Horizontal pair, imperf. between	30.00	—				
	Pair with full vertical gutter between	—					
	Perf. 10½ x 11						
902	3¢ Thirteenth Amendment, Oct. 20	.16	.15	3.00	(4)	5.00	44,389,550
	Issue of 1941, Perf. 11 x 10½						
903	3¢ Vermont Statehood, Mar. 4	.15	.15	1.75	(4)	6.00	54,574,550
	Issues of 1942						
904	3¢ Kentucky Statehood, June 1	.15	.15	1.10	(4)	4.00	63,558,400
905	3¢ Win the War, July 4	.15	.15	.40	(4)	3.75	
a	3¢ purple	20.00	8.00				
	Pair with full vertical or horizontal gutter between	175.00					
906	5¢ Chinese Resistance, July 7	.18	.16	9.50	(4)	6.00	21,272,800
	Issues of 1943						
907	2¢ Allied Nations, Jan. 14	.15	.15	.35	(4)	3.50	1,671,564,200
	Pair with full vertical or horizontal gutter between	225.00					
908	1¢ Four Freedoms, Feb. 12	.15	.15	.50	(4)	3.50	1,227,334,200

	Issues of 1943-44, Perf. 12	Un	U	PB	#	FDC	Q
	Overrun Countries Issue (#921 issued in 1944, rest in 1943)						
909	5¢ Poland, June 22	.18	.15	6.00*	(4)	5.00	19,999,646
910	5¢ Czechoslovakia, July 12	.18	.15	3.00*	(4)	4.00	19,999,646
911	5¢ Norway, July 27	.15	.15	1.50*	(4)	4.00	19,999,646
912	5¢ Luxembourg, Aug. 10	.15	.15	1.40*	(4)	4.00	19,999,646
913	5¢ Netherlands, Aug. 24	.15	.15	1.40*	(4)	4.00	19,999,646
914	5¢ Belgium, Sept. 14	.15	.15	1.25*	(4)	4.00	19,999,646
915	5¢ France, Sept. 28	.15	.15	1.40*	(4)	4.00	19,999,646
916	5¢ Greece, Oct. 12	.38	.25	13.00*	(4)	4.00	14,999,646
917	5¢ Yugoslavia, Oct. 26	.28	.15	6.50*	(4)	4.00	14,999,646
918	5¢ Albania, Nov. 9	.18	.15	6.00*	(4)	4.00	14,999,646
919	5¢ Austria, Nov. 23	.18	.15	4.00*	(4)	4.00	14,999,646
920	5¢ Denmark, Dec. 7	.18	.15	5.75*	(4)	4.00	14,999,646
921	5¢ Korea, Nov. 2, 1944	.15	.15	5.00*	(4)	5.00	14,999,646
	"KORPA" plate flaw	17.50	12.50				
	*Instead of plate numbers, the selvage is inscribed with the name of the country.						
	Issues of 1944, Perf. 11 x 10½						
922	3¢ Transcontinental Railroad, May 10	.18	.15	1.50	(4)	5.00	61,303,000
923	3¢ Steamship, May 22	.15	.15	1.25	(4)	4.00	61,001,450
924	3¢ Telegraph, May 24	.15	.15	.90	(4)	3.50	60,605,000
925	3¢ Philippines, Sept. 27	.15	.15	1.10	(4)	3.50	50,129,350
926	3¢ Motion Pictures, Oct. 31	.15	.15	.90	(4)	3.50	53,479,400

How was the telegraph invented?

Two discoveries formed the basis of research for the telegraph. In 1820, a Danish physicist, Hans Christian Oersted, discovered that an electric current causes a magnetized needle to move; and, in 1825, British electrician William Sturgeon invented the electromagnet. In 1837, British physicists William Cooke and Charles Wheatstone utilized these discoveries to make the first telegraph. In their system, an electric current passed through wires and caused a needle to move and point to a letter. American inventor Samuel Morse also invented an electromagnetic-based telegraph device. He developed a code for letters and numbers—the Morse code— made up of dots and dashes. Morse received a patent for his telegraph in 1840. **(#924)**

909

910

911

912

913

914

915

916

917

918

919

920

921

922

923

924

925

926

927

928

929

930

931

932

933

934

935

936

937

938

939

940

941

942

943

944

945

946

947

	Issues of 1945 (continued), Perf. 11 x 10½	Un	U	PB	#	FDC	Q
927	3¢ Florida Statehood, Mar. 3	.15	.15	.55	(4)	3.50	61,617,350
928	5¢ United Nations Conference, Apr. 25	.15	.15	.45	(4)	4.00	75,500,000
	Perf. 10½ x 11						
929	3¢ Iwo Jima (Marines), July 11	.15	.15	.38	(4)	6.75	137,321,000
	Issues of 1945-46, Franklin D. Roosevelt Issue, Perf. 11 x 10½						
930	1¢ Roosevelt and Hyde Park Residence, July 26, 1945	.15	.15	.16	(4)	2.50	128,140,000
931	2¢ Roosevelt and "The Little White House" at Warm Springs, Ga., Aug. 24, 1945	.15	.15	.24	(4)	2.50	67,255,000
932	3¢ Roosevelt and White House, June 27, 1945	.15	.15	.28	(4)	2.50	133,870,000
933	5¢ Roosevelt, Map of Western Hemisphere and Four Freedoms, Jan. 30, 1946	.15	.15	.40	(4)	3.00	76,455,400
934	3¢ Army, Sept. 28	.15	.15	.30	(4)	4.75	128,357,750
935	3¢ Navy, Oct. 27	.15	.15	.30	(4)	4.75	135,863,000
936	3¢ Coast Guard, Nov. 10	.15	.15	.30	(4)	4.75	111,616,700
937	3¢ Alfred E. Smith, Nov. 26	.15	.15	.30	(4)	2.50	308,587,700
	Pair with full vertical gutter between	—					
938	3¢ Texas Statehood, Dec. 29	.15	.15	.30	(4)	4.00	170,640,000
	Issues of 1946						
939	3¢ Merchant Marine, Feb. 26	.15	.15	.30	(4)	4.75	135,927,000
940	3¢ Veterans of World War II, May 9	.15	.15	.30	(4)	1.75	260,339,100
941	3¢ Tennessee Statehood, June 1	.15	.15	.30	(4)	1.50	132,274,500
942	3¢ Iowa Statehood, Aug. 3	.15	.15	.30	(4)	1.50	132,430,000
943	3¢ Smithsonian Institution, Aug. 10	.15	.15	.30	(4)	1.50	139,209,500
944	3¢ Kearny Expedition, Oct. 16	.15	.15	.30	(4)	1.50	114,684,450
	Issues of 1947, Perf. 10½ x 11						
945	3¢ Thomas A. Edison, Feb. 11	.15	.15	.30	(4)	2.00	156,540,510
	Perf. 11 x 10½						
946	3¢ Joseph Pulitzer, Apr. 10	.15	.15	.30	(4)	1.50	120,452,600
947	3¢ Postage Stamps Centenary, May 17	.15	.15	.30	(4)	1.50	127,104,300

Which museums are called "America's Attic"?

The museums and galleries that make up the Smithsonian Institution in Washington, D.C., contain more than 70 million American artifacts. The collections are so diverse and huge that the Smithsonian is sometimes called "America's Attic." The idea of the Smithsonian did not originate in this country, though.

An English scientist, James Smithson (1765-1829) left more than $500,000 "to found, at Washington under the name of the Smithsonian Institution, an Establishment for the increase and diffusion of knowledge among men." Interestingly, it is not known whether Smithson ever even visited the United States. **(#943)**

119

	Issues of 1947 (continued), Imperf.	Un	U	PB	#	FDC	Q
	Centenary International Philatelic Exhibition Issue Souvenir Sheet, May 19						
948	Souvenir sheet of 2 stamps (#1-2)	.60	.50			2.00	10,299,600
a	5¢ single stamp from sheet	.30	.25				10,299,600
b	10¢ single stamp from sheet	.30	.25				10,299,600
	Perf. 11 x 10¹/₂						
949	3¢ Doctors, June 9	.15	.15	.30	(4)	1.00	132,902,000
950	3¢ Utah Settlement, July 24	.15	.15	.30	(4)	1.00	131,968,000
951	3¢ U.S. Frigate Constitution, Oct. 21	.15	.15	.30	(4)	1.50	131,488,000
	Perf. 10¹/₂ x 11						
952	3¢ Everglades National Park, Dec. 5	.15	.15	.30	(4)	1.00	122,362,000
	Issues of 1948, Perf. 10¹/₂ x 11						
953	3¢ Dr. George Washington Carver, Jan. 5	.15	.15	.30	(4)	1.00	121,548,000
	Perf. 11 x 10¹/₂						
954	3¢ California Gold, Jan. 24	.15	.15	.30	(4)	1.00	131,109,500
955	3¢ Mississippi Territory, Apr. 7	.15	.15	.30	(4)	1.00	122,650,500
956	3¢ Four Chaplains, May 28	.15	.15	.30	(4)	1.00	121,953,500
957	3¢ Wisconsin Statehood, May 29	.15	.15	.30	(4)	1.00	115,250,000
958	5¢ Swedish Pioneer, June 4	.15	.15	.45	(4)	1.00	64,198,500
959	3¢ Progress of Women, July 19	.15	.15	.30	(4)	1.00	117,642,500
	Perf. 10¹/₂ x 11						
960	3¢ William Allen White, July 31	.15	.15	.30	(4)	1.00	77,649,600
	Perf. 11 x 10¹/₂						
961	3¢ U.S.-Canada Friendship, Aug. 2	.15	.15	.30	(4)	1.00	113,474,500
962	3¢ Francis Scott Key, Aug. 9	.15	.15	.30	(4)	1.00	120,868,500
963	3¢ Salute to Youth, Aug. 11	.15	.15	.30	(4)	1.00	77,800,500
964	3¢ Oregon Territory, Aug. 14	.15	.15	.30	(4)	1.00	52,214,000
	Perf. 10¹/₂ x 11						
965	3¢ Harlan F. Stone, Aug. 25	.15	.15	.60	(4)	1.00	53,958,100
966	3¢ Palomar Mountain Observatory, Aug. 30	.15	.15	1.10	(4)	1.50	61,120,100
a	Vertical pair, imperf. between	550.00					
	Perf. 11 x 10¹/₂						
967	3¢ Clara Barton, Sept. 7	.15	.15	.30	(4)	.90	57,823,000

Which fort inspired "The Star-Spangled Banner"?

Fort McHenry, in Baltimore Harbor, was the inspiration for Francis Scott Key's "The Star-Spangled Banner." During the War of 1812, the British captured his friend, William Beanes. Key, a well-known lawyer, boarded a truce ship to negotiate with the British for his friend's release. On board the ship, Key watched the British bombard Fort McHenry throughout the night. The next morning he saw that "our flag was still there." The event inspired Key to write the poem, "Defense of Fort M'Henry" and set the poem to a popular drinking song. **(#962)**

948

949

950

951

952

953

954

955

956

957

958

959

960

961

962

963

964

965

966

967

968

969

970

971

972

973

974

975

976

977

978

979

980

981

982

983

984

985

986

987

988

	Issues of 1948 (continued), Perf. 11 x 10½	Un	U	PB	#	FDC	Q
968	3¢ Poultry Industry, Sept. 9	.15	.15	.35	(4)	.90	52,975,000
	Perf. 10½ x 11						
969	3¢ Gold Star Mothers, Sept. 21	.15	.15	.35	(4)	1.00	77,149,000
	Perf. 11 x 10½						
970	3¢ Fort Kearny, Sept. 22	.15	.15	.35	(4)	1.00	58,332,000
971	3¢ Volunteer Firemen, Oct. 4	.15	.15	.35	(4)	1.50	56,228,000
972	3¢ Indian Centennial, Oct. 15	.15	.15	.35	(4)	1.00	57,832,000
973	3¢ Rough Riders, Oct. 27	.15	.15	.35	(4)	1.00	53,875,000
974	3¢ Juliette Gordon Low, Oct. 29	.15	.15	.35	(4)	1.00	63,834,000
	Perf. 10½ x 11						
975	3¢ Will Rogers, Nov. 4	.15	.15	.40	(4)	1.00	67,162,200
976	3¢ Fort Bliss, Nov. 5	.15	.15	1.25	(4)	1.00	64,561,000
	Perf. 11 x 10½						
977	3¢ Moina Michael, Nov. 9	.15	.15	.35	(4)	1.00	64,079,500
978	3¢ Gettysburg Address, Nov. 19	.15	.15	.35	(4)	1.00	63,388,000
	Perf. 10½ x 11						
979	3¢ American Turners, Nov. 20	.15	.15	.35	(4)	1.00	62,285,000
980	3¢ Joel Chandler Harris, Dec. 9	.15	.15	.55	(4)	1.00	57,492,600
	Issues of 1949, Perf. 11 x 10½						
981	3¢ Minnesota Territory, Mar. 3	.15	.15	.30	(4)	1.00	99,190,000
982	3¢ Washington and Lee University, Apr. 12	.15	.15	.30	(4)	1.00	104,790,000
983	3¢ Puerto Rico Election, Apr. 27	.15	.15	.30	(4)	1.00	108,805,000
984	3¢ Annapolis Tercentary, May 23	.15	.15	.30	(4)	1.00	107,340,000
985	3¢ Grand Army of the Republic, Aug. 29	.15	.15	.30	(4)	1.00	117,020,000
	Perf. 10½ x 11						
986	3¢ Edgar Allan Poe, Oct. 7	.15	.15	.45	(4)	1.00	122,633,000
	Thin outer frame line at top, inner frame line missing	6.00					
	Issues of 1950, Perf. 11 x 10½						
987	3¢ American Bankers Association, Jan. 3	.15	.15	.30	(4)	1.00	130,960,000
	Perf. 10½ x 11						
988	3¢ Samuel Gompers, Jan. 27	.15	.15	.30	(4)	1.00	128,478,000

Who founded the Girl Scouts of America?

Juliette Gordon Low (1860-1927), a talented sculptor, organized the Girl Scouts in the United States. She based her program on similar programs already established in England: the Boy Scouts and the Girl Guides.

Low organized a group of Girl Guides on her estate in Glenlyon, Scotland. After she moved to America, she held the first Girl Guide troop meeting in her home in Savannah, Georgia, in 1912. She soon changed the name to Girl Scouts and the national Girl Scout organization was incorporated in 1915. Low was its first president. **(#974)**

	Issues of 1950 (continued), Perf. 10¹/₂ x 11, 11 x 10¹/₂	Un	U	PB	#	FDC	Q
	National Capital Sesquicentennial Issue						
989	3¢ Statue of Freedom on Capitol Dome, Apr. 20	.15	.15	.30	(4)	1.00	132,090,000
990	3¢ Executive Mansion, June 12	.15	.15	.38	(4)	1.00	130,050,000
991	3¢ Supreme Court, Aug. 2	.15	.15	.30	(4)	1.00	131,350,000
992	3¢ U.S. Capitol, Nov. 22	.15	.15	.38	(4)	1.00	129,980,000
	Gripper cracks	1.00	.50				
	Perf. 11 x 10¹/₂						
993	3¢ Railroad Engineers, Apr. 29	.15	.15	.30	(4)	1.00	122,315,000
994	3¢ Kansas City, MO, June 3	.15	.15	.30	(4)	1.00	122,170,000
995	3¢ Boy Scouts, June 30	.15	.15	.35	(4)	3.00	131,635,000
996	3¢ Indiana Territory, July 4	.15	.15	.30	(4)	1.00	121,860,000
997	3¢ California Statehood, Sept. 9	.15	.15	.30	(4)	1.00	121,120,000
	Issues of 1951						
998	3¢ United Confederate Veterans, May 30	.15	.15	.30	(4)	1.00	119,120,000
999	3¢ Nevada Settlement, July 14	.15	.15	.30	(4)	1.00	112,125,000
1000	3¢ Landing of Cadillac, July 24	.15	.15	.30	(4)	1.00	114,140,000
1001	3¢ Colorado Statehood, Aug. 1	.15	.15	.30	(4)	1.00	114,490,000
1002	3¢ American Chemical Society, Sept. 4	.15	.15	.30	(4)	1.00	117,200,000
1003	3¢ Battle of Brooklyn, Dec. 10	.15	.15	.30	(4)	1.00	116,130,000
	Issues of 1952						
1004	3¢ Betsy Ross, Jan. 2	.15	.15	.35	(4)	1.00	116,175,000
1005	3¢ 4-H Club, Jan. 15	.15	.15	.30	(4)	1.00	115,945,000
1006	3¢ B&O Railroad, Feb. 28	.15	.15	.35	(4)	1.25	112,540,000
1007	3¢ American Automobile Association, Mar. 4	.15	.15	.30	(4)	1.00	117,415,000

How were the first trains on the B&O Railroad powered?

In 1827, when the Baltimore & Ohio (B&O) Railroad began operating, horses pulled the first trains. Many other experiments followed. The railroad also tried train cars equipped with sails, and during the summer of 1830, New York manufacturer Peter Cooper built a steam-powered

locomotive named *Tom Thumb*; however, it was too small for regular service on the B&O. Finally, in 1831, the railroad began regular passenger service with a locomotive called *York*. **(#1006)**

989

990

991

992

993

994

995

996

997

998

999

1000

1001

1002

1003

1004

1005

1006

1007

1008

1009

1010

1011

1012

1013

1014

1015

1016

1017

1018

1019

1020

1021

1022

1023

1024

1025

1026

1027

1028

1029

	Issues of 1952 (continued), Perf. 11 x 10½	Un	U	PB	#	FDC	Q
1008	3¢ NATO, Apr. 4	.15	.15	.30	(4)	1.00	2,899,580,000
1009	3¢ Grand Coulee Dam, May 15	.15	.15	.30	(4)	1.00	114,540,000
1010	3¢ Arrival of Lafayette, June 13	.15	.15	.30	(4)	1.00	113,135,000
	Perf. 10½ x 11						
1011	3¢ Mt. Rushmore Memorial, Aug. 11	.15	.15	.35	(4)	1.00	116,255,000
	Perf. 11 x 10½						
1012	3¢ Engineering, Sept. 6	.15	.15	.30	(4)	1.00	113,860,000
1013	3¢ Service Women, Sept. 11	.15	.15	.30	(4)	1.00	124,260,000
1014	3¢ Gutenberg Bible, Sept. 30	.15	.15	.30	(4)	1.00	115,735,000
1015	3¢ Newspaper Boys, Oct. 4	.15	.15	.30	(4)	1.00	115,430,000
1016	3¢ International Red Cross, Nov. 21	.15	.15	.30	(4)	1.00	136,220,000
	Issues of 1953						
1017	3¢ National Guard, Feb. 23	.15	.15	.35	(4)	1.00	114,894,600
1018	3¢ Ohio Statehood, Mar. 2	.15	.15	.35	(4)	1.00	118,706,000
1019	3¢ Washington Territory, Mar. 2	.15	.15	.30	(4)	1.00	114,190,000
1020	3¢ Louisiana Purchase, Apr. 30	.15	.15	.30	(4)	1.00	113,990,000
1021	5¢ Opening of Japan, July 14	.15	.15	.90	(4)	1.00	89,289,600
1022	3¢ American Bar Association, Aug. 24	.15	.15	.30	(4)	1.00	114,865,000
1023	3¢ Sagamore Hill, Sept. 14	.15	.15	.30	(4)	1.00	115,780,000
1024	3¢ Future Farmers, Oct. 13	.15	.15	.30	(4)	1.00	115,244,600
1025	3¢ Trucking Industry, Oct. 27	.15	.15	.30	(4)	1.00	123,709,600
1026	3¢ General George S. Patton, Nov. 11	.15	.15	.40	(4)	1.75	114,798,600
1027	3¢ New York City, Nov. 20	.15	.15	.35	(4)	1.00	115,759,600
1028	3¢ Gadsden Purchase, Dec. 30	.15	.15	.30	(4)	1.00	116,134,600
	Issue of 1954						
1029	3¢ Columbia University, Jan. 4	.15	.15	.30	(4)	1.00	118,540,000

When did women first take part in the U.S. military?

During the Revolutionary War, a woman nicknamed "Molly Pitcher" took up arms. Historians disagree about her real identity, but most say she was Mary Ludwig Hays McCauley. The legend is this: At Monmouth Courthouse in 1778, Mary helped bind wounds and dispense water during battle. Her husband, John Hays, was badly wounded, so she put down her water pitcher, swabbed his gun barrel and fired, staying at her post until she was relieved by an artillery man. Women's influence in the armed services has since grown, and they enjoy an essential place in the military today. (**#1013**)

127

	Issues of 1954-67 (continued), Perf. 11 x 10½	Un	U	PB	#	FDC
	Liberty Issue					
1030	½¢ Franklin, Oct. 20, 1954	.15	.15	.25	(4)	1.00
1031	1¢ Washington, Aug. 26, 1954	.15	.15	.25	(4)	1.00
	Pair with full vertical or horizontal gutter between	150.00				
b	Wet printing	.15	.15			
	Perf. 10½ x 11					
1031A	1¼¢ Palace of the Governors, June 17, 1960	.15	.15	.45	(4)	1.00
1032	1½¢ Mt. Vernon, Feb. 22, 1956	.15	.15	2.00	(4)	1.00
	Perf. 11 x 10½					
1033	2¢ Jefferson, Sept. 15, 1954	.15	.15	.22	(4)	1.00
	Pair with full vertical or horizontal gutter between	—				
1034	2½¢ Bunker Hill, June 17, 1959	.15	.15	.50	(4)	1.00
1035	3¢ Statue of Liberty, June 24, 1954	.15	.15	.30	(4)	1.00
a	Booklet pane of 6, June 30, 1954	4.50	.50			5.00
b	Tagged, July 6, 1966	.25	.25	5.00	(4)	15.00
c	Imperf. pair	1,500.00				
d	Horizontal pair, imperf. between	—				
e	Wet printing	.15	.15			
f	As "a," dry printing	4.50	.60			
1036	4¢ Lincoln, Nov. 19, 1954	.15	.15	.35	(4)	1.00
a	Booklet pane of 6, July 31, 1958	2.25	.50			4.00
b	Tagged, Nov. 2, 1963	.50	.40	6.50	(4)	50.00
	Perf. 10½ x 11					
1037	4½¢ The Hermitage, Mar. 16, 1959	.15	.15	.65	(4)	1.00
	Perf. 11 x 10½					
1038	5¢ James Monroe, Dec. 2, 1954	.15	.15	.50	(4)	1.00
	Pair with full vertical gutter between	200.00				
1039	6¢ T. Roosevelt, Nov. 18, 1955	.25	.15	1.10	(4)	1.00
a	Wet printing	.42	.15			
1040	7¢ Wilson, Jan. 10, 1956	.20	.15	1.00	(4)	1.00
	Perf. 11					
1041	8¢ Statue of Liberty, Apr. 9, 1954	.24	.15	2.25	(4)	1.00
a	Carmine double impression	650.00				
1042	8¢ Statue of Liberty, redrawn, Mar. 22, 1958	.20	.15	.95	(4)	1.00
	Perf. 11 x 10½					
1042A	8¢ Gen. John J. Pershing, Nov. 17, 1961	.22	.15	.95	(4)	1.00
	Perf. 10½ x 11					
1043	9¢ The Alamo, June 14, 1956	.28	.15	1.40	(4)	1.50
1044	10¢ Independence Hall, July 4, 1956	.22	.15	1.10	(4)	1.00
b	Tagged, July 6, 1966	2.00	.50	20.00	(4)	15.00
	Perf. 11					
1044A	11¢ Statue of Liberty, June 15, 1961	.28	.15	1.25	(4)	1.00
c	Tagged, Jan. 11, 1967	2.00	1.60	35.00	(4)	22.50

1030   **1031**

1031A

1032

1033   **1034**

1035   **1036**

1037

1038   **1039**   **1040**

1041   **1042**   **1042A**

1043   **1044**

1044A

129

1045   **1046**

1047

1048   **1049**   **1050**

1051   **1052**   **1053**

Have you noticed? We've improved the binding on your book so that it will stay open and lay flat. This new binding, called "Flex Binding," will make your guide a more convenient tool.

	Issues of 1954-67 (continued), Perf. 11 x 10½	Un	U	PB/LP	#	FDC
1045	12¢ Benjamin Harrison, June 6, 1959	.32	.15	1.50	(4)	1.00
a	Tagged, 1968	.45	.15	3.00	(4)	25.00
1046	15¢ John Jay, Dec. 12, 1958	.90	.15	3.00	(4)	1.00
a	Tagged, July 6, 1966	1.00	.35	7.50	(4)	20.00
	Perf. 10½ x 11					
1047	20¢ Monticello, Apr. 13, 1956	.45	.15	1.80	(4)	1.20
	Perf. 11 x 10½					
1048	25¢ Paul Revere, Apr. 18, 1958	1.40	.15	5.60	(4)	1.30
1049	30¢ Robert E. Lee, Sept. 21, 1955	.90	.15	5.65	(4)	1.50
a	Wet printing	1.75	.15	5.65	(4)	
1050	40¢ John Marshall, Sept. 24, 1955	1.90	.15	8.00	(4)	1.75
a	Wet printing	2.50	.25	8.00	(4)	
1051	50¢ Susan B. Anthony, Aug. 25, 1955	1.50	.15	6.75	(4)	6.00
a	Wet printing	2.50	.15	6.75	(4)	
1052	$1 Patrick Henry, Oct. 7, 1955	5.00	.15	24.00	(4)	10.00
a	Wet printing	6.50	.15	24.00	(4)	
	Perf. 11					
1053	$5 Alexander Hamilton, Mar. 19, 1956	75.00	6.75	325.00	(4)	55.00
	Issues of 1954-73, Coil Stamps, Perf. 10 Vertically					
1054	1¢ dark green Washington (1031), Oct. 8, 1954	.18	.15	.75	(2)	1.00
b	Imperf. pair	2,000.00	—			
c	Wet printing	.35	.16			
	Coil Stamp, Perf. 10 Horizontally					
1054A	1¼¢ turquoise Palace of the Governors (1031A), June 17, 1960	.15	.15	2.25	(2)	1.00
	Coil Stamps, Perf. 10 Vertically					
1055	2¢ rose carmine Jefferson (1033), Oct. 22, 1954	.15	.15	.45	(2)	1.00
a	Tagged, May 6, 1968	.15	.15			11.00
b	Imperf. pair (Bureau precanceled)		450.00			
c	As "a," imperf. pair	525.00				
d	Wet printing	.16	.15			
1056	2½¢ gray blue Bunker Hill (1034), Sept. 9, 1959	.25	.25	3.50	(2)	2.00
1057	3¢ deep violet Statue of Liberty (1035), July 20, 1954	.15	.15	.55	(2)	1.00
a	Imperf. pair	1,150.00	—	1,500.00	(2)	
b	Tagged, Oct. 1966	.50	.25			
c	Wet printing	.24	.15			
1058	4¢ red violet Lincoln (1036), July 31, 1958	.15	.15	.60	(2)	1.00
a	Imperf. pair	90.00	70.00	200.00	(2)	
b	Wet printing (Bureau precanceled)		.50			
	Coil Stamp, Perf. 10 Horizontally					
1059	4½¢ blue green The Hermitage (1037), May 1, 1959	1.50	1.20	14.00	(2)	1.75
	Coil Stamp, Perf. 10 Vertically					
1059A	25¢ green Revere (1048), Feb. 25, 1965	.50	.30	1.75	(2)	1.25
b	Tagged, Apr. 3, 1973	.55	.20			14.00
	Dull finish gum	.55				
c	Imperf. pair	40.00		75.00	(2)	

131

	Issues of 1954, Perf. 11 x 10½	Un	U	PB	#	FDC	Q
1060	3¢ Nebraska Territory, May 7	.15	.15	.30	(4)	1.00	115,810,000
1061	3¢ Kansas Territory, May 31	.15	.15	.30	(4)	1.00	113,603,700
	Perf. 10½ x 11						
1062	3¢ George Eastman, July 12	.15	.15	.35	(4)	1.00	128,002,000
	Perf. 11 x 10½						
1063	3¢ Lewis and Clark Expedition, July 28	.15	.15	.35	(4)	1.00	116,078,150
	Issues of 1955, Perf. 10½ x 11						
1064	3¢ Pennsylvania Academy of the Fine Arts, Jan. 15	.15	.15	.30	(4)	1.00	116,139,800
	Perf. 11 x 10½						
1065	3¢ Land-Grant Colleges, Feb. 12	.15	.15	.30	(4)	1.00	120,484,800
1066	8¢ Rotary International, Feb. 23	.16	.15	.80	(4)	1.75	53,854,750
1067	3¢ Armed Forces Reserve, May 21	.15	.15	.30	(4)	1.00	176,075,000
	Perf. 10½ x 11						
1068	3¢ New Hampshire, June 21	.15	.15	.35	(4)	1.00	125,944,400
	Perf. 11 x 10½						
1069	3¢ Soo Locks, June 28	.15	.15	.30	(4)	1.00	122,284,600
1070	3¢ Atoms for Peace, July 28	.15	.15	.35	(4)	1.00	133,638,850
1071	3¢ Fort Ticonderoga, Sept. 18	.15	.15	.35	(4)	1.00	118,664,600
1072	3¢ Andrew W. Mellon, Dec. 20	.15	.15	.30	(4)	1.00	112,434,000

What makes up the Armed Forces Reserve?

The Armed Forces Reserve is made up of all branches of the United States military forces: Air Force, Army, Coast Guard, Marines and Navy. On the third Saturday of May, Armed Forces Day is celebrated with military exercises on land, at sea and in the air. Armed Forces Day, as it was declared by President Truman, was first celebrated in May 1950 to replace three separate celebrations for the Air Force, Army and Navy. Military installations are usually open to the public on Armed Forces Day. **(#1067)**

1060

1061

1062

1063

1064

1065

1066

1067

1068

1069

1070

1071

1072

133

1956

1073

1074

1075

1076

1077

1078

1079

1080

1081

1082

1083

1084

1085

Issues of 1956, Perf. 10½ x 11	Un	U	PB/LP	#	FDC	Q
1073 3¢ Benjamin Franklin, Jan. 17	.15	.15	.30	(4)	1.00	129,384,550
Perf. 11 x 10½						
1074 3¢ Booker T. Washington, Apr. 5	.15	.15	.30	(4)	1.00	121,184,600
Fifth International Philatelic Exhibition Issues Souvenir Sheet, Imperf.						
1075 Sheet of 2 stamps (1035, 1041), Apr. 28	2.25	2.00	.90	(2)	5.00	2,900,731
a 3¢ (1035), single stamp from sheet	.90	.80				
b 8¢ (1041), single stamp from sheet	1.25	1.00				
Perf. 11 x 10½						
1076 3¢ New York Coliseum and Columbus Monument, Apr. 30	.15	.15	.30	(4)	1.00	119,784,200
Wildlife Conservation Issue						
1077 3¢ Wild Turkey, May 5	.15	.15	.35	(4)	1.10	123,159,400
1078 3¢ Pronghorn Antelope, June 22	.15	.15	.35	(4)	1.10	123,138,800
1079 3¢ King Salmon, Nov. 9	.15	.15	.35	(4)	1.10	109,275,000
Perf. 10½ x 11						
1080 3¢ Pure Food and Drug Laws, June 27	.15	.15	.30	(4)	1.00	112,932,200
Perf. 11 x 10½						
1081 3¢ Wheatland, Aug. 5	.15	.15	.30	(4)	1.00	125,475,000
Perf. 10½ x 11						
1082 3¢ Labor Day, Sept. 3	.15	.15	.30	(4)	1.00	117,855,000
Perf. 11 x 10½						
1083 3¢ Nassau Hall, Sept. 22	.15	.15	.30	(4)	1.00	122,100,000
Perf. 10½ x 11						
1084 3¢ Devils Tower, Sept. 24	.15	.15	.30	(4)	1.00	118,180,000
Pair with full horizontal gutter between	—					
Perf. 11 x 10½						
1085 3¢ Children's Stamp, Dec. 15	.15	.15	.00	(4)	1.00	100,975,000

How did a young girl help make steps toward world peace?

Samantha Smith (1972-1985), who lived with her family in Maine, would watch the news on television and get upset over the possibility of nuclear war between the United States and the former Soviet Union. When she was 10 years old, Samantha wrote a letter to then Soviet leader Yuri Andropov. Her letter said, "I have been worrying about Russia and the United States getting into a nuclear war. . . .God made the world for us to live together in peace and not to fight."

To her surprise, Andropov wrote a two-page letter back to her and invited her to the Soviet Union. Smith visited the country and became a young goodwill ambassador. In 1985, the Soviet government issued a stamp honoring Samantha Smith's work to help foster international friendship. (**#1085**)

	Issues of 1957, Perf. 11 x 10½	Un	U	PB	#	FDC	Q
1086	3¢ Alexander Hamilton, Jan. 11	.15	.15	.30	(4)	1.00	115,299,450
	Perf. 10½ x 11						
1087	3¢ Polio, Jan. 15	.15	.15	.30	(4)	1.00	186,949,600
	Perf. 11 x 10½						
1088	3¢ Coast and Geodetic Survey, Feb. 11	.15	.15	.30	(4)	1.00	115,235,000
1089	3¢ American Institute of Architects, Feb. 23	.15	.15	.30	(4)	1.00	106,647,500
	Perf. 10½ x 11						
1090	3¢ Steel Industry, May 22	.15	.15	.30	(4)	1.00	112,010,000
	Perf. 11 x 10½						
1091	3¢ International Naval Review-Jamestown Festival, June 10	.15	.15	.30	(4)	1.00	118,470,000
1092	3¢ Oklahoma Statehood, June 14	.15	.15	.35	(4)	1.00	102,230,000
1093	3¢ School Teachers, July 1	.15	.15	.30	(4)	1.00	102,410,000
	Perf. 11						
1094	4¢ Flag, July 4	.15	.15	.35	(4)	1.00	84,054,400
	Perf. 10½ x 11						
1095	3¢ Shipbuilding, Aug. 15	.15	.15	.30	(4)	1.00	126,266,000
	Champion of Liberty Issue, Ramon Magsaysay, Aug. 31, Perf. 11						
1096	8¢ Bust of Magsaysay on Medal	.16	.15	.70	(4)	1.00	39,489,600
	Plate block of 4, ultramarine P# omitted —						
	Perf. 10½ x 11						
1097	3¢ Lafayette, Sept. 6	.15	.15	.30	(4)	1.00	122,990,000
	Perf. 11						
1098	3¢ Wildlife Conservation, Nov. 22	.15	.15	.35	(4)	1.00	174,372,800
	Perf. 10½ x 11						
1099	3¢ Religious Freedom, Dec. 27	.15	.15	.30	(4)	1.00	114,365,000
	Issues of 1958						
1100	3¢ Gardening-Horticulture, Mar. 15	.15	.15	.30	(4)	1.00	122,765,200
1101-03	Not assigned						
	Perf. 11 x 10½						
1104	3¢ Brussels Universal and International Exhibition, Apr. 17	.15	.15	.30	(4)	1.00	113,660,200
1105	3¢ James Monroe, Apr. 28	.15	.15	.30	(4)	1.00	120,196,580
1106	3¢ Minnesota Statehood, May 11	.15	.15	.30	(4)	1.00	120,805,200
	Perf. 11						
1107	3¢ International Geophysical Year, May 31	.15	.15	.35	(4)	1.00	125,815,200
	Perf. 11 x 10½						
1108	3¢ Gunston Hall, June 12	.15	.15	.30	(4)	1.00	108,415,200

Minimum value listed for a stamp is 15 cents; for a First Day Cover (FDC), $1.00. This minimum represents a fair-market price for having a dealer locate and provide a single stamp or cover from his or her stock. Dealers may charge less per stamp or cover for a group of such stamps or covers, or less for a single stamp or cover.

1086

1087

1088

1089

1090

1091

1092

1093

1094

1095

1096

1097

1098

1099

1100

1104

1105

1106

1107

1108

137

1109

1110

1112

1113

1114

1115

1116

1117

1118

1119

1120

1121

1123

1124

1125

1126

1127

1128

1129

1130

1131

	Issues of 1958 (continued), Perf. 10½ x 11	Un	U	PB	#	FDC	Q
1109	3¢ Mackinac Bridge, June 25	.15	.15	.30	(4)	1.00	107,195,200
	Champion of Liberty Issue, Simon Bolivar, July 24						
1110	4¢ Bust of Bolivar on Medal	.15	.15	.35	(4)	1.00	115,745,280
	Perf. 11						
1111	8¢ Bust of Bolivar on Medal	.16	.15	1.40	(4)	1.00	39,743,670
	Plate block of four, ocher P# only	—					
	Perf. 11 x 10½						
1112	4¢ Atlantic Cable, Aug. 15	.15	.15	.40	(4)	1.00	114,570,200
	Issues of 1958-59, Lincoln Sesquicentennial Issue, Perf. 10½ x 11						
1113	1¢ Portrait by George Healy, Feb. 12, 1959	.15	.15	.25	(4)	1.00	120,400,200
1114	3¢ Sculptured Head by Gutzon Borglum, Feb. 27, 1959	.15	.15	.30	(4)	1.00	91,160,200
	Perf. 11 x 10½						
1115	4¢ Lincoln and Stephen Douglas Debating, by Joseph Boggs Beale, Aug. 27, 1958	.15	.15	.40	(4)	1.00	114,860,200
1116	4¢ Statue in Lincoln Memorial by Daniel Chester French, May 30, 1959	.15	.15	.40	(4)	1.00	126,500,000
	Champion of Liberty Issue, Lajos Kossuth, Sept. 19, Perf. 10½ x 11						
1117	4¢ Bust of Kossuth on Medal	.15	.15	.40	(4)	1.00	120,561,280
	Perf. 11						
1118	8¢ Bust of Kossuth on Medal	.16	.15	1.25	(4)	1.00	44,064,580
	Perf. 10½ x 11						
1119	4¢ Freedom of the Press, Sept. 22	.15	.15	.40	(4)	1.00	118,390,200
	Perf. 11 x 10½						
1120	4¢ Overland Mail, Oct. 10	.15	.15	.40	(4)	1.00	125,770,200
	Perf. 10½ x 11						
1121	4¢ Noah Webster, Oct. 16	.15	.15	.40	(4)	1.00	114,114,280
	Perf. 11						
1122	4¢ Forest Conservation, Oct. 27	.15	.15*	.40	(4)	1.00	156,600,200
	Perf. 11 x 10½						
1123	4¢ Fort Duquesne, Nov. 25	.15	.15	.40	(4)	1.00	124,200,200
	Issues of 1959						
1124	4¢ Oregon Statehood, Feb. 14	.15	.15	.40	(4)	1.00	120,740,200
	Champion of Liberty Issue, José de San Martin, Feb. 25, Perf. 10½ x 11						
1125	4¢ Bust of San Martin on Medal	.15	.15	.40	(4)	1.00	133,623,280
a	Horizontal pair, imperf. between	1,250.00					
	Perf. 11						
1126	8¢ Bust of San Martin on Medal	.16	.15	.80	(4)	1.00	45,568,000
	Perf. 10½ x 11						
1127	4¢ NATO, Apr. 1	.15	.15	.40	(4)	1.00	122,493,280
	Perf. 11 x 10½						
1128	4¢ Arctic Explorations, Apr. 6	.15	.15	.40	(4)	1.00	131,260,200
1129	8¢ World Peace Through World Trade, Apr. 20	.16	.15	.75	(4)	1.00	47,125,200
1130	4¢ Silver Centennial, June 8	.15	.15	.40	(4)	1.00	123,105,000
	Perf. 11						
1131	4¢ St. Lawrence Seaway, June 26	.15	.15	.40	(4)	1.00	126,105,050
	Pair with full horizontal gutter between	—					

	Issues of 1959 (continued), Perf. 11	Un	U	PB	#	FDC	Q
1132	4¢ 49-Star Flag, July 4	.15	.15	.40	(4)	1.00	209,170,000
1133	4¢ Soil Conservation, Aug. 26	.15	.15	.40	(4)	1.00	120,835,000
	Perf. 10¹/₂ x 11						
1134	4¢ Petroleum Industry, Aug. 27	.15	.15	.40	(4)	1.00	115,715,000
	Perf. 11 x 10¹/₂						
1135	4¢ Dental Health, Sept. 14	.15	.15	.40	(4)	1.00	118,445,000
	Champion of Liberty Issue, Ernst Reuter, Sept. 29, Perf. 10¹/₂ x 11						
1136	4¢ Bust of Reuter on Medal	.15	.15	.40	(4)	1.00	111,685,000
	Perf. 11						
1137	8¢ Bust of Reuter on Medal	.16	.15	.80	(4)	1.00	43,099,210
	Perf. 10¹/₂ x 11						
1138	4¢ Dr. Ephraim McDowell, Dec. 3	.15	.15	.40	(4)	1.00	115,444,000
a	Vertical pair, imperf. between	400.00					
b	Vertical pair, imperf. horizontally	300.00					
	Issues of 1960-61, American Credo Issue, Perf. 11						
1139	4¢ Quotation from Washington's Farewell Address, Jan. 20, 1960	.15	.15	.40	(4)	1.00	126,470,000
1140	4¢ Benjamin Franklin Quotation, Mar. 31, 1960	.15	.15	.40	(4)	1.00	124,560,000
1141	4¢ Thomas Jefferson Quotation, May 18, 1960	.15	.15	.45	(4)	1.00	115,455,000
1142	4¢ Francis Scott Key Quotation, Sept. 14, 1960	.15	.15	.45	(4)	1.00	122,060,000
1143	4¢ Abraham Lincoln Quotation, Nov. 19, 1960	.15	.15	.48	(4)	1.00	120,540,000
	Pair with full horizontal gutter between	—					
1144	4¢ Patrick Henry Quotation, Jan. 11, 1961	.15	.15	.50	(4)	1.00	113,075,000
	Issues of 1960						
1145	4¢ Boy Scouts, Feb. 8	.15	.15	.40	(4)	1.75	139,325,000
	Olympic Winter Games Issue, Feb. 18, Perf. 10¹/₂ x 11						
1146	4¢ Olympic Rings and Snowflake	.15	.15	.40	(4)	1.00	124,445,000
	Champion of Liberty Issue, Thomas G. Masaryk, Mar. 7						
1147	4¢ Bust of Masaryk on Medal	.15	.15	.35	(4)	1.00	113,792,100
a	Vertical pair, imperf. between	3,250.00					
	Perf. 11						
1148	8¢ Bust of Masaryk on Medal	.16	.15	1.00	(4)	1.00	44,215,500
a	Horizontal pair, imperf. between	—					
	Perf. 11 x 10¹/₂						
1149	4¢ World Refugee Year, Apr. 7	.15	.15	.40	(4)	1.00	113,195,000
	Perf. 11						
1150	4¢ Water Conservation, Apr. 18	.15	.15	.40	(4)	1.00	121,805,000
	Perf. 10¹/₂ x 11						
1151	4¢ SEATO, May 31	.15	.15	.40	(4)	1.00	115,353,000
a	Vertical pair, imperf. between	150.00					

1132

1133

1134

1135

1136

1137

1138

1139

1140

1141

1142

1143

1144

1145

1146

1147

1148

1149

1150

1151

1152

1153

1154

1155

1156

1157

1158

1159

1160

1161

1162

1163

1164

1165

1166

1167

1168

1169

1170

1171

1172

1173

	Issues of 1960 (continued), Perf. 11 x 10½	Un	U	PB	#	FDC	Q
1152	4¢ American Woman, June 2	.15	.15	.40	(4)	1.00	111,080,000
	Perf. 11						
1153	4¢ 50-Star Flag, July 4	.15	.15	.40	(4)	1.00	153,025,000
	Perf. 11 x 10½						
1154	4¢ Pony Express, July 19	.15	.15	.40	(4)	1.00	119,665,000
	Perf. 10½ x 11						
1155	4¢ Employ the Handicapped, Aug. 28	.15	.15	.40	(4)	1.00	117,855,000
1156	4¢ 5th World Forestry Congress, Aug. 29	.15	.15	.40	(4)	1.00	118,185,000
	Perf. 11						
1157	4¢ Mexican Independence, Sept. 16	.15	.15	.40	(4)	1.00	112,260,000
1158	4¢ U.S.-Japan Treaty, Sept. 28	.15	.15	.40	(4)	1.00	125,010,000
	Champion of Liberty Issue, Ignacy Jan Paderewski, Oct. 8, Perf. 10½ x 11						
1159	4¢ Bust of Paderewski on Medal	.15	.15	.40	(4)	1.00	119,798,000
	Perf. 11						
1160	8¢ Bust of Paderewski on Medal	.16	.15	1.10	(4)	1.00	42,696,050
	Perf. 10½ x 11						
1161	4¢ Sen. Robert A. Taft Memorial, Oct. 10	.15	.15	.40	(4)	1.00	106,610,000
	Perf. 11 x 10½						
1162	4¢ Wheels of Freedom, Oct. 15	.15	.15	.40	(4)	1.00	109,695,000
	Perf. 11						
1163	4¢ Boys' Clubs of America, Oct. 18	.15	.15	.40	(4)	1.00	123,690,000
1164	4¢ First Automated Post Office, Oct. 20	.15	.15	.40	(4)	1.00	123,970,000
	Champion of Liberty Issue, Gustaf Mannerheim, Oct. 26, Perf. 10½ x 11						
1165	4¢ Bust of Mannerheim on Medal	.15	.15	.40	(4)	1.00	124,796,000
	Perf. 11						
1166	8¢ Bust of Mannerheim on Medal	.16	.15	.80	(4)	1.00	42,076,720
1167	4¢ Camp Fire Girls, Nov. 1	.15	.15	.40	(4)	1.00	116,210,000
	Champion of Liberty Issue, Giusseppe Garibaldi, Nov. 2, Perf. 10½ x 11						
1168	4¢ Bust of Garibaldi on Medal	.15	.15	.40	(4)	1.00	126,252,000
	Perf. 11						
1169	8¢ Bust of Garibaldi on Medal	.16	.15	.80	(4)	1.00	42,746,200
	Perf. 10½ x 11						
1170	4¢ Sen. Walter F. George Memorial, Nov. 5	.15	.15	.40	(4)	1.00	124,117,000
1171	4¢ Andrew Carnegie, Nov. 25	.15	.15	.40	(4)	1.00	119,840,000
1172	4¢ John Foster Dulles Memorial, Dec. 6	.15	.15	.40	(4)	1.00	117,187,000
	Perf. 11 x 10½						
1173	4¢ Echo I-Communications for Peace, Dec. 15	.18	.15	.75	(4)	2.00	124,390,000

	Issues of 1961, Perf. 10½ x 11	Un	U	PB	#	FDC	Q
	Champion of Liberty Issue, Mahatma Gandhi, Jan. 26						
1174	4¢ Bust of Gandhi on Medal	.15	.15	.40	(4)	1.00	112,966,000
	Perf. 11						
1175	8¢ Bust of Gandhi on Medal	.16	.15	1.00	(4)	1.00	41,644,400
1176	4¢ Range Conservation, Feb. 2	.15	.15	.40	(4)	1.00	110,850,000
	Perf. 10½ x 11						
1177	4¢ Horace Greeley, Feb. 3	.15	.15	.40	(4)	1.00	98,616,000
	Issues of 1961-65, Civil War Centennial Issue, Perf. 11 x 10½						
1178	4¢ Fort Sumter, Apr. 12, 1961	.16	.15	.60	(4)	1.25	101,125,000
1179	4¢ Shiloh, Apr. 7, 1962	.15	.15	.48	(4)	1.25	124,865,000
	Perf. 11						
1180	5¢ Gettysburg, July 1, 1963	.15	.15	.55	(4)	1.25	79,905,000
1181	5¢ The Wilderness, May 5, 1964	.15	.15	.55	(4)	1.25	125,410,000
1182	5¢ Appomattox, Apr. 9, 1965	.25	.15	.95	(4)	1.25	112,845,000
a	Horizontal pair, imperf. vertically	4,500.00					
1183	4¢ Kansas Statehood, May 10	.15	.15	.40	(4)	1.00	106,210,000
	Perf. 11 x 10½						
1184	4¢ Sen. George W. Norris, July 11	.15	.15	.40	(4)	1.00	110,810,000
1185	4¢ Naval Aviation, Aug. 20	.15	.15	.40	(4)	1.00	116,995,000
	Pair with full vertical gutter between	150.00					
	Perf. 10½ x 11						
1186	4¢ Workmen's Compensation, Sept. 4	.15	.15	.40	(4)	1.00	121,015,000
	With plate # inverted			.60	(4)		
	Perf. 11						
1187	4¢ Frederic Remington, Oct. 4	.15	.15	.40	(4)	1.00	111,600,000
	Perf. 10½ x 11						
1188	4¢ Republic of China, Oct. 10	.15	.15	.40	(4)	1.00	110,620,000
1189	4¢ Naismith-Basketball, Nov. 6	.15	.15	.40	(4)	2.00	109,110,000
	Perf. 11						
1190	4¢ Nursing, Dec. 28	.15	.15	.40	(4)	1.00	145,350,000
	Issues of 1962						
1191	4¢ New Mexico Statehood, Jan. 6	.15	.15	.40	(4)	1.00	112,870,000
1192	4¢ Arizona Statehood, Feb. 14	.15	.15	.40	(4)	1.00	121,820,000
1193	4¢ Project Mercury, Feb. 20	.15	.15	.40	(4)	3.00	289,240,000
1194	4¢ Malaria Eradication, Mar. 30	.15	.15	.40	(4)	1.00	120,155,000
	Perf. 10½ x 11						
1195	4¢ Charles Evans Hughes, Apr. 11	.15	.15	.40	(4)	1.00	124,595,000

What was Project Mercury?

Project Mercury was a program designed to put a manned rocket into space. The purpose of the Project was to launch the craft in a controlled orbit around the earth, bring it back to earth safely, recover the capsule and study the effects of space on man. Project Mercury was first unveiled in the summer of 1958. On May 5, 1961, Project Mercury became a reality when Alan Shepard was launched into space for 15 minutes aboard the *Mercury 3*. **(#1193)**

1174

1175

1176

1177

1178

1179

1180

1181

1182

1183

1184

1185

1186

1187

1188

1189

1190

1191

1192

1193

1194

1195

145

1196

1197

1198

1199

1200

1201

1202

1203

1205

1206

1207

1208

1209   1213

1230

1231

1232

1233   1234

1235

146

	Issues of 1962 (continued), Perf. 11	Un	U	PB/LP	#	FDC	Q
1196	4¢ Seattle World's Fair, Apr. 25	.15	.15	.40	(4)	1.00	147,310,000
1197	4¢ Louisiana Statehood, Apr. 30	.15	.15	.40	(4)	1.00	118,690,000
	Perf. 11 x 10¹/₂						
1198	4¢ Homestead Act, May 20	.15	.15	.40	(4)	1.00	122,730,000
1199	4¢ Girl Scout Jubilee, July 24	.15	.15	.40	(4)	1.00	126,515,000
	Pair with full vertical gutter between *250.00*						
1200	4¢ Sen. Brien McMahon, July 28	.15	.15	.40	(4)	1.00	130,960,000
1201	4¢ Apprenticeship, Aug. 31	.15	.15	.40	(4)	1.00	120,055,000
	Perf. 11						
1202	4¢ Sam Rayburn, Sept. 16	.15	.15	.40	(4)	1.00	120,715,000
1203	4¢ Dag Hammarskjold, Oct. 23	.15	.15	.40	(4)	1.00	121,440,000
1204	4¢ black, brown and yellow (yellow inverted), Dag Hammarskjold, special printing, Nov. 16	.15	.15	1.25	(4)	6.00	40,270,000
	Christmas Issue, Nov. 1						
1205	4¢ Wreath and Candles	.15	.15	.40	(4)	1.00	861,970,000
1206	4¢ Higher Education, Nov. 14	.15	.15	.40	(4)	1.00	120,035,000
1207	4¢ Winslow Homer, Dec. 15	.15	.15	.48	(4)	1.00	117,870,000
a	Horizontal pair, imperf. between *4,500.00*						
	Issue of 1963-66						
1208	5¢ Flag over White House, Jan. 9, 1963	.25	.15	.50	(4)	1.00	
a	Tagged, Aug. 25, 1966	.16	.15	.80	(4)	11.50	
b	Horizontal pair, imperf. between *1,250.00*						
	Pair with full horizontal gutter between	—					
	Issues of 1962-66, Perf. 11 x 10¹/₂						
1209	1¢ Andrew Jackson, Mar. 22, 1963	.15	.15	.20	(4)	1.00	
a	Tagged, July 6, 1966	.15	.15	.30	(4)	5.75	
b	Horizontal pair, imperf. between, tagged —						
1210-12	Not assigned						
1213	5¢ George Washington, Nov. 23, 1962	.15	.15	.45	(4)	1.00	
a	Booklet pane of 5 + label	2.50	*1.50*			4.00	
b	Tagged, Oct. 28, 1963	.50	.22	3.00	(4)	5.75	
c	As "a," tagged	1.90	*1.50*				
1214-24	Not assigned						
	Coil Stamps, Perf. 10 Vertically						
1225	1¢ green Jackson (1209), May 31, 1963	.15	.15	1.75	(2)	1.00	
a	Tagged, July 6, 1966	.15	.15	5.75	(2)	5.00	
1226-28	Not assigned						
1229	5¢ dark blue gray Washington (1213), Nov. 23, 1962	1.00	.15	3.50	(2)	1.00	
a	Tagged, Oct. 28, 1963	1.25	.15			20.00	
b	Imperf. pair	375.00		1,150.00	(2)		
	Issues of 1963, Perf. 11						
1230	5¢ Carolina Charter, Apr. 6	.15	.15	.50	(4)	1.00	129,945,000
1231	5¢ Food for Peace- Freedom from Hunger, June 4	.15	.15	.50	(4)	1.00	135,620,000
1232	5¢ West Virginia Statehood, June 20	.15	.15	.50	(4)	1.00	137,540,000
1233	5¢ Emancipation Proclamation, Aug. 16	.15	.15	.50	(4)	1.00	132,435,000
1234	5¢ Alliance for Progress, Aug. 17	.15	.15	.50	(4)	1.00	135,520,000
	Perf. 10¹/₂ x 11						
1235	5¢ Cordell Hull, Oct. 5	.15	.15	.50	(4)	1.00	131,420,000

	Issues of 1963 (continued), Perf. 11 x 10½	Un	U	PB	#	FDC	Q
1236	5¢ Eleanor Roosevelt, Oct. 11	.15	.15	.50	(4)	1.00	133,170,000
	Perf. 11						
1237	5¢ The Sciences, Oct. 14	.15	.15	.50	(4)	1.00	130,195,000
1238	5¢ City Mail Delivery, Oct. 26	.15	.15	.50	(4)	1.00	128,450,000
1239	5¢ International Red Cross, Oct. 29	.15	.15	.50	(4)	1.00	118,665,000
	Christmas Issue, Nov. 1						
1240	5¢ National Christmas Tree and White House	.15	.15	.50	(4)	1.00	1,291,250,000
a	Tagged, Nov. 2	.65	.40	5.00	(4)	60.00	
	Pair with full horizontal gutter between	—					
1241	5¢ John James Audubon, Dec. 7 (See also #C71)	.15	.15	.50	(4)	1.00	175,175,000
	Issues of 1964, Perf. 10½ x 11						
1242	5¢ Sam Houston, Jan. 10	.15	.15	.50	(4)	1.00	125,995,000
	Perf. 11						
1243	5¢ Charles M. Russell, Mar. 19	.15	.15	.50	(4)	1.00	128,025,000
	Perf. 11 x 10½						
1244	5¢ New York World's Fair, Apr. 22	.15	.15	.50	(4)	1.00	145,700,000
	Perf. 11						
1245	5¢ John Muir, Apr. 29	.15	.15	.50	(4)	1.00	120,310,000
	Perf. 11 x 10½						
1246	5¢ President John Fitzgerald Kennedy Memorial, May 29	.15	.15	.50	(4)	1.00	511,750,000
	Perf. 10½ x 11						
1247	5¢ New Jersey Settlement, June 15	.15	.15	.50	(4)	1.00	123,845,000
	Perf. 11						
1248	5¢ Nevada Statehood, July 22	.15	.15	.50	(4)	1.00	122,825,000
1249	5¢ Register and Vote, Aug. 1	.15	.15	.50	(4)	1.00	453,090,000
	Perf. 10½ x 11						
1250	5¢ Shakespeare, Aug. 14	.15	.15	.50	(4)	1.00	123,245,000
1251	5¢ Doctors William and Charles Mayo, Sept. 11	.15	.15	.50	(4)	1.00	123,355,000
	Perf. 11						
1252	5¢ American Music, Oct. 15	.15	.15	.50	(4)	1.00	126,970,000
a	Blue omitted		950.00				
1253	5¢ Homemakers, Oct. 26	.15	.15	.50	(4)	1.00	121,250,000

How did John Muir become interested in conservation?

When John Muir (1838-1914) was 11 years old, his family moved to a farm in Kingston, Wisconsin where he developed a great love for nature. Muir worked at odd jobs until he was temporarily blinded in an industrial accident. After he recovered, Muir took a walking trip that lasted two and a half years. Along the way, he recorded his observations of plants and animals. In 1890, Muir influenced Congress to pass the Yosemite National Park Bill, where he lived for six years. And, in 1892, he founded the Sierra Club. **(#1245)**

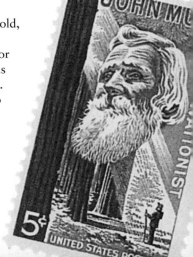

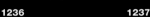

1236

1237

1238

1239

1240

1241

1242

1243

1244

1245

1246

1247

1248

1249

DOCTORS MAYO

1252

1253

1258

1259

1260

1254 1255 1257b
1256 1257

1261

1262

1263

1264

1265

1266

1267

1268

1270

1272

1269

1271

1274

1276

1273

1275

	Issues of 1964 (continued), Perf. 11	Un	U	PB	#	FDC	Q
	Christmas Issue, Nov. 9						
1254	5¢ Holly	.30	.15			1.00	351,940,000
1255	5¢ Mistletoe	.30	.15			1.00	351,940,000
1256	5¢ Poinsettia	.30	.15			1.00	351,940,000
1257	5¢ Sprig of Conifer	.30	.15			1.00	351,940,000
b	Block of four, #1254-57	1.25	1.00	1.50	(4)	3.00	
c	As "b," tagged, Nov. 10	4.25	2.00			57.50	
	Perf. 10¹/₂ x 11						
1258	5¢ Verrazano-Narrows Bridge, Nov. 21	.15	.15	.50	(4)	1.00	120,005,000
	Perf. 11						
1259	5¢ Fine Arts, Dec. 2	.15	.15	.50	(4)	1.00	125,800,000
	Perf. 10¹/₂ x 11						
1260	5¢ Amateur Radio, Dec. 15	.15	.15	.50	(4)	1.00	122,230,000
	Issues of 1965, Perf. 11						
1261	5¢ Battle of New Orleans, Jan. 8	.15	.15	.50	(4)	1.00	115,695,000
1262	5¢ Physical Fitness-Sokol, Feb. 15	.15	.15	.50	(4)	1.00	115,095,000
1263	5¢ Crusade Against Cancer, Apr. 1	.15	.15	.50	(4)	1.00	119,560,000
	Perf. 10¹/₂ x 11						
1264	5¢ Winston Churchill Memorial, May 13	.15	.15	.50	(4)	1.00	125,180,000
	Perf. 11						
1265	5¢ Magna Carta, June 15	.15	.15	.50	(4)	1.00	120,135,000
	Corner block of four, black PB# omitted	—					
1266	5¢ International Cooperation Year—United Nations, June 26	.15	.15	.50	(4)	1.00	115,405,000
1267	5¢ Salvation Army, July 2	.15	.15	.50	(4)	1.00	115,855,000
	Perf. 10¹/₂ x 11						
1268	5¢ Dante Alighieri, July 17	.15	.15	.50	(4)	1.00	115,340,000
1269	5¢ President Herbert Hoover Memorial, Aug. 10	.15	.15	.50	(4)	1.00	114,840,000
	Perf. 11						
1270	5¢ Robert Fulton, Aug. 19	.15	.15	.50	(4)	1.00	116,140,000
1271	5¢ Florida Settlement, Aug. 28	.15	.15	.50	(4)	1.00	116,900,000
a	Yellow omitted	550.00					
1272	5¢ Traffic Safety, Sept. 3	.15	.15	.50	(4)	1.00	114,085,000
1273	5¢ John Singleton Copley, Sept. 17	.15	.15	.50	(4)	1.00	114,880,000
1274	11¢ International Telecommunication Union, Oct. 6	.32	.16	5.75	(4)	1.00	26,995,000
1275	5¢ Adlai E. Stevenson Memorial, Oct. 23	.15	.15	.50	(4)	1.00	128,495,000
	Christmas Issue, Nov. 2						
1276	5¢ Angel with Trumpet (1840 Weather Vane)	.15	.15	.50	(4)	1.00	1,139,930,000
a	Tagged, Nov. 15	.75	.25	7.50	(4)	42.50	
1277	Not assigned						

The stamp listings contain a number of "a," "b," "c," etc. additions which include recognized varieties and errors. These listings are as complete as space permits.

	Issues of 1965-78, Perf. 11 x 10½, 10½ x 11 (See also #1299, 1303-05C)	Un	U	PB	#	FDC
	Prominent Americans Issue					
1278	1¢ Jefferson, Jan. 12, 1968	.15	.15	.20	(4)	1.00
a	Booklet pane of 8	1.00	.25			2.50
b	Bklt. pane of 4 + 2 labels, May 10, 1971	.75	.20			12.50
c	Untagged (Bureau precanceled)		.15			
1279	1¼¢ Albert Gallatin, Jan. 30, 1967	.15	.15	10.00	(4)	1.00
1280	2¢ Frank Lloyd Wright, Jan. 8, 1968	.15	.15	.25	(4)	1.00
a	Booklet pane of 5 + label	1.20	.40			4.00
b	Untagged (Bureau precanceled)		.15			
c	Booklet pane of 6, May 7, 1971	1.00	.35			15.00
	Pair with full vertical gutter between	—				
1281	3¢ Francis Parkman, Sept. 16, 1967	.15	.15	.30	(4)	1.00
a	Untagged (Bureau precanceled)		.15			
1282	4¢ Lincoln, Nov. 19, 1965	.15	.15	.38	(4)	1.00
a	Tagged, Dec. 1, 1965	.15	.15	.38	(4)	20.00
	Pair with full horizontal gutter between	—				
1283	5¢ Washington, Feb. 22, 1966	.15	.15	.50	(4)	1.00
a	Tagged, Feb. 23, 1966	.15	.15	.50	(4)	22.50
1283B	5¢ redrawn, Nov. 17, 1967	.15	.15	.50	(4)	1.00
	Dull finish gum	.20		1.00	(4)	
d	Untagged (Bureau precanceled)		.15			
1284	6¢ Roosevelt, Jan. 29, 1966	.15	.15	.60	(4)	1.00
a	Tagged, Dec. 29, 1966	.15	.15	.80	(4)	20.00
b	Booklet pane of 8, Dec. 28, 1967	1.50	.50			3.00
c	Booklet pane of 5 + label, Jan. 9, 1968	1.25	.50			100.00
1285	8¢ Albert Einstein, Mar. 14, 1966	.20	.15	.85	(4)	1.50
a	Tagged, July 6, 1966	.20	.15	.75	(4)	14.00
1286	10¢ Jackson, Mar. 15, 1967	.20	.15	1.00	(4)	1.00
b	Untagged (Bureau precanceled)		.20			
1286A	12¢ Henry Ford, July 30, 1968	.25	.15	1.00	(4)	1.00
c	Untagged (Bureau precanceled)		.25			
1287	13¢ John F. Kennedy, May 29, 1967	.25	.15	1.20	(4)	1.50
a	Untagged (Bureau precanceled)		.25			
1288	15¢ Oliver Wendell Holmes, Mar. 8, 1968	.30	.15	1.25	(4)	1.00
a	Untagged (Bureau precanceled)		.30			
	Booklet Stamp, Perf. 10					
1288B	15¢ dark rose claret Holmes (1288), Single from booklet	.28	.15			1.00
c	Booklet pane of 8, June 14, 1978	2.25	1.25			3.00
e	As "c," vert. imperf. between	—				
	Perf. 11 x 10½, 10½ x 11					
1289	20¢ George C. Marshall, Oct. 24, 1967	.45	.15	1.90	(4)	1.00
a	Tagged, Apr. 3, 1973	.45	.15	1.75	(4)	12.50
1290	25¢ Frederick Douglass, Feb. 14, 1967	.55	.15	2.25	(4)	1.25
a	Tagged, Apr. 3, 1973	.55	.15	2.00	(4)	14.00
1291	30¢ John Dewey, Oct. 21, 1968	.65	.15	3.00	(4)	1.25
a	Tagged, Apr. 3, 1973	.60	.15	2.75	(4)	14.00
1292	40¢ Thomas Paine, Jan. 29, 1968	.85	.15	3.25	(4)	1.60
a	Tagged, Apr. 3, 1973	.80	.15	3.00	(4)	15.00
1293	50¢ Lucy Stone, Aug. 13, 1968	1.00	.15	4.50	(4)	3.25
a	Tagged, Apr. 3, 1973	.85	.15	4.50	(4)	20.00
1294	$1 Eugene O'Neill, Oct. 16, 1967	2.50	.15	10.00	(4)	7.50
a	Tagged, Apr. 3, 1973	2.00	.15	8.00	(4)	22.50

152

1278

1279

1280

1281

1282

1283

1283B

1284

1285

1286

1286A

1287

1288

1289

1290

1291

1292

1293

1294

1295

1305

1306

1307

1308

1309

1310

1311

1312

1313

1314

	Issues of 1965-78 (continued), Perf. 11 x 10½, 10½ x 11	Un	U	PB/LP	#	FDC	Q
1295	$5 John Bassett Moore, Dec. 3, 1966	13.50	2.00	50.00	(4)	40.00	
a	Tagged, Apr. 3, 1973	8.50	2.00	35.00	(4)	65.00	
1296	Not assigned						
	Issues of 1966-81, Coil Stamps, Perf. 10 Horizontally						
1297	3¢ violet Parkman (1281), Nov. 4, 1975	.15	.15	.45	(2)	1.00	
a	Imperf. pair	30.00		50.00	(2)		
b	Untagged (Bureau precanceled)		.15				
c	As "b," imperf. pair		6.00	40.00	(2)		
1298	6¢ Roosevelt (1284), Dec. 28, 1967	.15	.15	1.25	(2)	1.00	
a	Imperf. pair	2,500.00					
	Coil Stamps, Perf. 10 Vertically (See also #1279-96)						
1299	1¢ green Jefferson (1278), Jan. 12, 1968	.15	.15	.20	(2)	1.00	
a	Untagged (Bureau precanceled)		.15				
b	Imperf. pair	30.00	—	65.00	(2)		
1300-02	Not assigned						
1303	4¢ blk. Lincoln (1282), May 28, 1966	.15	.15	.75	(2)	1.00	
a	Untagged (Bureau precanceled)		.15				
b	Imperf. pair	675.00		1,200.00	(2)		
1304	5¢ bl. Washington (1283), Sept. 8, 1966	.15	.15	.40	(2)	1.00	
a	Untagged (Bureau precanceled)		.15				
b	Imperf. pair	200.00		350.00	(2)		
e	As "a," imperf. pair		450.00				
1304C	5¢ redrawn (1283B), 1981	.15	.15	.60	(2)		
d	Imperf. pair	—					
1305	6¢ gray brown Roosevelt, Feb. 28, 1968	.15	.15	.55	(2)	1.00	
a	Imperf. pair	65.00		135.00	(2)		
b	Untagged (Bureau precanceled)		.20				
1305E	15¢ rose claret Holmes (1288), June 14, 1978	.25	.15	1.25	(2)	1.00	
	Dull finish gum	.60					
f	Untagged (Bureau precanceled)		.30				
g	Imperf. pair	30.00		90.00	(2)		
h	Pair, imperf. between	200.00		600.00	(2)		
1305C	$1 dull purple Eugene O'Neill (1294), Jan. 12, 1973	1.50	.20	5.00	(2)	5.00	
d	Imperf. pair	2,250.00		4,000.00	(2)		
	Issues of 1966, Perf. 11						
1306	5¢ Migratory Bird Treaty, Mar. 16	.15	.15	.50	(4)	1.00	116,835,000
1307	5¢ Humane Treatment of Animals, Apr. 9	.15	.15	.50	(4)	1.00	117,470,000
1308	5¢ Indiana Statehood, Apr. 16	.15	.15	.50	(4)	1.00	123,770,000
1309	5¢ American Circus, May 2	.15	.15	.50	(4)	2.50	131,270,000
	Sixth International Philatelic Exhibition Issue						
1310	5¢ Stamped Cover, May 21	.15	.15	.50	(4)	1.00	122,285,000
	Souvenir Sheet, Imperf.						
1311	5¢ Stamped Cover (1310) and Washington, D.C., Scene, May 23	.15	.15			1.00	14,680,000
	Perf. 11						
1312	5¢ The Bill of Rights, July 1	.15	.15	.50	(4)	1.00	114,160,000
	Perf. 10½ x 11						
1313	5¢ Poland's Millennium, July 30	.15	.15	.50	(4)	1.00	128,475,000
	Perf. 11						
1314	5¢ National Park Service, Aug. 25	.15	.15	.50	(4)	1.00	119,535,000
a	Tagged, Aug. 26	.30	.20	2.00	(4)	20.00	

	Issues of 1966 (continued), Perf. 11	Un	U	PB	#	FDC	Q
1315	5¢ Marine Corps Reserve, Aug. 29	.15	.15	.50	(4)	1.00	125,110,000
a	Tagged	.30	.20	2.00	(4)	20.00	
b	Black and bister omitted	—					
1316	5¢ General Federation of Women's Clubs, Sept. 12	.15	.15	.50	(4)	1.00	114,853,200
a	Tagged, Sept. 13	.30	.20	2.00	(4)	22.50	

American Folklore Issue, Johnny Appleseed, Sept. 24

		Un	U	PB	#	FDC	Q
1317	5¢ Appleseed Carrying Shovel and Seed Sack, Apple in Background	.15	.15	.50	(4)	1.00	124,290,000
a	Tagged, Sept. 26	.30	.20	2.00	(4)	22.50	
1318	5¢ Beautification of America, Oct. 5	.15	.15	.50	(4)	1.00	128,460,000
a	Tagged	.30	.20	1.50	(4)	20.00	
1319	5¢ Great River Road, Oct. 21	.15	.15	.50	(4)	1.00	127,585,000
a	Tagged, Oct. 22	.30	.20	2.00	(4)	22.50	
1320	5¢ Savings Bond-Servicemen, Oct. 26	.15	.15	.50	(4)	1.00	115,875,000
a	Tagged, Oct. 27	.30	.20	2.00	(4)	22.50	
b	Red, dark bl. and blk. omitted	4,500.00					
c	Dark blue omitted	4,000.00					

Christmas Issue, Nov. 1

		Un	U	PB	#	FDC	Q
1321	5¢ Madonna and Child, by Hans Memling	.15	.15	.50	(4)	1.00	1,173,547,400
a	Tagged, Nov. 2	.30	.20	1.90	(4)	9.50	
1322	5¢ Mary Cassatt, Nov. 17	.15	.15	.60	(4)	1.00	114,015,000
a	Tagged	.30	.20	1.75	(4)	20.00	

Issues of 1967

		Un	U	PB	#	FDC	Q
1323	5¢ National Grange, Apr. 17	.15	.15	.50	(4)	1.00	121,105,000
a	Tagging omitted	3.50					
1324	5¢ Canada, May 25	.15	.15	.50	(4)	1.00	132,045,000
1325	5¢ Erie Canal, July 4	.15	.15	.50	(4)	1.00	118,780,000
1326	5¢ Search for Peace— Lions International, July 5	.15	.15	.50	(4)	1.00	121,985,000
1327	5¢ Henry David Thoreau, July 12	.15	.15	.50	(4)	1.00	111,850,000
1328	5¢ Nebraska Statehood, July 29	.15	.15	.50	(4)	1.00	117,225,000
a	Tagging omitted	4.00					
1329	5¢ Voice of America, Aug. 1	.15	.15	.50	(4)	1.00	111,515,000

American Folklore Issue, Davy Crockett, Aug. 17

		Un	U	PB	#	FDC	Q
1330	5¢ Davy Crockett with Rifle and Scrub Pine	.15	.15	.50	(4)	1.00	114,270,000
a	Vertical pair, imperf. between	—					
b	Green omitted	—					
c	Black and green omitted	—					
d	Yellow and green omitted	—					

Accomplishments in Space Issue, Sept. 29

		Un	U	PB	#	FDC	Q
1331	5¢ Space-Walking Astronaut	.50	.15			3.00	60,432,500
a	Attached pair, #1331-32	1.40	1.25	3.50	(4)	8.00	
1332	5¢ Gemini 4 Capsule and Earth	.50	.15			3.00	60,432,500
1333	5¢ Urban Planning, Oct. 2	.15	.15	.50	(4)	1.00	110,675,000
1334	5¢ Finland Independence, Oct. 6	.15	.15	.50	(4)	1.00	110,670,000

Minimum value listed for a stamp is 15 cents; for a First Day Cover (FDC), $1.00. This minimum represents a fair-market price for having a dealer locate and provide a single stamp or cover from his or her stock. Dealers may charge less per stamp or cover for a group of such stamps or covers, or less for a single stamp or cover.

1315

1316

1317

1318

1319

1320

1321

1322

1323

1324

1325

1326

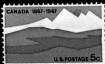

1327

1328

1329

1330

1331

1332

1331a

1333

1334

157

1335

1336

1337

1338

1339

1340

1341

1342

1343

1344

1345

1346

1347

1348

1349

1350

1351

1352

1353

1354

1355

158

	Issues of 1967 (continued), Perf. 12	Un	U	PB	#	FDC	Q
1335	5¢ Thomas Eakins, Nov. 2	.15	.15	.50	(4)	1.00	113,825,000
	Christmas Issue, Nov. 6, Perf. 11						
1336	5¢ Madonna and Child, by Hans Memling	.15	.15	.45	(4)	1.00	1,208,700,000
1337	5¢ Mississippi Statehood, Dec. 11	.15	.15	.50	(4)	1.00	113,330,000
	Issues of 1968-1971						
1338	6¢ Flag over White House (design 19 x 22mm), Jan. 24, 1968	.15	.15	.45	(4)	1.00	
k	Vertical pair, imperf. between	600.00					
	Coil Stamp, Perf. 10 Vertically						
1338A	6¢ dark blue, red and green (1338), May 30, 1969	.15	.15			1.00	
b	Imperf. pair	450.00					
	Perf. 11 x 10½						
1338D	6¢ dark blue, red and green (1338, design 18¼ x 21mm), Aug. 7, 1970	.15	.15	2.60	(20)	1.00	
e	Horizontal pair, imperf. between	110.00					
1338F	8¢ dark blue, red and slate green (1338), May 10, 1971	.16	.15	3.50	(20)	1.00	
i	Imperf., vertical pair	45.00					
j	Horizontal pair, imperf. between	40.00					
	Coil Stamp, Perf. 10 Vertically						
1338G	8¢ dark blue, red and slate green (1338), May 10, 1971	.18	.15			1.00	
h	Imperf. pair	55.00					
	Issues of 1968, Perf. 11						
1339	6¢ Illinois Statehood, Feb. 12	.15	.15	.50	(4)	1.00	141,350,000
1340	6¢ HemisFair '68, Mar. 30	.15	.15	.55	(4)	1.00	144,345,000
a	White omitted	1,500.00					
1341	$1 Airlift, Apr. 4	2.50	1.25	12.50	(4)	6.50	
	Pair with full horizontal gutter between	—					
1342	6¢ Support Our Youth-Elks, May 1	.15	.15	.50	(4)	1.00	147,120,000
1343	6¢ Law and Order, May 17	.15	.15	.50	(4)	1.00	130,125,000
1344	6¢ Register and Vote, June 27	.15	.15	.50	(4)	1.00	158,700,000
	Historic Flag Issue, July 4						
1345	6¢ Ft. Moultrie Flag, 1776	.50	.25			3.00	22,804,000
1346	6¢ U.S. Flag, 1795-1818 (Ft. McHenry Flag)	.35	.25			3.00	22,804,000
1347	6¢ Washington's Cruisers Flag, 1775	.30	.25			3.00	22,804,000
1348	6¢ Bennington Flag, 1777	.30	.25			3.00	22,804,000
1349	6¢ Rhode Island Flag, 1775	.30	.25			3.00	22,804,000
1350	6¢ First Stars and Stripes, 1777	.30	.25			3.00	22,804,000
1351	6¢ Bunker Hill Flag, 1775	.30	.25			3.00	22,804,000
1352	6¢ Grand Union Flag, 1776	.30	.25			3.00	22,804,000
1353	6¢ Philadelphia Light Horse Flag, 1775	.30	.25			3.00	22,804,000
1354	6¢ First Navy Jack, 1775	.30	.25			3.00	22,804,000
a	Strip of 10, #1345-54	3.25	3.00	6.75	(20)	15.00	
	Perf. 12						
1355	6¢ Walt Disney, Sept. 11	.16	.15	.70	(4)	2.50	153,015,000
a	Ocher omitted	800.00					
b	Vertical pair, imperf. horizontally	825.00					
c	Imperf. pair	850.00					
d	Black omitted	2,000.00					
e	Horizontal pair, imperf. between	3,250.00					
f	Blue omitted	2,000.00					

159

	Issues of 1968 (continued), Perf. 11	Un	U	PB	#	FDC	Q
1356	6¢ Father Marquette, Sept. 20	.15	.15	.50	(4)	1.00	132,560,000
	American Folklore Issue, Daniel Boone, Sept. 26						
1357	6¢ Pennsylvania Rifle, Powder Horn, Tomahawk, Pipe and Knife	.15	.15	.50	(4)	1.00	130,385,000
a	Tagging omitted	—					
1358	6¢ Arkansas River Navigation, Oct. 1	.15	.15	.50	(4)	1.00	132,265,000
1359	6¢ Leif Erikson, Oct. 9	.15	.15	.50	(4)	1.00	128,710,000
	Perf. 11 x 10½						
1360	6¢ Cherokee Strip, Oct. 15	.15	.15	.55	(4)	1.00	124,775,000
a	Tagging omitted	4.50					
	Perf. 11						
1361	6¢ John Trumbull, Oct. 18	.15	.15	.60	(4)	1.00	128,295,000
1362	6¢ Waterfowl Conservation, Oct. 24	.15	.15	.70	(4)	1.00	142,245,000
a	Vertical pair, imperf. between	550.00					
b	Red and dark blue omitted	1,400.00					
	Christmas Issue, Nov. 1						
1363	6¢ Angel Gabriel, from "The Annunciation," by Jan Van Eyck	.15	.15	2.25	(10)	1.00	1,410,580,000
a	Untagged, Nov. 2	.15	.15	2.25	(10)	6.50	
b	Imperf. pair tagged	275.00					
c	Light yellow omitted	125.00					
d	Imperf. pair (untagged)	400.00					
1364	6¢ American Indian, Nov. 4	.16	.15	.70	(4)	1.00	125,100,000
	Issues of 1969, Beautification of America Issue, Jan. 16						
1365	6¢ Capitol, Azaleas and Tulips	.40	.15			1.00	48,142,500
1366	6¢ Washington Monument, Potomac River and Daffodils	.40	.15			1.00	48,142,500
1367	6¢ Poppies and Lupines along Highway	.40	.15			1.00	48,142,500
1368	6¢ Blooming Crabapple Trees Lining Avenue	.40	.15			1.00	48,142,500
a	Block of 4, #1365-68	1.70	1.25	2.25	(4)	4.00	
b	As "a," tagging omitted	—					
1369	6¢ American Legion, Mar. 15	.15	.15	.50	(4)	1.00	148,770,000
	American Folklore Issue, Grandma Moses, May 1						
1370	6¢ "July Fourth," by Grandma Moses	.15	.15	.50	(4)	1.00	139,475,000
a	Horizontal pair, imperf. between	275.00					
b	Black and Prussian blue omitted	950.00					
1371	6¢ Apollo 8, May 5	.15	.15	.65	(4)	3.00	187,165,000
a	Imperf. pair	—					
1372	6¢ W.C. Handy, May 17	.15	.15	.50	(4)	1.00	125,555,000
a	Tagging omitted	4.50					
1373	6¢ California Settlement, July 16	.15	.15	.50	(4)	1.00	144,425,000
1374	6¢ John Wesley Powell, Aug. 1	.15	.15	.50	(4)	1.00	135,875,000
1375	6¢ Alabama Statehood, Aug. 2	.15	.15	.50	(4)	1.00	151,110,000

1356

1357

1358

1359

1360

1361

1362

1363

1304

1365   1366   1368a
1367   1368

1369

1370

1371

1372

1373

1374

1375

1380

1376   1377   1379a
1378   1379

1381   1382

1383

1384

1385

1386

1384 Precancel

1391

1387   1388   1390a   1392
1389   1390

	Issues of 1969 (continued), Perf. 11	Un	U	PB	#	FDC	Q
	Botanical Congress Issue, Aug. 23						
1376	6¢ Douglas Fir (Northwest)	.75	.15			1.00	39,798,750
1377	6¢ Lady's Slipper (Northeast)	.75	.15			1.00	39,798,750
1378	6¢ Ocotillo (Southwest)	.75	.15			1.00	39,798,750
1379	6¢ Franklinia (Southeast)	.75	.15			1.00	39,798,750
a	Block of 4, #1376-79	3.00	3.00	3.75	(4)	5.00	
	Perf. 10½ x 11						
1380	6¢ Dartmouth College Case, Sept. 22	.15	.15	.50	(4)	1.00	129,540,000
	Perf. 11						
1381	6¢ Professional Baseball, Sept. 24	.75	.15	2.50	(4)	6.00	130,925,000
a	Black omitted	1,250.00					
1382	6¢ College Football, Sept. 26	.15	.15	.80	(4)	3.00	139,055,000
1383	6¢ Dwight D. Eisenhower, Oct. 14	.15	.15	.50	(4)	1.00	150,611,200
	Christmas Issue, Nov. 3, Perf. 11 x 10½						
1384	6¢ Winter Sunday in Norway, Maine	.15	.15	1.40	(10)	1.00	1,709,795,000
	Precanceled	.50	.15				
b	Imperf. pair	1,250.00					
c	Light green omitted	25.00					
d	Light green and yellow omitted	1,000.00	—				
e	Yellow omitted	—					
f	Tagging omitted	2.50					
	Precanceled versions issued on an experimental basis in four cities whose names appear on the stamps: Atlanta, GA; Baltimore, MD; Memphis, TN; and New Haven, CT.						
	Perf. 11						
1385	6¢ Hope for the Crippled, Nov. 20	.15	.15	.50	(4)	1.00	127,545,000
1386	6¢ William M. Harnett, Dec. 3	.15	.15	.50	(4)	1.00	145,788,800
	Issues of 1970, Natural History Issue, May 6						
1387	6¢ American Bald Eagle	.15	.15			1.50	50,448,550
1388	6¢ African Elephant Herd	.15	.15			1.50	50,448,550
1389	6¢ Tlingit Chief in Haida Ceremonial Canoe	.15	.15			1.50	50,448,550
1390	6¢ Brontosaurus, Stegosaurus and Allosaurus from Jurassic Period	.15	.15			1.50	50,448,550
a	Block of 4, #1387-90	.50	.50	.65	(4)	4.00	
1391	6¢ Maine Statehood, July 9	.15	.15	.50	(4)	1.00	171,850,000
	Perf. 11 x 10½						
1392	6¢ Wildlife Conservation, July 20	.15	.15	.50	(4)	1.00	142,205,000

What are the differences between African and Asian elephants?

The different ears of the African and Asian elephants are the most obvious clues to their species. African elephants, whose ears are shaped somewhat like the continent of Africa, have much larger ears than Asian elephants. Male African elephants usually are about 10 feet tall at the shoulder, while Asian elephants only reach 8 feet at the shoulder. Both male and female African elephants have long tusks. But only male Asian elephants grow tusks. **(#1388)**

AFRICAN ELEPHANT H

	Issues of 1970-74, Perf. 11 x 10½	Un	U	PB/LP	#	FDC	Q
1393	6¢ Eisenhower, Aug. 6, 1970	.15	.15	.50	(4)	1.00	
a	Booklet pane of 8	1.25	*.50*			3.00	
b	Booklet pane of 5 + label	1.25	*.50*			1.50	
c	Untagged (Bureau precanceled)		.15				
	Perf. 10½ x 11						
1393D	7¢ Franklin, Oct. 20, 1972	.15	.15	.60	(4)	1.00	
e	Untagged (Bureau precanceled)		.15				
	Perf. 11						
1394	8¢ Eisenhower, May 10, 1971	.16	.15	.60	(4)	1.00	
	Pair with full vertical gutter between	—					
	Perf. 11 x 10½						
1395	8¢ deep claret Eisenhower (1394), Single from booklet	.18	.15			1.00	
a	Booklet pane of 8, May 10, 1971	1.80	*1.25*			3.00	
b	Booklet pane of 6, May 10, 1971	1.25	*.75*			3.00	
c	Booklet pane of 4 + 2 labels, Jan. 28, 1972	1.65	*.50*			2.25	
d	Booklet pane of 7 + label, Jan. 28, 1972	1.75	*1.00*			2.00	
1396	8¢ U.S. Postal Service, July 1, 1971	.15	.15	2.00	(12)	1.00	
1397	14¢ Fiorello H. LaGuardia, Apr. 24, 1972	.25	.15	1.15	(4)	1.00	
a	Untagged (Bureau precanceled)		.25				
1398	16¢ Ernie Pyle, May 7, 1971	.28	.15	1.25	(4)	1.00	
a	Untagged (Bureau precanceled)		.35				
1399	18¢ Dr. Elizabeth Blackwell, Jan. 23, 1974	.32	.15	1.40	(4)	1.00	
1400	21¢ Amadeo P. Giannini, June 27, 1973	.35	.15	1.50	(4)	1.00	
	Coil Stamps, Perf. 10 Vertically						
1401	6¢ dark blue gray Eisenhower (1393), Aug. 6, 1970	.15	.15	.50	(2)	1.00	
a	Untagged (Bureau precanceled)		.15				
b	Imperf. pair	*1,500.00*		—	(2)		
1402	8¢ deep claret Eisenhower (1394), May 10, 1971	.15	.15	.45	(2)	1.00	
a	Imperf. pair	45.00		70.00	(2)		
b	Untagged (Bureau precanceled)		.15				
c	Pair, imperf. between	*6,250.00*					
1403-04	Not assigned						
	Issues of 1970, Perf. 11						
1405	6¢ Edgar Lee Masters, Aug. 22	.15	.15	.50	(4)	1.00	137,660,000
a	Tagging omitted	7.50					
1406	6¢ Woman Suffrage, Aug. 26	.15	.15	.50	(4)	1.00	135,125,000
1407	6¢ South Carolina Settlement, Sept. 12	.15	.15	.50	(4)	1.00	135,895,000
1408	6¢ Stone Mountain Memorial, Sept. 19	.15	.15	.50	(4)	1.00	132,675,000
1409	6¢ Ft. Snelling, Oct. 17	.15	.15	.50	(4)	1.00	134,795,000
	Anti-Pollution Issue, Oct. 28, Perf. 11 x 10½						
1410	6¢ Save Our Soil— Globe and Wheat Field	.22	.15			1.25	40,400,000
1411	6¢ Save Our Cities— Globe and City Playground	.22	.15			1.25	40,400,000
1412	6¢ Save Our Water— Globe and Bluegill Fish	.22	.15			1.25	40,400,000
1413	6¢ Save Our Air— Globe and Seagull	.22	.15			1.25	40,400,000
a	Block of 4, #1410-13	1.00	1.00	2.50	(10)	3.00	

1393   **1393D**   **1394**   **1396**

1397   **1398**   **1399**   **1400**

1406   **1407**

1405

1408   **1409**

1410   **1411**   **1413a**

1412   **1413**

1414

1414a

1415
1417

1416
1418

1418b

1419

1420

1421
1422

1421a

1423

1424

1425

1426

1427
1429

1428
1430

1430a

	Issues of 1970 (continued), Perf. 10½ x 11	Un	U	PB	#	FDC	Q
	Christmas Issue, Nov. 5						
1414	6¢ Nativity, by Lorenzo Lotto	.15	.15	1.15	(8)	1.40	638,730,000*
a	Precanceled	.15	.15	1.90	(8)		358,245,000
b	Black omitted	650.00					
c	As "a," blue omitted	2,000.00					
	#1414a-18a were furnished to 68 cities. Unused prices are for copies with gum and used prices are for copies with or without gum but with an additional cancellation. *Includes #1414a.						
	Perf. 11 x 10½						
1415	6¢ Tin and Cast-iron Locomotive	.40	.15			1.40	122,313,750
a	Precanceled	.90	.15				109,912,500
b	Black omitted	1,500.00					
1416	6¢ Toy Horse on Wheels	.40	.15			1.40	122,313,750
a	Precanceled	.90	.15				109,912,500
b	Black omltted	1,500.00					
c	Imperf. pair		4,000.00				
1417	6¢ Mechanical Tricycle	.40	.15			1.40	122,313,750
a	Precanceled	.90	.15				109,912,500
b	Black omitted	1,500.00					
1418	6¢ Doll Carriage	.40	.15			1.40	122,313,750
a	Precanceled	.90	.15				109,912,500
b	Block of 4, #1415-18	1.90	1.75	3.75	(8)	3.50	
c	Block of 4, #1415a-18a	3.75	3.50	9.00	(8)		
d	Black omitted	1,500.00					
	Perf. 11						
1419	6¢ United Nations, Nov. 20	.15	.15	.50	(4)	1.00	127,610,000
	Pair with full horizontal gutter between	—					
1420	6¢ Landing of the Pilgrims, Nov. 21	.15	.15	.50	(4)	1.00	129,785,000
a	Orange and yellow omitted	1,200.00					
	Disabled American Veterans and Servicemen Issue, Nov. 24						
1421	6¢ Disabled American Veterans Emblem	.15	.15			1.00	67,190,000
a	Attached pair, #1421-22	.25	.25	1.00	(4)	1.25	
1422	6¢ U.S. Servicemen	.15	.15			1.00	67,190,000
	Issues of 1971						
1423	6¢ American Wool Industry, Jan. 19	.15	.15	.50	(4)	1.00	136,305,000
a	Tagging omitted	3.50	—				
1424	6¢ Gen. Douglas MacArthur, Jan. 26	.15	.15	.50	(4)	1.00	134,840,000
1425	6¢ Blood Donor, Mar. 12	.15	.15	.50	(4)	1.00	130,975,000
a	Tagging omitted	4.50					
	Perf. 11 x 10½						
1426	8¢ Missouri Statehood, May 8	.15	.15	2.00	(12)	1.00	161,235,000
	Wildlife Conservation Issue, June 12, Perf. 11						
1427	8¢ Trout	.16	.15			1.25	43,920,000
1428	8¢ Alligator	.16	.15			1.25	43,920,000
1429	8¢ Polar Bear	.16	.15			1.25	43,920,000
1430	8¢ California Condor	.16	.15			1.25	43,920,000
a	Block of 4, #1427-30	.65	.65	.75	(4)	3.00	
b	As "a," light green and dark green omitted from #1427-28	3,500.00					
c	As "a," red omitted from #1427, 1429-30	9,000.00					

	Issues of 1971 (continued), Perf. 11	Un	U	PB	#	FDC	Q
1431	8¢ Antarctic Treaty, June 23	.15	.15	.70	(4)	1.00	138,700,000
a	Tagging omitted	4.00					
	American Revolution Bicentennial Issue, July 4						
1432	8¢ Bicentennial Commission Emblem	.16	.15	.85	(4)	1.00	138,165,000
a	Gray and black omitted	650.00					
b	Gray omitted	1,100.00					
1433	8¢ John Sloan, Aug. 2	.15	.15	.70	(4)	1.00	152,125,000
a	Tagging omitted	—					
	Space Achievement Decade Issue, Aug. 2						
1434	8¢ Earth, Sun and Landing Craft on Moon	.15	.15				88,147,500
a	Attached pair, #1434-35	.30	.25	.70	(4)	2.50	
b	As "a," blue and red omitted	1,500.00					
1435	8¢ Lunar Rover and Astronauts	.15	.15				88,147,500
a	Tagging omitted	6.00					
1436	8¢ Emily Dickinson, Aug. 28	.15	.15	.70	(4)	1.00	142,845,000
a	Black and olive omitted	950.00					
b	Pale rose omitted	7,500.00					
1437	8¢ San Juan, Puerto Rico, Sept. 12	.15	.15	.70	(4)	1.00	148,755,000
a	Tagging omitted	5.00					
	Perf. 10½ x 11						
1438	8¢ Prevent Drug Abuse, Oct. 4	.15	.15	1.00	(6)	1.00	139,080,000
1439	8¢ CARE, Oct. 27	.15	.15	1.25	(8)	1.00	130,755,000
a	Black omitted	4,500.00					
b	Tagging omitted	2.50					
	Historic Preservation Issue, Oct. 29, Perf. 11						
1440	8¢ Decatur House, Washington, D.C.	.16	.15			1.25	42,552,000
1441	8¢ Whaling Ship *Charles W. Morgan*, Mystic, Connecticut	.16	.15			1.25	42,552,000
1442	8¢ Cable Car, San Francisco	.16	.15			1.25	42,552,000
1443	8¢ San Xavier del Bac Mission, Tucson, Arizona	.16	.15			1.25	42,552,000
a	Block of 4, #1440-43	.65	.65	.75	(4)	3.00	
b	As "a," black brown omitted	2,400.00					
c	As "a," ocher omitted	—					
	Christmas Issue, Nov. 10, Perf. 10½ x 11						
1444	8¢ Adoration of the Shepherds, by Giorgione	.15	.15	2.00	(12)	1.00	1,074,350,000
a	Gold omitted	500.00					
1445	8¢ Partridge in a Pear Tree	.15	.15	2.00	(12)	1.00	979,540,000
	Issues of 1972, Perf. 11						
1446	8¢ Sidney Lanier, Feb. 3	.15	.15	.70	(4)	1.00	137,355,000
	Perf. 10½ x 11						
1447	8¢ Peace Corps, Feb. 11	.15	.15	1.00	(6)	1.00	150,400,000

The stamp listings contain a number of "a," "b," "c," etc. additions which include recognized varieties and errors. These listings are as complete as space permits.

1431

1433

1432

1434　　**1435**　　**1434a**

1436　　**1437**　　**1438**　　**1439**

1440　　**1441**　　**1443a**

1442　　**1443**

1444　　**1445**　　**1446**　　**1447**

1452

1448
1450

1449
1451

1451a

1453

1454

1455

1456
1458

1457
1459

1459a

1460

1461

1462

1463

1464
1466

1465
1467

1467a

	Issues of 1972 (continued). Perf. 11	Un	U	PB	#	FDC	Q
	National Parks Centennial Issue, Cape Hatteras, Apr. 5 (See also #C84)						
1448	2¢ Ship at Sea	.15	.15				43,182,500
1449	2¢ Cape Hatteras Lighthouse	.15	.15				43,182,500
1450	2¢ Laughing Gulls on Driftwood	.15	.15				43,182,500
1451	2¢ Laughing Gulls and Dune	.15	.15				43,182,500
a	Block of 4, #1448-51	.20	.20	.45	(4)	1.25	
b	As "a," black omitted	2,500.00					
	Wolf Trap Farm, June 26						
1452	6¢ Performance at Shouse Pavilion	.15	.15	.55	(4)	1.00	104,090,000
1453	8¢ Old Faithful, Yellowstone, Mar. 1	.15	.15	.70	(4)	1.00	164,096,000
a	Tagging omitted	10.00					
	Mount McKinley, July 28						
1454	15¢ View of Mount McKinley in Alaska	.30	.18	1.30	(4)	1.00	53,920,000
	Note: Beginning with this National Parks Centennial issue, the USPS began to offer stamp collectors first day cancellations affixed to 8" x 10½" souvenir pages. The pages are similar to the stamp announcements that have appeared on Post Office bulletin boards beginning with Scott #1132.						
1455	8¢ Family Planning, Mar. 18	.15	.15	.70	(4)	1.00	153,025,000
a	Yellow omitted	—					
b	Dark brown and olive omitted	—					
	American Bicentennial Issue, Colonial American Craftsmen, July 4, Perf. 11 x 10½						
1456	8¢ Glassblower	.16	.15			1.00	50,472,500
1457	8¢ Silversmith	.16	.15			1.00	50,472,500
1458	8¢ Wigmaker	.16	.15			1.00	50,472,500
1459	8¢ Hatter	.16	.15			1.00	50,472,500
a	Block of 4, #1456-59	.65	.65	.75	(4)	2.50	
	Olympic Games Issue, Aug. 17 (See also #C85)						
1460	8¢ Bicycling and Olympic Rings	.15	.15	1.25	(10)	1.00	67,335,000
	Plate flaw (broken red ring)	7.50					
1461	8¢ Bobsledding and Olympic Rings	.15	.15	1.60	(10)	1.00	179,675,000
1462	15¢ Running and Olympic Rings	.28	.18	3.00	(10)	1.00	46,340,000
1463	8¢ Parent Teachers Association, Sept. 15	.15	.15	.70	(4)	1.00	180,155,000
	Wildlife Conservation Issue, Sept. 20, Perf. 11						
1464	8¢ Fur Seals	.16	.15			1.50	49,591,200
1465	8¢ Cardinal	.16	.15			1.50	49,591,200
1466	8¢ Brown Pelican	.16	.15			1.50	49,591,200
1467	8¢ Bighorn Sheep	.16	.15			1.50	49,591,200
a	Block of 4, #1464-67	.65	.65	.75	(4)	3.00	
b	As "a," brown omitted	3,750.00					
c	As "a," green and blue omitted	—					

Note: With this Wildlife Conservation issue the USPS introduced the "American Commemorative Series" Stamp Panels. Each panel contains a block of four mint stamps with text and background illustrations.

	Issues of 1972 (continued), Perf. 11 x 10¹/₂	Un	U	PB	#	FDC	Q
1468	8¢ Mail Order Business, Sept. 27	.15	.15	1.90	(12)	1.00	185,490,000
	Perf. 10¹/₂ x 11						
1469	8¢ Osteopathic Medicine, Oct. 9	.15	.15	1.00	(6)	1.00	162,335,000
	American Folklore Issue, Tom Sawyer, Oct. 13, Perf. 11						
1470	8¢ Tom Sawyer Whitewashing a Fence, by Norman Rockwell	.15	.15	.70	(4)	1.00	162,789,950
a	Horizontal pair, imperf. between	4,500.00					
b	Red and black omitted	1,500.00					
c	Yellow and tan omitted	1,800.00					
	Christmas Issue, Nov. 9, Perf. 10¹/₂ x 11						
1471	8¢ Angels from "Mary, Queen of Heaven," by the Master of the St. Lucy Legend	.15	.15	1.90	(12)	1.00	1,003,475,000
a	Pink omitted	250.00					
b	Black omitted	3,750.00					
1472	8¢ Santa Claus	.15	.15	1.90	(12)	1.00	1,017,025,000
	Perf. 11						
1473	8¢ Pharmacy, Nov. 10	.16	.15	.70	(4)	1.00	165,895,000
a	Blue and orange omitted	1,000.00					
b	Blue omitted	2,000.00					
c	Orange omitted	2,000.00					
1474	8¢ Stamp Collecting, Nov. 17	.15	.15	.70	(4)	1.00	166,508,000
a	Black omitted	1,100.00					
	Issues of 1973, Perf. 11 x 10¹/₂						
1475	8¢ Love, Jan. 26	.15	.15	1.00	(6)	1.00	320,055,000
	American Bicentennial Issue, Communications in Colonial Times, Perf. 11						
1476	8¢ Printer and Patriots Examining Pamphlet, Feb. 16	.15	.15	.70	(4)	1.00	166,005,000
1477	8¢ Posting a Broadside, Apr. 13	.15	.15	.70	(4)	1.00	163,050,000
	Pair with full horizontal gutter between	—					
1478	8¢ Postrider, June 22	.15	.15	.70	(4)	1.00	159,005,000
1479	8¢ Drummer, Sept. 28	.15	.15	.70	(4)	1.00	147,295,000
	Boston Tea Party, July 4						
1480	8¢ British Merchantman	.15	.15			1.00	49,068,750
1481	8¢ British Three-Master	.15	.15			1.00	49,068,750
1482	8¢ Boats and Ship's Hull	.15	.15			1.00	49,068,750
1483	8¢ Boat and Dock	.15	.15			1.00	49,068,750
a	Block of 4, #1480-83	.65	.45	.70	(4)	3.00	
b	As "a," blk. (engraved) omitted	1,750.00					
c	As "a," blk. (lithographed) omitted	1,650.00					

1468

1469

1470

1473

1474

1471

1472

1475

1476

1477

1478

1479

1480   **1481**   **1483a**
1482   **1483**

173

1484

1485

1486

1487

1488

Nearly 27 billion
U.S. stamps
are sold yearly
to carry
your letters to
every corner
of the world.

Mail is
picked up
from nearly
a third of a million
local collection
boxes, as well
as your mailbox.

More than
87 billion letters
and packages
are handled
yearly—almost
300 million every
delivery day.

The People
in your
Postal Service
handle and
deliver more
than 500 million
packages yearly.

Thousands of
machines, buildings,
and vehicles
must be operated
and maintained
to keep your
mail moving.

People Serving You

People Serving You

People Serving You

People Serving You

People Serving You

1489   1490   1491   1492   1493

The skill
of sorting mail
manually
is still vital
to delivery of
your mail.

Employees
use modern, high-
speed equipment
to sort and process
huge volumes of
mail in central
locations.

Thirteen billion
pounds of mail are
handled yearly by
postal employees
as they speed
your letters and
packages.

Our customers
include
54 million urban
and 12 million
rural families,
plus 9 million
businesses.

Employees
cover
4 million miles
each delivery day
to bring mail to
your home or
business.

People Serving You

People Serving You

People Serving You

People Serving You

People Serving You

1498a

1494   1495   1496   1497   1498

Issues of 1973 (continued), Perf. 11		Un	U	PB	#	FDC	Q
	American Arts Issue						
1484	8¢ George Gershwin and Scene from "Porgy and Bess," Feb. 28	.15	.15	1.85	(12)	1.00	139,152,000
a	Vertical pair, imperf. horizontally	250.00					
1485	8¢ Robinson Jeffers, Man and Children of Carmel with Burro, Aug. 13	.15	.15	1.85	(12)	1.00	128,048,000
a	Vertical pair, imperf. horizontally	300.00					
1486	8¢ Henry Ossawa Tanner, Palette and Rainbow, Sept. 10	.15	.15	1.85	(12)	1.00	146,008,000
1487	8¢ Willa Cather, Pioneer Family and Covered Wagon, Sept. 20	.15	.15	1.85	(12)	1.00	139,608,000
a	Vertical pair, imperf. horizontally	350.00					
1488	8¢ Nicolaus Copernicus, Apr. 23	.15	.15	.70	(4)	1.00	159,475,000
a	Orange omitted	1,100.00					
b	Black omitted	1,600.00					
	Postal Service Employees Issue, Apr. 30, Perf. 10½ x 11						
1489	8¢ Stamp Counter	.15	.15			1.00	48,602,000
1490	8¢ Mail Collection	.15	.15			1.00	48,602,000
1491	8¢ Letter Facing on Conveyor	.15	.15			1.00	48,602,000
1492	8¢ Parcel Post Sorting	.15	.15			1.00	48,602,000
1493	8¢ Mail Canceling	.15	.15			1.00	48,602,000
1494	8¢ Manual Letter Routing	.15	.15			1.00	48,602,000
1495	8¢ Electronic Letter Routing	.15	.15			1.00	48,602,000
1496	8¢ Loading Mail on Truck	.15	.15			1.00	48,602,000
1497	8¢ Carrier Delivering Mail	.15	.15			1.00	48,602,000
1498	8¢ Rural Mail Delivery	.15	.15			1.00	48,602,000
a	Strip of 10, #1489-98	1.50	1.00	3.10	(20)	5.00	

#1489-98 were the first United States stamps to have printing on the back (See also #1559-62).

Did George Gershwin have to study music to be successful?

George Gershwin (1898-1937), whose real name was Jacob Gershvin, was a gifted American composer of popular music. Gershwin studied with many different teachers and continued to take private lessons even when he was a famous composer. But his genius for melodies and rhythms, more than any studies, led to his success.

He wrote one of his earliest successful songs, "Swanee," when he was just 19. A milestone in his career was the orchestral *Rhapsody in Blue* (1924). Gershwin went on to produce musical comedies. He is best known for his works of popular music, like the folk opera *Porgy and Bess* (1935). His political satire *Of Thee I Sing* (1931) was the first musical to win a Pulitzer Prize. (**#1484**)

	Issues of 1973 (continued), Perf. 11	Un	U	PB	#	FDC	Q
1499	8¢ Harry S. Truman, May 8	.15	.15	.65	(4)	1.00	157,052,800
	Progress in Electronics Issue, July 10 (See also #C86)						
1500	6¢ Marconi's Spark Coil and Gap	.15	.15	.55	(4)	1.00	53,005,000
1501	8¢ Transistors and Printed Circuit Board	.15	.15	.70	(4)	1.00	159,775,000
a	Black omitted	750.00					
b	Tan and lilac omitted	2,000.00					
1502	15¢ Microphone, Speaker, Vacuum Tube, TV Camera Tube	.28	.15	1.20	(4)	1.00	39,005,000
a	Black omitted	1,600.00					
1503	8¢ Lyndon B. Johnson, Aug. 27	.15	.15	1.85	(12)	1.00	152,624,000
a	Horizontal pair, imperf. vertically	300.00					
	Issues of 1973-74, Rural America Issue						
1504	8¢ Angus and Longhorn Cattle, by F.C. Murphy, Oct. 5, 1973	.15	.15	.70	(4)	1.00	145,840,000
a	Green and red brown omitted	1,150.00					
b	Vertical pair, imperf. between	—					
1505	10¢ Chautauqua Tent and Buggies, Aug. 6, 1974	.18	.15	.80	(4)	1.00	151,335,000
1506	10¢ Wheat Fields and Train, Aug. 16, 1974	.18	.15	.80	(4)	1.00	141,085,000
a	Black and blue omitted	750.00					
	Issues of 1973, Christmas Issue, Nov. 7, Perf. 10½ x 11						
1507	8¢ Small Cowper Madonna, by Raphael	.15	.15	1.85	(12)	1.00	885,160,000
	Pair with full vertical gutter between	—					
1508	8¢ Christmas Tree in Needlepoint	.15	.15	1.85	(12)	1.00	939,835,000
a	Vertical pair, imperf. between	500.00					
	Pair with full horizontal gutter between	—					
	Issues of 1973-74, Perf. 11 x 10½						
1509	10¢ 50-Star and 13-Star Flags, Dec. 8, 1973	.18	.15	3.75	(20)	1.00	
a	Horizontal pair, imperf. between	50.00					
b	Blue omitted	150.00					
c	Imperf. pair	1,150.00					
1510	10¢ Jefferson Memorial, Dec. 14, 1973	.18	.15	.80	(4)	1.00	
a	Untagged (Bureau precanceled)		.18				
b	Booklet pane of 5 + label	1.50	.30			2.25	
c	Booklet pane of 8	1.65	.30			2.50	
d	Booklet pane of 6, Aug. 5, 1974	5.25	.30			3.00	
e	Vertical pair, imperf. horizontally	250.00					
f	Vertical pair, imperf. between	—					

1499

1500

1501

1502

1503

1504

1505

1506

1507

1508

1509

1510

177

1511   **1518**

1525

1526

1527

1528   **1529**

1530   **1531**   **1532**   **1533**   **1537a**

1534   **1535**   **1536**   **1537**

	Issues of 1973-74 (continued), Perf. 11 x 10½	Un	U	PB/LP	#	FDC	Q
1511	10¢ ZIP Code, Jan. 4, 1974	.18	.15	1.50	(8)	1.00	
a	Yellow omitted	50.00					
	Pair with full horizontal gutter between	—					
1512-17	Not assigned						
	Coil Stamps, Perf. 10 Vertically						
1518	6.3¢ Liberty Bell, Oct. 1, 1974	.15	.15	.65	(2)	1.00	
a	Untagged (Bureau precanceled)		.15	.80	(2)		
b	Imperf. pair	250.00		400.00	(2)		
c	As "a," imperf. pair		125.00	250.00	(2)		
1519	10¢ red and blue Flags (1509), Dec. 8, 1973	.18	.15			1.00	
a	Imperf. pair	30.00					
1520	10¢ blue Jefferson Memorial (1510), Dec. 14, 1973	.18	.15	.55	(2)	1.00	
a	Untagged (Bureau precanceled)		.25				
b	Imperf. pair	40.00		70.00	(2)		
1521-24	Not assigned						
	Issues of 1974, Perf. 11						
1525	10¢ Veterans of Foreign Wars, Mar. 11	.18	.15	.80	(4)	1.00	149,930,000
	Perf. 10½ x 11						
1526	10¢ Robert Frost, Mar. 26	.18	.15	.80	(4)	1.00	145,235,000
	Perf. 11						
1527	10¢ Expo '74 World's Fair, Apr. 18	.18	.15	2.20	(12)	1.00	135,052,000
	Perf. 11 x 10½						
1528	10¢ Horse Racing, May 4	.18	.15	2.20	(12)	1.00	156,750,000
a	Blue omitted	1,000.00					
b	Red omitted	—					
	Perf. 11						
1529	10¢ Skylab, May 14	.18	.15	.80	(4)	1.50	164,670,000
a	Vertical pair, imperf. between	—					
	Universal Postal Union Issue, June 6						
1530	10¢ Michelangelo, from "School of Athens," by Raphael	.20	.15			1.00	23,769,600
1531	10¢ "Five Feminine Virtues," by Hokusai	.20	.15			1.00	23,769,600
1532	10¢ "Old Scraps," by John Fredrick Peto	.20	.15			1.00	23,769,600
1533	10¢ "The Lovely Reader," by Jean Etienne Liotard	.20	.15			1.00	23,769,600
1534	10¢ "Lady Writing Letter," by Gerard Terborch	.20	.15			1.00	23,769,600
1535	10¢ Inkwell and Quill, from "Boy with a Top," by Jean-Baptiste Simeon Chardin	.20	.15			1.00	23,769,600
1536	10¢ Mrs. John Douglas, by Thomas Gainsborough	.20	.15			1.00	23,769,600
1537	10¢ Don Antonio Noriega, by Francisco de Goya	.20	.15			1.00	23,769,600
a	Block of 8, #1530-37	1.60	1.50	3.50	(16)	4.00	
b	As "a," imperf. vertically	7,500.00					

	Issues of 1974 (continued), Perf. 11	Un	U	PB	#	FDC	Q
	Mineral Heritage Issue, June 13						
1538	10¢ Petrified Wood	.18	.15			1.00	41,803,200
a	Light blue and yellow omitted	—					
1539	10¢ Tourmaline	.18	.15			1.00	41,803,200
a	Light blue omitted	—					
b	Black and purple omitted	—					
1540	10¢ Amethyst	.18	.15			1.00	41,803,200
a	Light blue and yellow omitted	—					
1541	10¢ Rhodochrosite	.18	.15			1.00	41,803,200
a	Block of 4, #1538-41	.80	.80	.85	(4)	2.50	
b	As "a," light blue and yellow omitted	2,000.00					
c	Light blue omitted	—					
d	Black and red omitted	—					
1542	10¢ First Kentucky Settlement- Ft. Harrod, June 15	.18	.15	.80	(4)	1.00	156,265,000
a	Dull black omitted	1,000.00					
b	Green, black and blue omitted	3,250.00					
c	Green omitted	—					
d	Green and black omitted	—					
	American Bicentennial Issue, First Continental Congress, July 4						
1543	10¢ Carpenters' Hall	.18	.15			1.00	48,896,250
1544	10¢ "We Ask but for Peace, Liberty and Safety"	.18	.15			1.00	48,896,250
1545	10¢ "Deriving Their Just Powers from the Consent of the Governed"	.18	.15			1.00	48,896,250
1546	10¢ Independence Hall	.18	.15			1.00	48,896,250
a	Block of 4, #1543-46	.75	.75	.85	(4)	2.75	
1547	10¢ Energy Conservation, Sept. 23	.18	.15	.80	(4)	1.00	148,850,000
a	Blue and orange omitted	800.00					
b	Orange and green omitted	900.00					
c	Green omitted	950.00					
	American Folklore Issue, The Legend of Sleepy Hollow, Oct. 10						
1548	10¢ Headless Horseman and Ichabod Crane	.18	.15	.80	(4)	1.00	157,270,000
1549	10¢ Retarded Children, Oct. 12	.18	.15	.80	(4)	1.00	150,245,000
	Christmas Issue, Perf. 10¹/₂ x 11						
1550	10¢ Angel from Perussis Altarpiece, Oct. 23	.18	.15	1.85	(10)	1.00	835,180,000
	Perf. 11 x 10¹/₂						
1551	10¢ "The Road-Winter," by Currier and Ives, Oct. 23	.18	.15	2.20	(12)	1.00	882,520,000
	Precanceled Self-Adhesive, Imperf.						
1552	10¢ Dove Weather Vane atop Mount Vernon, Nov. 15	.18	.15	3.70	(20)	1.00	213,155,000
	Issues of 1975, American Arts Issue, Perf. 10¹/₂ x 11						
1553	10¢ Benjamin West, Self-Portrait, Feb. 10	.18	.15	1.85	(10)	1.00	156,995,000
	Perf. 11						
1554	10¢ Paul Laurence Dunbar and Lamp, May 1	.18	.15	1.85	(10)	1.00	146,365,000
a	Imperf. pair	1,250.00					
1555	10¢ D.W. Griffith and Motion-Picture Camera, May 27	.18	.15	.80	(4)	1.00	148,805,000
a	Brown omitted	700.00					

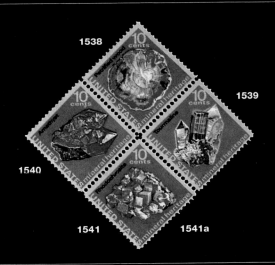

1538

10 cents

1539

1540

1541   1541a

1542

1543   1544   1546a

1545   1546

1547

1548

1549   1550

1551

1552

1553   1554

1555

1556   1557   1558

YOUTHFUL HEROINE
On the dark night of April 26, 1777, 16-year-old Sybil Ludington rode her horse "Star" alone through the Connecticut countryside rallying her father's militia to repel a raid by the British on Danbury.

GALLANT SOLDIER
The conspicuously courageous actions of black foot soldier Salem Poor at the Battle of Bunker Hill on June 17, 1775, earned him citations for his bravery and leadership ability.

FINANCIAL HERO
Businessman and broker Haym Salomon was responsible for raising most of the money needed to finance the American Revolution and later to save the new nation from collapse.

1559   1560   1561

FIGHTER EXTRAORDINARY
Peter Francisco's strength and bravery made him a legend around campfires. He fought with distinction at Brandywine, Yorktown and Guilford Court House.

1563

1564

1562

1565   1566   1568a
1567   1568

1569   1569a
1570

Issues of 1975 (continued), Perf. 11	Un	U	PB	#	FDC	Q
Space Issues						
1556 10¢ Pioneer 10 Passing Jupiter, Feb. 28	.18	.15	.80	(4)	2.00	173,685,000
a Red and yellow omitted	1,500.00					
b Blue omitted	1,000.00					
1557 10¢ Mariner 10, Venus and Mercury, Apr. 4	.18	.15	.80	(4)	2.00	158,600,000
a Red omitted	750.00					
b Ultramarine and bister omitted	1,800.00					
1558 10¢ Collective Bargaining, Mar. 13	.18	.15	1.60	(8)	1.00	153,355,000
Imperfs. of #1558 exist from printer's waste.						
American Bicentennial Issue, Contributors to the Cause, Mar. 25, Perf. 11 x 10½						
1559 8¢ Sybil Ludington Riding Horse	.16	.15	1.65	(10)	1.00	63,205,000
a Back inscription omitted	275.00					
1560 10¢ Salem Poor Carrying Musket	.18	.15	1.85	(10)	1.00	157,865,000
a Back inscription omitted	300.00					
1561 10¢ Haym Salomon Figuring Accounts	.18	.15	1.85	(10)	1.00	166,810,000
a Back inscription omitted	350.00					
b Red omitted	250.00					
1562 18¢ Peter Francisco Shouldering Cannon	.35	.20	3.60	(10)	1.00	44,825,000
Battle of Lexington & Concord, Apr. 19, Perf. 11						
1563 10¢ "Birth of Liberty," by Henry Sandham	.18	.15	2.20	(12)	1.00	144,028,000
a Vertical pair, imperf. horizontally	500.00					
Battle of Bunker Hill, June 17						
1564 10¢ "Battle of Bunker Hill," by John Trumbull	.18	.15	2.20	(12)	1.00	139,928,000
Military Uniforms, July 4						
1565 10¢ Soldier with Flintlock Musket, Uniform Button	.18	.15			1.00	44,963,750
1566 10¢ Sailor with Grappling Hook, First Navy Jack, 1775	.18	.15			1.00	44,963,750
1567 10¢ Marine with Musket, Full-Rigged Ship	.18	.15			1.00	44,963,750
1568 10¢ Militiaman with Musket, Powder Horn	.18	.15			1.00	44,963,750
a Block of 4, #1565-68	.75	.75	2.30	(12)	2.50	
Apollo Soyuz Space Issue, July 15						
1569 10¢ Apollo and Soyuz after Docking, and Earth	.18	.15			2.00	80,931,600
a Attached pair, #1569-70	.40	.25	2.20	(12)	4.00	
b As "a," vertical pair, imperf. horizontally	1,050.00					
Pair with full horizontal gutter between	—					
1570 10¢ Spacecraft before Docking, Earth and Project Emblem	.18	.15			2.00	80,931,600

	Issues of 1975 (continued), Perf. 11 x 10½	Un	U	PB	#	FDC	Q
1571	10¢ International Women's Year, Aug. 26	.18	.15	1.15	(6)	1.00	145,640,000
	Postal Service Bicentennial Issue, Sept. 3						
1572	10¢ Stagecoach and Trailer Truck	.18	.15			1.00	42,163,750
1573	10¢ Old and New Locomotives	.18	.15			1.00	42,163,750
1574	10¢ Early Mail Plane and Jet	.18	.15			1.00	42,163,750
1575	10¢ Satellite for Transmission of Mailgrams	.18	.15			1.00	42,163,750
a	Block of 4, #1572-75	.80	.80	2.30	(12)	1.25	
b	As "a," red "10¢" omitted	—					
	Perf. 11						
1576	10¢ World Peace Through Law, Sept. 29	.18	.15	.80	(4)	1.00	146,615,000
	Banking and Commerce Issue, Oct. 6						
1577	10¢ Engine Turning, Indian Head Penny and Morgan Silver Dollar	.18	.15			1.00	73,098,000
a	Attached pair, #1577-78	.40	.20	.80	(4)	1.25	
b	Brown and blue omitted	1,250.00					
c	As "a," brn., blue and yel. omitted	—					
1578	10¢ Seated Liberty Quarter, $20 Gold Piece and Engine Turning	.18	.15			1.00	73,098,000
	Christmas Issue, Oct. 14						
1579	(10¢) Madonna and Child, by Domenico Ghirlandaio	.18	.15	2.20	(12)	1.00	739,430,000
a	Imperf. pair	110.00					
	Plate flaw ("d" damaged)	5.00	—				
1580	(10¢) Christmas Card, by Louis Prang, 1878	.18	.15	2.20	(12)	1.00	878,690,000
a	Imperf. pair	120.00					
b	Perf. 10½ x 11	.60	.15	7.25	(12)		
	Issues of 1975-81, Americana Issue, Perf. 11 x 10½ (Designs 18½ x 22½mm; #1590-90a, 17½ x 20mm; see also #1606, 1608, 1610-19, 1622-23, 1625, 1811, 1813, 1816)						
1581	1¢ Inkwell & Quill, Dec. 8, 1977	.15	.15	.25	(4)	1.00	
a	Untagged (Bureau precanceled)		.15				
1582	2¢ Speaker's Stand, Dec. 8, 1977	.15	.15	.25	(4)	1.00	
a	Untagged (Bureau precanceled)		.15				
1583	Not assigned						
1584	3¢ Early Ballot Box, Dec. 8, 1977	.15	.15	.28	(4)	1.00	
a	Untagged (Bureau precanceled)		.15				
1585	4¢ Books, Bookmark, Eyeglasses, Dec. 8, 1977	.15	.15	.38	(4)	1.00	
a	Untagged (Bureau precanceled)		1.25				
1586-89	Not assigned						
	Booklet Stamp						
1590	9¢ Capitol Dome (1591), single from booklet (1623a), Mar. 11, 1977	.50	.20			1.00	
	Booklet Stamp, Perf. 10						
a	Single (1591) from booklet (1623c)	18.50	10.00				
	#1590 is on white paper; #1591 is on gray paper.						
	Perf. 11 x 10½						
1591	9¢ Capitol Dome, Nov. 24, 1975	.16	.15	.70	(4)	1.00	
a	Untagged (Bureau precanceled)		.18				
1592	10¢ Contemplation of Justice, Nov. 17, 1977	.18	.15	.90	(4)	1.00	
a	Untagged (Bureau precanceled)		.25				
1593	11¢ Printing Press, Nov. 13, 1975	.20	.15	.90	(4)	1.00	
1594	12¢ Torch, Apr. 8, 1981	.22	.15	1.25	(4)	1.00	

1571

1572   **1573**   **1575a**

1574   **1575**

1576

1577   **1578**   **1577a**

1579   **1580**

1581   **1582**

1584   **1585**

1591   **1592**

1593   **1594**

1595   **1596**   **1597**   **1599**

1603   **1604**   **1605**   **1606**

1608   **1610**   **1611**   **1612**

1613   **1614**   **1615**   **1615C**

186

	Issues of 1975-79, Perf. 11 x 10½	Un	U	PB/LP	#	FDC
	Americana Issue (continued) (See also #1581-82, 1584-85, 1590-99, 1603-08, 1610-19, 1622-23, 1625, 1811, 1813, 1816)					
1595	13¢ Liberty Bell, single from booklet	.25	.15			1.00
a	Booklet pane of 6, Oct. 31, 1975	1.90	.50			2.00
b	Booklet pane of 7 + label	1.75	.50			2.75
c	Booklet pane of 8	2.00	.50			2.50
d	Booklet pane of 5 + label, Apr. 2, 1976	1.40	.50			2.25
	Perf. 11					
1596	13¢ Eagle and Shield, Dec. 1, 1975	.26	.15	3.25	(12)	1.00
a	Imperf. pair	50.00				
b	Yellow omitted	225.00				
1597	15¢ Ft. McHenry Flag, June 30, 1978	.28	.15	1.75	(6)	1.00
a	Imperf. pair	17.50				
b	Gray omitted	250.00				
	Booklet Stamp, Perf. 11 x 10½					
1598	15¢ Ft. McHenry Flag (1597), single from booklet	.30	.15			1.00
a	Booklet pane of 8, June 30, 1978	3.50	.60			2.50
1599	16¢ Head of Liberty, Mar. 31, 1978	.34	.15	1.90	(4)	1.00
1600-02	Not assigned					
1603	24¢ Old North Church, Nov. 14, 1975	.45	.15	1.90	(4)	1.00
1604	28¢ Ft. Nisqually, Aug. 11, 1978	.55	.15	2.30	(4)	1.25
	Dull finish gum	1.10				
1605	29¢ Sandy Hook Lighthouse, Apr. 14, 1978	.55	.15	2.60	(4)	1.25
	Dull finish gum	2.00				
	Perf. 11 x 10½					
1606	30¢ One-Rm. Schoolhouse, Aug. 27, 1979	.55	.15	2.30	(4)	1.25
1607	Not assigned					
	Perf. 11					
1608	50¢ Whale Oil Lamp, Sept. 11, 1979	.95	.15	4.00	(4)	1.50
a	Black omitted	400.00				
b	Vertical pair, imperf. horizontally	—				
1609	Not assigned					
1610	$1 Candle and Rushlight Holder, July 2, 1979	1.75	.20	7.50	(4)	3.00
a	Brown omitted	300.00				
b	Tan, orange and yellow omitted	300.00				
c	Brown inverted	12,500.00				
1611	$2 Kerosene Table Lamp, Nov. 16, 1978	3.75	.45	15.50	(4)	5.00
1612	$5 Railroad Lantern, Aug. 23, 1979	9.00	1.50	37.50	(4)	12.50
	Coil Stamps, Perf. 10 Vertically					
1613	3.1¢ Guitar, Oct. 25, 1979	.15	.15	1.50	(2)	1.00
a	Untagged (Bureau precanceled)		.50			
b	Imperf. pair	1,250.00		3,600.00	(2)	
1614	7.7¢ Saxhorns, Nov. 20, 1976	.18	.15	1.00	(2)	1.00
a	Untagged (Bureau precanceled)		.35			
b	As "a," imperf. pair		1,400.00	4,400.00	(2)	
1615	7.9¢ Drum, Apr. 23, 1976	.15	.15	.65	(2)	1.00
a	Untagged (Bureau precanceled)		.16			
b	Imperf. pair	650.00				
1615C	8.4¢ Piano, July 13, 1978	.22	.15	3.25	(2)	1.00
d	Untagged (Bureau precanceled)		.16			
e	As "d," pair, imperf. between		60.00	—	(2)	
f	As "d," imperf. pair		15.00	30.00	(2)	

187

	Issues of 1975-81, Perf. 10 Vertically	Un	U	PB/LP	#	FDC
	Americana Issue (continued) (See also #1581-82, 1584-85, 1590-99, 1603-05, 1811, 1813, 1816)					
1616	9¢ slate green Capitol Dome (1591), Mar. 5, 1976	.20	.15	.90	(2)	1.00
a	Imperf. pair	*125.00*		*250.00*	(2)	
b	Untagged (Bureau precanceled)		.28			
c	As "b," imperf. pair		*190.00*	—		
1617	10¢ purple Contemplation of Justice (1592), Nov. 4, 1977	.24	.15	1.10	(2)	1.00
a	Untagged (Bureau precanceled)		.25			
b	Imperf. pair	*60.00*		*125.00*	(2)	
	Dull finish gum	.20				
1618	13¢ brown Liberty Bell (1595), Nov. 25, 1975	.25	.15	.60	(2)	1.00
a	Untagged (Bureau precanceled)		.45			
b	Imperf. pair	25.00		65.00	(2)	
g	Pair, imperf. between	—				
1618C	15¢ Ft. McHenry Flag (1597), June 30, 1978	.40	.15			1.00
d	Imperf. pair	20.00				
e	Pair, imperf. between	*150.00*				
f	Gray omitted	*40.00*				
1619	16¢ blue Head of Liberty (1599), Mar. 31, 1978	.32	.15	1.50	(2)	1.00
a	Huck Press printing (white background with a bluish tinge, fraction of a millimeter smaller)	.50	.15			
	Perf. 11 x 10¹/₂					
1620-21	Not assigned					
1622	13¢ Flag over Independence Hall, Nov. 15, 1975	.24	.15	5.75	(20)	1.00
a	Horizontal pair, imperf. between	60.00				
b	Imperf. pair	*1,250.00*				
c	Perf. 11, 1981	.65	.15	*80.00*	(20)	
d	As "c," vertical pair, imperf.	*200.00*				
e	Horizontal pair, imperf. vertically	—				
	Booklet Stamps					
1623	13¢ Flag over Capitol, single from booklet (1623a)	.22	.15			1.00
a	Booklet pane of 8, (1 #1590 and 7 #1623), Mar. 11, 1977	2.50	*.60*			25.00
	Booklet Stamps, Perf. 10					
b	13¢ Single from booklet	1.00	1.00			
c	Booklet pane of 8, (1 #1590a and 7 #1623b)	30.00	—			12.50
	#1623, 1623b issued only in booklets. All stamps are imperf. at one side or imperf. at one side and bottom.					
	Booklet Stamps, Perf. 11 x 10¹/₂					
d	Attached pair, #1590 and 1623	.75	—			
	Booklet Stamps, Perf. 10					
e	Attached pair, #1590a and 1623b	20.00	—			
1624	Not assigned					
	Coil Stamp, Perf. 10 Vertically					
1625	13¢ Flag over Independence Hall (1622), Nov. 15, 1975	.30	.15			1.00
a	Imperf. pair	22.50				

1622

1623a

1632

1629   1630   1631   1631a

1633

1635

1636

1637

1638

1639

1640

1641

1642

1643

1644

	Issues of 1976, Perf. 11	Un	U	PB	#	FDC	Q
	American Bicentennial Issue, The Spirit of '76, Jan. 1						
1629	13¢ Drummer Boy	.25	.15			1.25	73,152,000
1630	13¢ Old Drummer	.25	.15			1.25	73,152,000
1631	13¢ Fife Player	.25	.15			1.25	73,152,000
a	Strip of 3, #1629-31	.75	.60	3.10	(12)	2.00	
b	As "a," imperf.	1,200.00					
c	Imperf. pair, #1631	800.00					
1632	13¢ Interphil 76, Jan. 17	.24	.15	1.05	(4)	1.00	157,825,000
	State Flags, Feb. 23						
1633	13¢ Delaware	.25	.20			1.25	8,720,100
1634	13¢ Pennsylvania	.25	.20			1.25	8,720,100
1635	13¢ New Jersey	.25	.20			1.25	8,720,100
1636	13¢ Georgia	.25	.20			1.25	8,720,100
1637	13¢ Connecticut	.25	.20			1.25	8,720,100
1638	13¢ Massachusetts	.25	.20			1.25	8,720,100
1639	13¢ Maryland	.25	.20			1.25	8,720,100
1640	13¢ South Carolina	.25	.20			1.25	8,720,100
1641	13¢ New Hampshire	.25	.20			1.25	8,720,100
1642	13¢ Virginia	.25	.20			1.25	8,720,100
1643	13¢ New York	.25	.20			1.25	8,720,100
1644	13¢ North Carolina	.25	.20			1.25	8,720,100

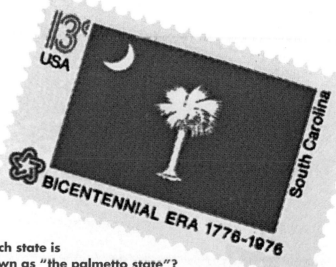

Which state is known as "the palmetto state"?

During the Revolutionary War in 1776, colonists in a small fort built of palmetto logs defeated a British fleet that tried to capture Charleston Harbor. The next day, the colonial commander, William Moultrie, saw a column of smoke rising from a burning British ship, which reminded Moultrie of the palmetto tree that grows widely in South Carolina. According to legend, these war-time events gave South Carolina its nickname of "the palmetto state." **(#1640)**

	Issues of 1976 (continued), Perf. 11	Un	U		FDC	Q
	American Bicentennial Issue (continued), State Flags, Feb. 23					
1645	13¢ Rhode Island	.25	.20		1.25	8,720,100
1646	13¢ Vermont	.25	.20		1.25	8,720,100
1647	13¢ Kentucky	.25	.20		1.25	8,720,100
1648	13¢ Tennessee	.25	.20		1.25	8,720,100
1649	13¢ Ohio	.25	.20		1.25	8,720,100
1650	13¢ Louisiana	.25	.20		1.25	8,720,100
1651	13¢ Indiana	.25	.20		1.25	8,720,100
1652	13¢ Mississippi	.25	.20		1.25	8,720,100
1653	13¢ Illinois	.25	.20		1.25	8,720,100
1654	13¢ Alabama	.25	.20		1.25	8,720,100
1655	13¢ Maine	.25	.20		1.25	8,720,100
1656	13¢ Missouri	.25	.20		1.25	8,720,100
1657	13¢ Arkansas	.25	.20		1.25	8,720,100
1658	13¢ Michigan	.25	.20		1.25	8,720,100
1659	13¢ Florida	.25	.20		1.25	8,720,100
1660	13¢ Texas	.25	.20		1.25	8,720,100
1661	13¢ Iowa	.25	.20		1.25	8,720,100
1662	13¢ Wisconsin	.25	.20		1.25	8,720,100
1663	13¢ California	.25	.20		1.25	8,720,100
1664	13¢ Minnesota	.25	.20		1.25	8,720,100
1665	13¢ Oregon	.25	.20		1.25	8,720,100

Which is the only state that produces diamonds?

Arkansas has many mineral resources, mostly found in the lowlands and the Arkansas River valley; and, it is the only state that produces diamonds. It is said that in 1906 an Arkansas farmer found a diamond in his field. Supposedly, the farmer's field was once the crater of an ancient volcano. Today, diamonds, as well as other minerals and stones, hide in the volcanic rock, and visitors can search for them in a public diamond field.

In addition to diamonds, Arkansas produces oil, natural gas, clay, coal and bauxite. The state is also known for other natural wonders, including its vast forests of oak, hickory and pine trees and the hot, soothing mineral springs. **(#1657)**

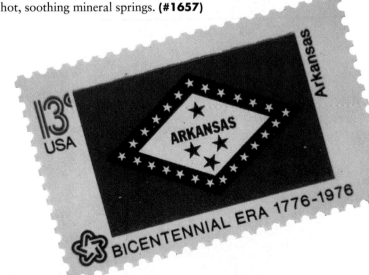

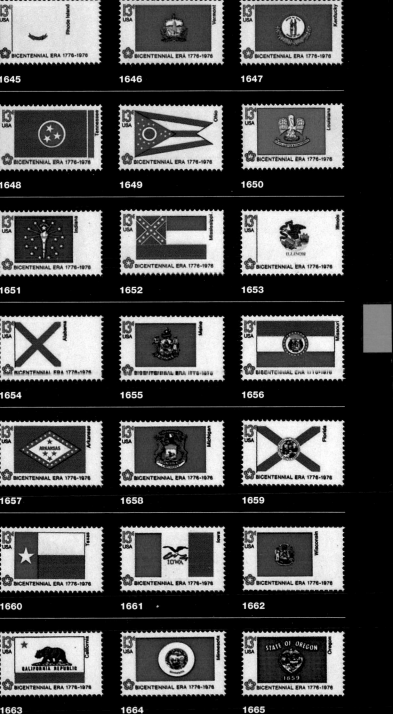

1645   1646   1647

1648   1649   1650

1651   1652   1653

1654   1655   1656

1657   1658   1659

1660   1661   1662

1663   1664   1665

1666

1667

1668

1669

1670

1671

1672

1673

1674

1675

1676

1677

1678

1679

1680

1681

1682

1683

1684

1685

	Issues of 1976 (continued), Perf. 11	Un	U	PB	#	FDC	Q
	American Bicentennial Issue (continued), State Flags, Feb. 23						
1666	13¢ Kansas	.25	.20			1.25	8,720,100
1667	13¢ West Virginia	.25	.20			1.25	8,720,100
1668	13¢ Nevada	.25	.20			1.25	8,720,100
1669	13¢ Nebraska	.25	.20			1.25	8,720,100
1670	13¢ Colorado	.25	.20			1.25	8,720,100
1671	13¢ North Dakota	.25	.20			1.25	8,720,100
1672	13¢ South Dakota	.25	.20			1.25	8,720,100
1673	13¢ Montana	.25	.20			1.25	8,720,100
1674	13¢ Washington	.25	.20			1.25	8,720,100
1675	13¢ Idaho	.25	.20			1.25	8,720,100
1676	13¢ Wyoming	.25	.20			1.25	8,720,100
1677	13¢ Utah	.25	.20			1.25	8,720,100
1678	13¢ Oklahoma	.25	.20			1.25	8,720,100
1679	13¢ New Mexico	.25	.20			1.25	8,720,100
1680	13¢ Arizona	.25	.20			1.25	8,720,100
1681	13¢ Alaska	.25	.20			1.25	8,720,100
1682	13¢ Hawaii	.25	.20			1.25	8,720,100
a	Pane of 50, #1633-82	13.00	—	13.00	(50)	27.50	
1683	13¢ Telephone Centennial, Mar. 10	.24	.15	1.05	(4)	1.00	158,915,000
1684	13¢ Commercial Aviation, Mar. 19	.24	.15	2.50	(10)	1.00	156,960,000
1685	13¢ Chemistry, Apr. 6	.24	.15	3.00	(12)	1.00	158,470,000
	Pair with full vertical gutter between	—					

When was the first commercial airplane flight?

In 1914, pilot Tony Jannus started the world's
first commercial airline. It flew across Tampa Bay, between St. Petersburg
and Tampa, Florida. Because the plane could only carry one person at a
time, it soon went out of business. Commercial aviation gained popularity
after World War I when military planes became available for civilian use.
During the early '20s, several small passenger airlines started in America,
but most of them did not stay in business long. At that time, many
Americans thought that flying was dangerous. However, the industry
grew rapidly by the 1930s. **(#1684)**

	Issues of 1976 (continued), Perf. 11	Un	U	FDC	Q
	American Bicentennial Issue Souvenir Sheets, May 29, 5 stamps each				
1686	13¢ The Surrender of Lord Cornwallis at Yorktown, by John Trumbull	3.50	—	6.00	1,990,000
a	13¢ Two American Officers	.45	.40		1,990,000
b	13¢ Gen. Benjamin Lincoln	.45	.40		1,990,000
c	13¢ George Washington	.45	.40		1,990,000
d	13¢ John Trumbull, Col. David Cobb, General Friedrich von Steuben, Marquis de Lafayette and Thomas Nelson	.45	.40		1,990,000
e	13¢ Alexander Hamilton, John Laurens and Walter Stewart	.45	.40		1,990,000
f	"USA/13¢" omitted on "b," "c" and "d," imperf.	—	1,500.00		
g	"USA/13¢" omitted on "a" and "e"	450.00	—		
h	Imperf. (untagged)		1,750.00		
i	"USA/13¢" omitted on "b," "c" and "d"	450.00			
j	"USA/13¢" double on "b"	—			
k	"USA/13¢" omitted on "c" and "d"	—			
l	"USA/13¢" omitted on "e"	500.00			
m	"USA/13¢" omitted, imperf. (untaggged)	—	—		
1687	18¢ The Declaration of Independence, 4 July 1776 at Philadelphia, by John Trumbull	4.50	—	7.50	1,983,000
a	18¢ John Adams, Roger Sherman and Robert R. Livingston	.55	.55		1,983,000
b	18¢ Thomas Jefferson and Benjamin Franklin	.55	.55		1,983,000
c	18¢ Thomas Nelson, Jr., Francis Lewis, John Witherspoon and Samuel Huntington	.55	.55		1,983,000
d	18¢ John Hancock and Charles Thomson	.55	.55		1,983,000
e	18¢ George Read, John Dickinson and Edward Rutledge	.55	.55		1,983,000
f	Design and marginal inscriptions omitted	4,750.00			
g	"USA/18¢" omitted on "a" and "c"	—			
h	"USA/18¢" omitted on "b," "d" and "e"	500.00			
i	"USA/18¢" omitted on "d"	500.00			
j	Black omitted in design	1,200.00			
k	"USA/18¢" omitted, imperf. (untagged)	2,250.00			
m	"USA/18¢" omitted on "b" and "e"	500.00			

The Surrender of Lord Cornwallis at Yorktown
From a Painting by John Trumbull

1686

The Declaration of Independence, 4 July 1776 at Philadelphia
From a Painting by John Trumbull

1687

Washington Crossing the Delaware
From a Painting by Emanuel Leutze / Eastman Johnson

1688

Washington Reviewing His Ragged Army at Valley Forge
From a Painting by William T. Trego

1689

	Issues of 1976 (continued), Perf. 11	Un	U	FDC	Q
	American Bicentennial Issue (continued) Souvenir Sheets, May 29, 5 stamps each				
1688	24¢ Washington Crossing the Delaware, by Emanuel Leutze/ Eastman Johnson	5.50	—	8.50	1,953,000
a	24¢ Boatmen	.70	.70		1,953,000
b	24¢ George Washington	.70	.70		1,953,000
c	24¢ Flagbearer	.70	.70		1,953,000
d	24¢ Men in Boat	.70	.70		1,953,000
e	24¢ Steersman and Men on Shore	.70	.70		1,953,000
f	"USA/24¢" omitted, imperf.	2,850.00			
g	"USA/24¢" omitted on "d" and "e"	—	450.00		
h	Design and marginal inscriptions omitted	2,250.00			
i	"USA/24¢" omitted on "a," "b" and "c"	—	—		
j	Imperf. (untagged)	2,250.00			
k	"USA/24¢" inverted on "d" and "e"	—			
1689	31¢ Washington Reviewing His Ragged Army at Valley Forge, by William T. Trego	6.50		9.50	1,903,000
a	31¢ Two Officers	.85	.85		1,903,000
b	31¢ George Washington	.85	.85		1,903,000
c	31¢ Officer and Brown Horse	.85	.85		1,903,000
d	31¢ White Horse and Officer	.85	.85		1,903,000
e	31¢ Three Soldiers	.85	.85		1,903,000
f	"USA/31¢" omitted, imperf.	2,100.00			
g	"USA/31¢" omitted on "a" and "c"	—			
h	"USA/31¢" omitted on "b," "d" and "e"	—	—		
i	"USA/31¢" omitted on "e"	600.00			
j	Black omitted in design	1,350.00			
k	Imperf. (untagged)		2,000.00		
l	"USA/31¢" omitted on "b" and "d"	—			
m	"USA/31¢" omitted on "a," "c" and "e"	—			
n	As "m," imperf. (untagged)	—			
p	As "h," imperf. (untagged)		2,400.00		
q	As "g," imperf. (untagged)	2,500.00			

Why did soldiers die at Valley Forge?

General George Washington led his troops to Valley Forge during the winter of 1777 through 1778 after defeats at Brandywine and Germantown, Pennsylvania. The winter was hard. The soldiers had little food and lived in crude log huts that they built themselves. Long marches had destroyed shoes, supplies and morale. Many soldiers died when they were hit by a smallpox epidemic. Others died of typhoid, dysentery and pneumonia. Just when it seemed all was lost, Baron von Steuben, a former Prussian soldier, trained the American soldiers to be a well-disciplined army. Conditions and morale improved, and the soldiers went on to victory. (**#1689**)

Washington Reviewing His Ragged Army at Valley Forge, From a Painting by William T. Trego

	Issues of 1976 (continued), Perf.11	Un	U	PB	#	FDC	Q
	American Bicentennial Issue, Benjamin Franklin, June 1						
1690	13¢ Bust of Franklin, Map of North America, 1776	.20	.15	.90	(4)	1.00	164,890,000
a	Light blue omitted	400.00					
	Declaration of Independence, by John Trumbull, July 4						
1691	13¢ Delegates	.22	.15			1.00	41,222,500
1692	13¢ Delegates and John Adams	.22	.15			1.00	41,222,500
1693	13¢ Roger Sherman, Robert R. Livingston, Thomas Jefferson and Benjamin Franklin	.22	.15			1.00	41,222,500
1694	13¢ John Hancock, Charles Thomson, George Read, John Dickinson and Edward Rutledge	.22	.15			1.00	41,222,500
a	Strip of 4, #1691-94	.95	.75	4.75	(20)	2.00	
	Olympic Games Issue, July 16						
1695	13¢ Diver and Olympic Rings	.28	.15			1.00	46,428,750
1696	13¢ Skier and Olympic Rings	.28	.15			1.00	46,428,750
1697	13¢ Runner and Olympic Rings	.28	.15			1.00	46,428,750
1698	13¢ Skater and Olympic Rings	.28	.15			1.00	46,428,750
a	Block of 4, #1695-98	1.15	.85	3.50	(12)	2.00	
b	As "a," imperf.	750.00					
1699	13¢ Clara Maass, Aug. 18	.26	.15	3.40	(12)	1.00	130,592,000
a	Horizontal pair, imperf. vertically	400.00					
1700	13¢ Adolph S. Ochs, Sept. 18	.24	.15	1.05	(4)	1.00	158,332,400
	Christmas Issue, Oct. 27						
1701	13¢ Nativity, by John Singleton Copley	.24	.15	3.00	(12)	1.00	809,955,000
a	Imperf. pair	110.00					
1702	13¢ "Winter Pastime," by Nathaniel Currier	.24	.15	2.50	(10)	1.00	481,685,000*
a	Imperf. pair	120.00					
	*Includes #1703 printing						
1703	13¢ as #1702	.24	.15	5.00	(20)	1.00	
a	Imperf. pair	140.00					
b	Vertical pair, imperf. between	—					

#1702 has overall tagging. Lettering at base is black and usually 1/2mm below design. As a rule, no "snowflaking" in sky or pond. Pane of 50 has margins on 4 sides with slogans. #1703 has block tagging the size of the printed area. Lettering at base is gray-black and usually 3/4mm below design. "Snowflaking" generally in sky and pond. Pane of 50 has margin only at right or left and no slogans.

	Issues of 1977, American Bicentennial Issue, Washington at Princeton, Jan. 3						
1704	13¢ Washington, Nassau Hall, Hessian Prisoners and 13-star Flag, by Charles Willson Peale	.24	.15	2.50	(10)	1.00	150,328,000
a	Horizontal pair, imperf. vertically	450.00					
1705	13¢ Sound Recording, Mar. 23	.24	.15	1.05	(4)	1.00	176,830,000

1690

1691   1692   1693   1694   1694a

1699

1700

1695
1697

1696
1698

1698a

1701

1702

1703

1704

1705

1710

1711

1706   **1707**   **1709a**
1708   **1709**

Lafayette
US Bicentennial 13c

1716

1712   **1713**   **1715a**
1714   **1715**

1721

1717   **1718**   **1720a**
1719   **1720**

	Issues of 1977 (continued), Perf. 11	Un	U	PB	#	FDC	Q
	American Folk Art Issue, Pueblo Pottery, Apr. 13						
1706	13¢ Zia Pot	.24	.15			1.00	48,994,000
1707	13¢ San Ildefonso Pot	.24	.15			1.00	48,994,000
1708	13¢ Hopi Pot	.24	.15			1.00	48,994,000
1709	13¢ Acoma Pot	.24	.15			1.00	48,994,000
a	Block of 4, #1706-09	1.00	.60	2.50	(10)	2.00	
b	As "a," imperf. vertically	2,500.00					
1710	13¢ Solo Transatlantic Flight, May 20	.24	.15	3.00	(12)	1.00	208,820,000
a	Imperf. pair	1,250.00					
1711	13¢ Colorado Statehood, May 21	.24	.15	3.00	(12)	1.00	192,250,000
a	Horizontal pair, imperf. between	500.00					
b	Horizontal pair, imperf. vertically	800.00					
c	Perf. 11.2	.35	.25				
	Butterfly Issue, June 6						
1712	13¢ Swallowtail	.24	.15			1.00	54,957,500
1713	13¢ Checkerspot	.24	.15			1.00	54,957,500
1714	13¢ Dogface	.24	.15			1.00	54,957,500
1715	13¢ Orange-Tip	.24	.15			1.00	54,957,500
a	Block of 4, #1712-15	1.00	.60	3.10	(12)	2.00	
b	As "a," imperf. horizontally	—					
	American Bicentennial Issue, Lafayette's Landing in South Carolina, June 13						
1716	13¢ Marquis de Lafayette	.24	.15	1.05	(4)	1.00	159,852,000
	Skilled Hands for Independence, July 4						
1717	13¢ Seamstress	.24	.15			1.00	47,077,500
1718	13¢ Blacksmith	.24	.15			1.00	47,077,500
1719	13¢ Wheelwright	.24	.15			1.00	47,077,500
1720	13¢ Leatherworker	.24	.15			1.00	47,077,500
a	Block of 4, #1717-20	1.00	.80	3.10	(12)	1.75	
	Perf. 11 x 10¹/₂						
1721	13¢ Peace Bridge, Aug. 4	.24	.15	1.05	(4)	1.00	163,625,000

Who makes things "go around"?

A wheelwright makes or repairs wheels. The wheel, which was invented in ancient Mesopotamia between 3500 and 3000 B.C., is one of the world's most notable inventions. Before the wheel, people and oxen pulled heavy loads on sleds. People also put sleds on logs, which acted as rollers. As the sled rolled forward, people picked up the logs from behind and laid them down in front of the sled. Early wheels evolved from this practice. (**#1719**)

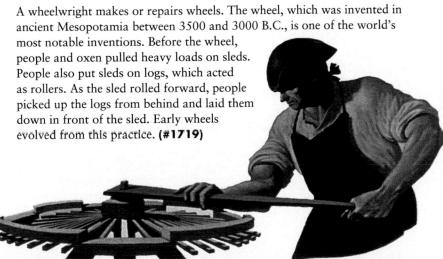

	Issues of 1977 (continued), Perf. 11	Un	U	PB	#	FDC	Q
	American Bicentennial Issue, Battle of Oriskany, Aug. 6						
1722	13¢ Herkimer at Oriskany, by Frederick Yohn	.24	.15	2.50	(10)	1.25	156,296,000
	Energy Issue, Oct. 20						
1723	13¢ Energy Conservation	.24	.15			1.00	79,338,000
a	Attached pair, #1723-24	.50	.40	3.00	(12)	1.25	
1724	13¢ Energy Development	.24	.15			1.00	79,338,000
1725	13¢ First Civil Settlement— Alta, California, Sept. 9	.24	.15	1.05	(4)	1.00	154,495,000
	American Bicentennial Issue, Articles of Confederation, Sept. 30						
1726	13¢ Members of Continental Congress in Conference	.24	.15	1.05	(4)	1.00	168,050,000
1727	13¢ Talking Pictures, Oct. 6	.24	.15	1.05	(4)	1.00	156,810,000
	American Bicentennial Issue, Surrender at Saratoga, Oct. 7						
1728	13¢ Surrender of Burgoyne, by John Trumbull	.24	.15	2.50	(10)	1.00	153,736,000
	Christmas Issue, Oct. 21						
1729	13¢ Washington at Valley Forge, by J.C. Leyendecker	.24	.15	5.75	(20)	1.00	882,260,000
a	Imperf. pair	75.00					
1730	13¢ Rural Mailbox	.24	.15	2.50	(10)	1.00	921,530,000
a	Imperf. pair	275.00					
	Issues of 1978						
1731	13¢ Carl Sandburg, Jan. 6	.24	.15	1.05	(4)	1.00	156,560,000
	Captain Cook Issue, Jan. 20						
1732	13¢ Capt. James Cook– Alaska, by Nathaniel Dance	.24	.15			1.00	101,077,500
a	Attached pair, #1732-33	.50	.30	5.25	(20)	1.50	
b	As "a," imperf. between	4,500.00					
1733	13¢ *Resolution* and *Discovery*– Hawaii, by John Webber	.24	.15			1.00	101,077,500
a	Vertical pair, imperf. horizontally	—					
1734	13¢ Indian Head Penny, Jan. 11	.24	.15	1.50	(4)	1.00	
	Pair with full horizontal gutter between	—					
a	Horizontal pair, imperf. vertically	300.00					
1735	15¢ A Stamp, May 22	.24	.15	1.05	(4)	1.00	
a	Imperf. pair	80.00					
b	Vertical pair, imperf. horizontally	300.00					
	Booklet Stamp, Perf. 11 x 10½						
1736	15¢ orange Eagle (1735), single from booklet	.25	.15			1.00	
a	Booklet pane of 8, May 22	2.25	.60			2.50	
	Roses Booklet Issue, July 11, Perf. 10						
1737	15¢ Roses, single from booklet	.25	.15			1.00	
a	Booklet pane of 8	2.25	.60			2.50	
b	As "a," imperf.	—					

#1736-37 issued only in booklets. All stamps are imperf. on one side or on one side and bottom.

Minimum value listed for a stamp is 15 cents; for a First Day Cover (FDC), $1.00. This minimum represents a fair-market price for having a dealer locate and provide a single stamp or cover from his or her stock. Dealers may charge less per stamp or cover for a group of such stamps or covers, or less for a single stamp or cover.

US Bicentennial 13 cents

1722

1723   **1723a**
1724

First Civil Settlement·Alta California·1777

1725

1726

1727

US Bicentennial 13 cents

1728

1729   **1730**

1731

1732   **1732a**
1733

1734

1735

1737

205

1738 1739 1740 1741 1742 1742a

1744

1745 1746 1748a
1747 1748

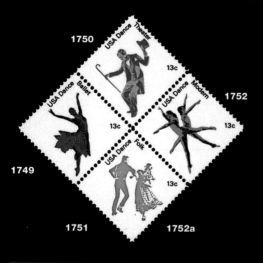

1750

1752

1753

1749

1751 1752a

1754 1755 1756

	Issues of 1980, Perf. 11	Un	U	PB/LP	#	FDC	Q
	Windmills Booklet Issue, Feb. 7						
1738	15¢ Virginia, 1720	.30	.15			1.00	
1739	15¢ Rhode Island, 1790	.30	.15			1.00	
1740	15¢ Massachusetts, 1793	.30	.15			1.00	
1741	15¢ Illinois, 1860	.30	.15			1.00	
1742	15¢ Texas, 1890	.30	.15			1.00	
a	Booklet pane of 10, #1738-42	3.60	.60			3.50	
	#1737-42 issued only in booklets. All stamps are imperf. top or bottom, or top or bottom and right side.						
	Issues of 1978 (continued), Coil Stamp, Perf. 10 Vertically						
1743	15¢ orange Eagle (1735), May 22	.25	.15	.65	(2)	1.00	
a	Imperf. pair	100.00		—	(2)		
	Black Heritage Issue, Harriet Tubman, Feb. 1, Perf. 10½ x 11						
1744	13¢ Harriet Tubman and Cart Carrying Slaves	.24	.15	3.00	(12)	1.00	156,525,000
	American Folk Art Issue, Quilts, Mar. 8, Perf. 11						
1745	13¢ Basket design, red and orange	.24	.15			1.00	41,295,600
1746	13¢ Basket design, red	.24	.15			1.00	41,295,600
1747	13¢ Basket design, orange	.24	.15			1.00	41,295,600
1748	13¢ Basket design, brown	.24	.15			1.00	41,295,600
a	Block of 4, #1745-48	1.00	.60	3.10	(12)	2.00	
	American Dance Issue, Apr. 26						
1749	13¢ Ballet	.24	.15			1.00	39,399,600
1750	13¢ Theater	.24	.15			1.00	39,399,600
1751	13¢ Folk	.24	.15			1.00	39,399,600
1752	13¢ Modern	.24	.15			1.00	39,399,600
a	Block of 4, #1749-52	1.00	.60	3.10	(12)	1.75	
	American Bicentennial Issue, French Alliance, May 4						
1753	13¢ King Louis XVI and Benjamin Franklin, by Charles Gabriel Sauvage	.24	.15	1.05	(4)	1.00	102,920,000
	Perf. 10½ x 11						
1754	13¢ Early Cancer Detection, May 18	.24	.15	1.05	(4)	1.00	152,355,000
	Performing Arts Issue, Jimmie Rodgers, May 24, Perf. 11						
1755	13¢ Jimmie Rodgers with Locomotive, Guitar and Brakeman's Cap	.24	.15	3.00	(12)	1.00	94,625,000
	George M. Cohan, July 3						
1756	15¢ George M. Cohan, "Yankee Doodle Dandy" and Stars	.28	.15	3.50	(12)	1.00	151,570,000

Who is the "Father of Country Music"?

Jimmie (James Charles) Rodgers (1897-1933) is recognized for pioneering American country music. His country-and-western style was then known as blues yodeling. Rodgers' previous work on the railroad earned him the nickname "the singing brakeman." During the last six years of his life, Rodgers recorded more than 100 songs, including "T. for Texas" and "Waitin' for a Train." In 1961, Rodgers was the first person to be honored by the Country Music Hall of Fame in Nashville. **(#1755)**

	Issues of 1978 (continued), Perf. 11	Un	U	PB	#	FDC	Q
	CAPEX '78 Souvenir Sheet, June 10						
1757	13¢ Souvenir sheet of 8	1.65	1.65	1.90	(8)	2.75	15,170,400
a	13¢ Cardinal	.20	.15				15,170,400
b	13¢ Mallard	.20	.15				15,170,400
c	13¢ Canada Goose	.20	.15				15,170,400
d	13¢ Blue Jay	.20	.15				15,170,400
e	13¢ Moose	.20	.15				15,170,400
f	13¢ Chipmunk	.20	.15				15,170,400
g	13¢ Red Fox	.20	.15				15,170,400
h	13¢ Raccoon	.20	.15				15,170,400
i	Yellow, green, red, brown and black (litho.) omitted	3,500.00					
1758	15¢ Photography, June 26	.26	.15	3.25	(12)	1.00	163,200,000
1759	15¢ Viking Missions to Mars, July 20	.28	.15	1.20	(4)	2.00	158,880,000
	Wildlife Conservation Issue, American Owls, Aug. 26						
1760	15¢ Great Gray Owl	.28	.15			1.00	46,637,500
1761	15¢ Saw-Whet Owl	.28	.15			1.00	46,637,500
1762	15¢ Barred Owl	.28	.15			1.00	46,637,500
1763	15¢ Great Horned Owl	.28	.15			1.00	46,637,500
a	Block of 4, #1760-63	1.15	.85	1.25	(4)	2.00	
	American Trees Issue, Oct. 9						
1764	15¢ Giant Sequoia	.28	.15			1.00	42,034,000
1765	15¢ White Pine	.28	.15			1.00	42,034,000
1766	15¢ White Oak	.28	.15			1.00	42,034,000
1767	15¢ Gray Birch	.28	.15			1.00	42,034,000
a	Block of 4, #1764-67	1.15	.85	3.50	(12)	2.00	
b	As "a," imperf. horizontally	12,500.00					
	Christmas Issue, Oct. 18						
1768	15¢ Madonna and Child with Cherubim, by Andrea della Robbia	.28	.15	3.50	(12)	1.00	963,370,000
a	Imperf. pair	90.00					
1769	15¢ Child on Hobby Horse and Christmas Trees	.28	.15	3.50	(12)	1.00	916,800,000
a	Imperf. pair	100.00					
b	Vertical pair, imperf. horizontally	1,750.00					
	Pair with full horizontal gutter between	—					

How did the giant sequoia trees get their name?

The name "sequoia" comes from the name of a Cherokee Indian. In 1809, a Cherokee named Sequoya (1770?-1843) developed the first written Native American language. He realized the value of reading and writing, and thought a written alphabet would help his people advance. Sequoya presented his system of writing to his tribal council in 1821. The alphabet had 85 symbols, each representing a syllable in the Cherokee language. In his honor, the giant trees are named "sequoia." **(#1764)**

1757a, b, c, d

1757e, f, g, h

1757

1758

1759

1760	1761	1763a
1762	1763	

1764   1765   1767a
1766   1767

1768   1769

International Year of the Child

1772

1770

1771

1773

1774

1775   **1776**   **1778a**

1777   **1778**

1779   **1780**   **1782a**

1781   **1782**

1783   **1784**   **1786a**

1785   **1786**

	Issues of 1979, Perf. 11	Un	U	PB	#	FDC	Q
1770	15¢ Robert F. Kennedy, Jan. 12	.28	.15	1.20	(4)	2.00	159,297,600
	Black Heritage Issue, Martin Luther King, Jr., Jan. 13						
1771	15¢ Martin Luther King, Jr., and Civil Rights Marchers	.28	.15	3.50	(12)	1.00	166,435,000
a	Imperf. pair	—					
1772	15¢ International Year of the Child, Feb. 15	.28	.15	1.20	(4)	1.00	162,535,000
	Literary Arts Issue, John Steinbeck, Feb. 27, Perf. 10½ x 11						
1773	15¢ John Steinbeck, by Philippe Halsman	.28	.15	1.20	(4)	1.00	155,000,000
1774	15¢ Albert Einstein, Mar. 4	.28	.15	1.20	(4)	1.50	157,310,000
	Pair with full horizontal gutter between	—					
	American Folk Art Issue, Pennsylvania Toleware, Apr. 19, Perf. 11						
1775	15¢ Straight-Spout Coffeepot	.28	.15			1.00	43,524,000
1776	15¢ Tea Caddy	.28	.15			1.00	43,524,000
1777	15¢ Sugar Bowl	.28	.15			1.00	43,524,000
1778	15¢ Curved-Spout Coffeepot	.28	.15			1.00	43,524,000
a	Block of 4, #1775-78	1.15	.85	2.90	(10)	2.00	
b	As "a," imperf. horizontally	3,750.00					
	American Architecture Issue, June 4						
1779	15¢ Virginia Rotunda, by Thomas Jefferson	.30	.15			1.00	41,198,400
1780	15¢ Baltimore Cathedral, by Benjamin Latrobe	.30	.15			1.00	41,198,400
1781	15¢ Boston State House, by Charles Bulfinch	.30	.15			1.00	41,198,400
1782	15¢ Philadelphia Exchange, by William Strickland	.30	.15			1.00	41,198,400
a	Block of 4, #1779-82	1.25	.85	1.25	(4)	2.00	
	Endangered Flora Issue, June 7						
1783	15¢ Persistent Trillium	.28	.15			1.00	40,763,750
1784	15¢ Hawaiian Wild Broadbean	.28	.15			1.00	40,763,750
1785	15¢ Contra Costa Wallflower	.28	.15			1.00	40,763,750
1786	15¢ Antioch Dunes Evening Primrose	.28	.15			1.00	40,763,750
a	Block of 4, #1783-86	1.25	.85	3.50	(12)	2.00	
b	As "a," imperf.	600.00					
	As "a," full vertical gutter between	—					

Who used nonviolent action to gain equal rights for African-Americans?

Martin Luther King, Jr., (1929-1968) fought for equal rights for African-Americans based on nonviolent action. King's actions were instrumental in getting the 1964 Civil Rights Act and 1965 Voting Rights Act passed. In December 1964, King was awarded the Nobel Peace Prize. In one of King's many famous speeches he said, "I have a dream that my four little children will one day live in a nation where they will not be judged by the color of their skin, but by the content of their character." **(#1771)**

	Issues of 1979 (continued), Perf. 11	Un	U	PB	#	FDC	Q
1787	15¢ Seeing Eye Dogs, June 15	.28	.15	5.75	(20)	1.00	161,860,000
a	Imperf. pair	400.00					
1788	15¢ Special Olympics, Aug. 9	.28	.15	2.90	(10)	1.00	165,775,000
	American Bicentennial Issue, John Paul Jones, Sept. 23, Perf. 11 x 12						
1789	15¢ John Paul Jones, by Charles Willson Peale	.28	.15	2.90	(10)	1.00	160,000,000
a	Perf. 11	.30	.15	3.10	(10)		
b	Perf. 12	2,000.00	1,000.00				
c	Vertical pair, imperf. horizontally	200.00					
d	As "a," vertical pair, imperf. horizontally	160.00					
	Numerous varieties of printer's waste of #1789 exist.						
	Olympic Summer Games Issue, Sept. 5, Perf. 11 (See also #C97)						
1790	10¢ Javelin Thrower	.20	.20	2.50	(12)	1.00	67,195,000
	Sept. 28						
1791	15¢ Runner	.28	.15			1.00	46,726,250
1792	15¢ Swimmer	.28	.15			1.00	46,726,250
1793	15¢ Rowers	.28	.15			1.00	46,726,250
1794	15¢ Equestrian Contestant	.28	.15			1.00	46,726,250
a	Block of 4, #1791-94	1.15	.85	3.50	(12)	2.00	
b	As "a," imperf.	1,400.00					
	Issues of 1980, Olympic Winter Games Issue, Feb. 1, Perf. 11 x 10½						
1795	15¢ Speed Skater	.50	.15			1.00	52,073,750
1796	15¢ Downhill Skier	.50	.15			1.00	52,073,750
1797	15¢ Ski Jumper	.50	.15			1.00	52,073,750
1798	15¢ Hockey Goaltender	.50	.15			1.00	52,073,750
a	Perf. 11	1.05	—				
b	Block of 4, #1795-98	2.00	1.00	4.00	(12)	2.00	
c	Block of 4, #1795a-98a	4.25	—	13.00	(12)		
	Issues of 1979 (continued), Christmas Issue, Oct. 18, Perf. 11						
1799	15¢ Virgin and Child with Cherubim, by Gerard David	.28	.15	3.40	(12)	1.00	873,710,000
a	Imperf. pair	100.00					
b	Vertical pair, imperf. horizontally	700.00					
c	Vertical pair, imperf. between	—					
1800	15¢ Santa Claus, Christmas Tree Ornament	.28	.15	3.40	(12)	1.00	931,880,000
a	Green and yellow omitted	800.00					
b	Green, yellow and tan omitted	850.00					
	Performing Arts Issue, Will Rogers, Nov. 4						
1801	15¢ Will Rogers Portrait and Rogers as a Cowboy Humorist	.28	.15	3.40	(12)	1.00	161,290,000
a	Imperf. pair	250.00					
1802	15¢ Vietnam Veterans, Nov. 11	.28	.15	2.90	(10)	2.50	172,740,000
	Issues of 1980 (continued), Performing Arts Issue, W.C. Fields, Jan. 29						
1803	15¢ W.C. Fields Portrait and Fields as a Juggler	.28	.15	3.40	(12)	1.25	168,995,000
	Black Heritage Issue, Benjamin Banneker, Feb. 15						
1804	15¢ Benjamin Banneker Portrait and Banneker as Surveyor	.28	.15	3.40	(12)	1.00	160,000,000
a	Horizontal pair, imperf. vertically	800.00					

1787   **1788**   **1789**

1790

1791   **1792**   **1794a**
1793   **1794**

1795   **1796**   **1798b**
1797   **1798**

1799   **1800**

1801

1802

1803   **1804**

1813   **1816**

1805   **1807**   **1809**
1806   **1808**   **1810**

1822

1818

1821   **1823**

1824   **1825**   **1826**

1827   **1828** **1830a**
1829   **1830**

	Issues of 1980 (continued), Perf. 11	Un	U	PB/LP	#	FDC	Q
	Letter Writing Issue, Feb. 25						
1805	15¢ Letters Preserve Memories	.28	.15			1.00	38,933,000
1806	15¢ purple P.S. Write Soon	.28	.15			1.00	38,933,000
1807	15¢ Letters Lift Spirits	.28	.15			1.00	38,933,000
1808	15¢ green P.S. Write Soon	.28	.15			1.00	38,933,000
1809	15¢ Letters Shape Opinions	.28	.15			1.00	38,933,000
1810	15¢ red and blue P.S. Write Soon	.28	.15			1.00	38,933,000
a	Vertical Strip of 6, #1805-10	1.75	1.50	10.00	(36)	2.50	
	Issues of 1980-81, Americana Issue, Coil Stamps, Perf. 10 Vertically						
	(See also #1581-82, 1584-85, 1590-99, 1603-06, 1608, 1610-19, 1622-23, 1625)						
1811	1¢ dark blue, greenish Inkwell and Quill (1581), Mar. 6, 1980	.15	.15	.30	(2)	1.00	
a	Imperf. pair	175.00		275.00	(2)		
1812	Not assigned						
1813	3.5¢ Weaer Violins, June 23, 1980	.15	.15	.90	(2)	1.00	
a	Untagged (Bureau precanceled)		.15				
b	Imperf. pair	225.00		—	(2)		
1814-15	Not assigned						
1816	12¢ red brown, *beige* Torch from Statue of Liberty (1594), Apr. 8, 1981	.24	.15	1.25	(2)	1.00	
a	Untagged (Bureau precanceled)		.25				
b	Imperf. pair	225.00		250.00	(2)		
1817	Not assigned						
	Issues of 1981, Perf. 11 x 10½						
1818	18¢ B Stamp, Mar. 15	.32	.15	1.50	(4)	1.00	
	Booklet Stamp, Perf. 10						
1819	18¢ B Stamp (1818), single from booklet	.40	.15			1.00	
a	Booklet pane of 8, Mar. 15	3.50	*1.50*			3.00	
	Coil Stamp, Perf. 10 Vertically						
1820	18¢ B Stamp (1818), Mar. 15	.40	.15	1.60	(2)	1.00	
a	Imperf. pair	90.00		110.00	(2)		
	Issues of 1980 (continued), Perf. 10½ x 11						
1821	15¢ Frances Perkins, April 10	.28	.15	1.20	(4)	1.00	163,510,000
	Perf. 11						
1822	15¢ Dolley Madison, May 20	.28	.15	1.40	(4)	1.00	256,620,000
1823	15¢ Emily Bissell, May 31	.28	.15	1.20	(4)	1.00	95,695,000
a	Vertical pair, imperf. horizontally	250.00					
1824	15¢ Helen Keller/Anne Sullivan, June 27	.28	.15	1.20	(4)	1.00	153,975,000
1825	15¢ Veterans Administration, July 21	.28	.15	1.20	(4)	1.00	160,000,000
a	Horizontal pair, imperf. vertically	500.00					
	American Bicentennial Issue, General Bernardo de Galvez, July 23						
1826	15¢ General Bernardo de Galvez and Revolutionary Flag at Battle of Mobile	.28	.15	1.20	(4)	1.00	100,000,000
a	Red, brown and blue omitted	800.00					
b	Bl., brn., red and yel. omitted	1,400.00					
	Coral Reefs Issue, Aug. 26						
1827	15¢ Brain Coral, Beaugregory Fish	.30	.15			1.00	51,291,250
1828	15¢ Elkhorn Coral, Porkfish	.30	.15			1.00	51,291,250
1829	15¢ Chalice Coral, Moorish Idol	.30	.15			1.00	51,291,250
1830	15¢ Finger Coral, Sabertooth Blenny	.30	.15			1.00	51,291,250
a	Block of 4, #1827-30	1.20	.85	3.65	(12)	2.00	
b	As "a," imperf.	1,250.00					
c	As "a," imperf. between, vertically	—					
d	As "a," imperf. vertically	3,000.00					

215

	Issues of 1980 (continued), Perf. 11	Un	U	PB	#	FDC	Q
1831	15¢ Organized Labor, Sept. 1	.28	.15	3.50	(12)	1.00	166,590,000
a	Imperf. pair	400.00					
	Literary Arts Issue, Edith Wharton, Sept. 5, Perf. 10½ x 11						
1832	15¢ Edith Wharton Reading Letter	.28	.15	1.20	(4)	1.00	163,275,000
	Perf. 11						
1833	15¢ Education, Sept. 12	.28	.15	1.70	(6)	1.00	160,000,000
a	Horizontal pair, imperf. vertically	250.00					
	American Folk Art Issue, Pacific Northwest Indian Masks, Sept. 25						
1834	15¢ Heiltsuk, Bella Bella Tribe	.30	.15			1.00	38,101,000
1835	15¢ Chilkat Tlingit Tribe	.30	.15			1.00	38,101,000
1836	15¢ Tlingit Tribe	.30	.15			1.00	38,101,000
1837	15¢ Bella Coola Tribe	.30	.15			1.00	38,101,000
a	Block of 4, #1834-37	1.25	.85	3.10	(10)	2.00	
	American Architecture Issue, Oct. 9						
1838	15¢ Smithsonian Institution, by James Renwick	.30	.15			1.00	38,756,000
1839	15¢ Trinity Church, by Henry Hobson Richardson	.30	.15			1.00	38,756,000
1840	15¢ Pennsylvania Academy of Fine Arts, by Frank Furness	.30	.15			1.00	38,756,000
1841	15¢ Lyndhurst, by Alexander Jefferson Davis	.30	.15			1.00	38,756,000
a	Block of 4, #1838-41	1.25	.85	1.30	(4)	2.00	
	Christmas Issue, Oct. 31						
1842	15¢ Madonna and Child from Epiphany Window, Washington Cathedral	.28	.15	3.40	(12)	1.00	693,250,000
a	Imperf. pair	100.00					
	Pair with full vertical gutter between	—					
1843	15¢ Wreath and Toys	.28	.15	5.75	(20)	1.00	718,715,000
a	Imperf. pair	100.00					
b	Buff omitted	—					

Why is Edith Wharton recognized as a great writer?

Edith Newbold Jones Wharton (1862-1937) is praised for her short stories and novels. Wharton's stories give an emotional depth to her characters and examine social behavior. Many of the themes of Wharton's work came from her background. Wharton was born in New York City to a high-society family. She valued the refined manners of fashionable society, but was also conscious of its shallowness. Wharton was fluent in several languages and knowledgeable about history, art, sociology and science. Her novel, *The Age of Innocence*, won the Pulitzer Prize. **(#1832)**

1831   1832   1833

1834   1835   1837a

1836   1837

1842   1843

1838   1839   1841a

1840   1841

Dorothea Dix
USA 1c

1844

Igor Stravinsky
USA 2c

1845

Henry Clay
USA 3c

1846

Carl Schurz
4c USA

1847

Pearl Buck
USA 5c

1848

Walter Lippmann
6 USA

1849

Abraham Baldwin
USA 7

1850

Henry Knox
USA 8

1851

Sylvanus Thayer
USA 9

1852

Richard Russell
USA 10c

1853

Alden Partridge
USA 11

1854

USA 13c
Crazy Horse

1855

Sinclair Lewis
USA 14

1856

Rachel Carson
USA 17c

1857

George Mason
USA 18c

1858

USA 19c
Sequoyah

1859

Ralph Bunche
USA 20c

1860

Thomas H. Gallaudet
USA 20c

1861

Harry S Truman
USA 20c

1862

John J. Audubon
USA 22

1863

Frank C. Laubach
USA 30c

1864

Charles R. Drew MD
USA 35c

1865

Robert Millikan
37c USA

1866

Grenville Clark
USA 39

1867

Lillian M. Gilbreth
USA 40c

1868

USA 50
Chester W. Nimitz

1869

218

	Issues of 1980-85, Perf. 11	Un	U	PB	#	FDC
	Great Americans Issue (See also #2168-73, 2176-80, 2182-86, 2188, 2190-92, 2194-97)					
1844	1¢ Dorothea Dix, Sept. 23, 1983	.15	.15	.35	(6)	1.00
a	Imperf. pair	350.00				
b	Vertical pair, imperf. between	—				
	Perf. 10½ x 11					
1845	2¢ Igor Stravinsky, Nov. 18, 1982	.15	.15	.25	(4)	1.00
a	Vertical pair, full gutter between	—				
1846	3¢ Henry Clay, July 13, 1983	.15	.15	.35	(4)	1.00
1847	4¢ Carl Schurz, June 3, 1983	.15	.15	.40	(4)	1.00
1848	5¢ Pearl Buck, June 25, 1983	.15	.15	.50	(4)	1.00
	Perf. 11					
1849	6¢ Walter Lippman, Sept. 19, 1985	.15	.15	.75	(6)	1.00
a	Vertical pair, imperf. between	2,300				
1850	7¢ Abraham Baldwin, Jan. 25, 1985	.15	.15	.75	(6)	1.00
1851	8¢ Henry Knox, July 25, 1985	.15	.15	.70	(4)	1.00
1852	9¢ Sylvanus Thayer, June 7, 1985	.16	.15	1.00	(6)	1.00
1853	10¢ Richard Russell, May 31, 1984	.18	.15	1.10	(6)	1.00
a	Vertical pair, imperf. between	1,100.00				
b	Horizontal pair, imperf. between	—				
1854	11¢ Alden Partridge, Feb. 12, 1985	.20	.15	1.10	(4)	1.00
	Perf. 10½ x 11					
1855	13¢ Crazy Horse, Jan. 15, 1982	.24	.15	1.35	(4)	1.00
	Perf. 11					
1856	14¢ Sinclair Lewis, Mar. 21, 1985	.25	.15	1.55	(6)	1.00
a	Vertical pair, imperf. horizontally	150.00				
b	Horizontal pair, imperf. between	8.50				
c	Vertical pair, imperf. between	2,000.00				
	Perf. 10½ x 11					
1857	17¢ Rachel Carson, May 28, 1981	.32	.15	1.40	(4)	1.00
1858	18¢ George Mason, May 7, 1981	.32	.15	2.25	(4)	1.00
1859	19¢ Sequoyah, Dec. 27, 1980	.35	.15	2.00	(4)	1.00
1860	20¢ Ralph Bunche, Jan. 12, 1982	.40	.15	2.75	(4)	1.00
1861	20¢ Thomas H. Gallaudet, June 10, 1983	.38	.15	2.75	(4)	1.00
	Perf. 11					
1862	20¢ Harry S. Truman, Jan. 26, 1984	.38	.15	2.40	(6)	1.00
b	Overall tagging, 1990	—	—			
1863	22¢ John J. Audubon, Apr. 23, 1985	.40	.15	2.50	(6)	1.00
a	Vertical pair, imperf. horizontally	2,500.00				
b	Vertical pair, imperf. between	—				
c	Horizontal pair, imperf. between	—				
1864	30¢ Frank C. Laubach, Sept. 2, 1984	.55	.15	3.50	(6)	1.00
	Perf. 10½ x 11					
1865	35¢ Charles R. Drew, MD, June 3, 1981	.65	.15	2.75	(4)	1.25
1866	37¢ Robert Millikan, Jan. 26, 1982	.70	.15	2.90	(4)	1.25
	Perf. 11					
1867	39¢ Grenville Clark, May 20, 1985	.70	.15	4.25	(6)	1.25
a	Vertical pair, imperf. horizontally	600.00				
b	Vertical pair, imperf. between	1,250.00				
1868	40¢ Lillian M. Gilbreth, Feb. 24, 1984	.70	.15	4.60	(6)	1.25
1869	50¢ Chester W. Nimitz, Feb. 22, 1985	.90	.15	4.50	(4)	1.25
1870-73	Not assigned					

219

	Issues of 1981, Perf. 11	Un	U	PB/PNC	#	FDC	Q
1874	15¢ Everett Dirksen, Jan. 4	.28	.15	1.20	(4)	1.00	160,155,000
	Black Heritage Issue, Whitney Moore Young, Jan. 30						
1875	15¢ Whitney Moore Young at Desk	.28	.15	1.25	(4)	1.00	159,505,000
	Flower Issue, April 23						
1876	18¢ Rose	.35	.15			1.00	52,654,000
1877	18¢ Camellia	.35	.15			1.00	52,654,000
1878	18¢ Dahlia	.35	.15			1.00	52,654,000
1879	18¢ Lily	.35	.15			1.00	52,654,000
a	Block of 4, #1876-79	1.40	.85	1.50	(4)	2.50	
	Wildlife Booklet Issue, May 14						
1880	18¢ Bighorn Sheep	.35	.15			1.00	
1881	18¢ Puma	.35	.15			1.00	
1882	18¢ Harbor Seal	.35	.15			1.00	
1883	18¢ Bison	.35	.15			1.00	
1884	18¢ Brown Bear	.35	.15			1.00	
1885	18¢ Polar Bear	.35	.15			1.00	
1886	18¢ Elk (Wapiti)	.35	.15			1.00	
1887	18¢ Moose	.35	.15			1.00	
1888	18¢ White-Tailed Deer	.35	.15			1.00	
1889	18¢ Pronghorn Antelope	.35	.15			1.00	
a	Booklet pane of 10, #1880-89	9.00				5.00	

#1880-89 issued only in booklets. All stamps are imperf. at one side or imperf. at one side and bottom.

	Flag and Anthem Issue, April 24						
1890	18¢ "...for amber waves of grain"	.32	.15	2.00	(6)	1.00	
a	Imperf. pair	100.00					
b	Vertical pair, imperf. horizontally	—					
	Coil Stamp, Perf. 10 Vertically						
1891	18¢ "...from sea to shining sea"	.36	.15	5.00	(3)	1.00	
a	Imperf. pair	20.00					

Beginning with #1891, all coil stamps except #1947 feature a small plate number at the bottom of the design at varying intervals in a roll, depending on the press used. The basic "plate number coil" (PNC) collecting unit is a strip of three stamps, with the plate number appearing on the middle stamp. PNC values are for the most common plate number.

	Booklet Stamps, Perf. 11						
1892	6¢ USA Circle of Stars, single from booklet (1893a)	.55	.15			1.00	
1893	18¢ "...for purple mountain majesties," single from booklet (1893a)	.32	.15			1.00	
a	Booklet pane of 8 (2 #1892 & 6 #1893)	3.25	—			2.50	
b	As "a," imperf. vertically between	*80.00*	—				

#1892-93 issued only in booklets. All stamps are imperf. at one side or imperf. at one side and bottom.

	Flag Over Supreme Court Issue, Dec. 17 (Except #1896b, issued June 1, 1982)						
1894	20¢ Flag Over Supreme Court	.35	.15	2.25	(6)	1.00	
a	Imperf. pair	40.00					
b	Vertical pair, imperf. horizontally	*650.00*					
c	Dark blue omitted	*100.00*					
d	Black omitted	*300.00*					
	Coil Stamp, Perf. 10 Vertically						
1895	20¢ Flag Over Supreme Court (1894)	.35	.15	4.75	(3)	1.00	
a	Imperf. pair	10.00					
b	Black omitted	40.00					
c	Blue omitted	—					
e	Untagged (Bureau precanceled)	.50	.50	45.00	(3)		

1874   **1875**

1876   **1877**   **1879a**
1878   **1879**

1880   **1881**   **1889a**
1882   **1883**   **1892**   **1893a**
1884   **1885**   **1893**
1886   **1887**
1888   **1889**

1890   **1891**   **1894**

Omnibus 1880s
USA 1c

1897

Locomotive 1870s
USA 2c

1897A

Handcar 1880s
USA 3c

1898

Stagecoach 1890s
USA 4c

1898A

Motorcycle
1913
USA 5c

1899

Sleigh 1880s
USA 5.2c Auth
Nonprofit
Org

1900

Bicycle 1870s
USA 5.9c
Auth
Nonprofit
Org

1901

Baby Buggy 1880s
USA 7.4c

1902

Mail Wagon 1880s
USA 9.3c
Bulk
Rate

1903

Hansom Cab 1890s
USA 10.9c
Bulk
Rate

1904

RR Caboose 1890s
USA 11c
Bulk Rate

1905

Electric Auto 1917
USA 17c

1906

Surrey 1890s
USA 18c

1907

Fire Pumper
1860s
USA 20c

1908

USA $9.35

1909

The Gift of Self
USA
18c
American Red Cross
1881-1981

1910

SAVINGS AND LOANS
SAVE
USA 18c

1911

	Issues of 1981 (continued), Perf. 11 x 10½	Un	U	PB/PNC	#	FDC	Q
	Booklet Stamp						
1896	20¢ Flag over Supreme Court (1894), single from booklet	.35	.15			1.00	
a	Booklet pane of 6	2.25	—			6.00	
b	Booklet pane of 10, June 1, 1982	4.00	—			10.00	
	Issues of 1981-84, Perf. 10 Vertically						
	Coil Stamps, Transportation Issue (See also #2123-36, 2225-26, 2228, 2231, 2252-66, 2452-53A, 2457, 2464, 2468)						
1897	1¢ Omnibus 1880s, Aug. 19, 1983	.15	.15	.55	(3)	1.00	
a	Imperf. pair	800.00		—	(3)		
1897A	2¢ Locomotive 1870s, May 20, 1982	.15	.15	.60	(3)	1.00	
e	Imperf. pair	70.00		—	(3)		
1898	3¢ Handcar 1880s, Mar. 25, 1983	.15	.15	.95	(3)	1.00	
1898A	4¢ Stagecoach 1890s, Aug. 19, 1982	.15	.15	1.65	(3)	1.00	
b	Untagged (Bureau precanceled)	.15	.15	4.75	(3)	1.00	
c	As "b," imperf. pair	750.00					
d	Imperf. pair	950.00	—				
1899	5¢ Motorcycle 1913, Oct. 10, 1983	.15	.15	1.40	(3)	1.00	
a	Imperf. pair	—					
1900	5.2¢ Sleigh 1880s, Mar. 21, 1983	.15	.15	10.00	(3)	1.00	
a	Untagged (Bureau precanceled)	.15	.15	11.00	(3)	1.00	
1901	5.9¢ Bicycle 1870s, Feb. 17, 1982	.18	.15	11.00	(3)	1.00	
a	Untagged (Bureau precanceled)	.18	.18	20.00	(3)	1.00	
b	As "a," imperf. pair	225.00		—	(2)		
1902	7.4¢ Baby Buggy 1880s, April 7, 1984	.18	.15	9.00	(3)	1.00	
a	Untagged (Bureau precanceled)	.20	.20	3.50	(3)	1.00	
1903	9.3¢ Mail Wagon 1880s, Dec. 15, 1981	.25	.15	13.00	(3)	1.00	
a	Untagged (Bureau precanceled)	.22	.22	4.00	(3)	1.00	
b	As "a," imperf. pair	140.00		—	(2)		
1904	10.9¢ Hansom Cab 1890s, Mar. 26, 1982	.24	.15	20.00	(3)	1.00	
a	Untagged (Bureau precanceled)	.24	.24	30.00	(3)	1.00	
b	As "a," imperf. pair	200.00		—	(2)		
1905	11¢ RR Caboose 1890s, Feb. 3, 1984	.24	.15	4.50	(3)	1.00	
a	Untagged (Bureau precanceled)	.24	.15	3.75	(3)	1.00	
1906	17¢ Electric Auto 1917, June 25, 1981	.32	.15	3.25	(3)	1.00	
a	Untagged (Bureau precanceled)	.35	.35	4.75	(3)	1.00	
b	Imperf. pair	165.00		—	(2)		
c	As "a," imperf. pair	650.00		—	(2)		
1907	18¢ Surrey 1890s, May 18, 1981	.34	.15	4.50	(3)	1.00	
a	Imperf. pair	120.00		—	(2)		
1908	20¢ Fire Pumper 1860s, Dec. 10, 1981	.32	.15	3.25	(3)	1.00	
a	Imperf. pair	100.00		300.00	(2)		

Values for plate # coil strips of 3 stamps for #1897-1908 are for the most common plate numbers. Other plate #s and strips of 5 stamps may have higher values.

	Issue of 1983, Express Mail Booklet Issue, Aug. 12, Perf. 10 Vertically						
1909	$9.35 Eagle and Moon, single from booklet	22.50	14.00			45.00	
a	Booklet pane of 3	62.50				125.00	

#1909 issued only in booklets. All stamps are imperf. at top and bottom or imperf. at top, bottom and right side.

	Issues of 1981 (continued), Perf. 10½ x 11						
1910	18¢ American Red Cross, May 1	.32	.15	1.35	(4)	1.00	165,175,000
	Perf. 11						
1911	18¢ Savings and Loans, May 8	.32	.15	1.40	(4)	1.00	107,240,000

223

	Issues of 1981 (continued), Perf. 11	Un	U	PB	#	FDC	Q
	Space Achievement Issue, May 21						
1912	18¢ Exploring the Moon—Moon Walk	.32	.15			1.00	42,227,375
1913	18¢ Benefiting Mankind (upper left)—Columbia Space Shuttle	.32	.15			1.00	42,227,375
1914	18¢ Benefiting Mankind (upper right)	.32	.15			1.00	42,227,375
1915	18¢ Understanding the Sun—Skylab	.32	.15			1.00	42,227,375
1916	18¢ Probing the Planets—Pioneer II	.32	.15			1.00	42,227,375
1917	18¢ Benefiting Mankind (lower left)—Columbia Space Shuttle	.32	.15			1.00	42,227,375
1918	18¢ Benefiting Mankind (lower right)	.32	.15			1.00	42,227,375
1919	18¢ Comprehending the Universe—Telescope	.32	.15			1.00	42,227,375
a	Block of 8, #1912-19	3.00	2.75	3.00	(8)	3.00	
b	As "a," imperf.	8,000.00					
1920	18¢ Professional Management, June 18	.32	.15	1.40	(4)	1.00	99,420,000
	Preservation of Wildlife Habitats Issue, June 26						
1921	18¢ Save Wetland Habitats— Great Blue Heron	.35	.15			1.00	44,732,500
1922	18¢ Save Grassland Habitats— Badger	.35	.15			1.00	44,732,500
1923	18¢ Save Mountain Habitats— Grizzly Bear	.35	.15			1.00	44,732,500
1924	18¢ Save Woodland Habitats— Ruffled Grouse	.35	.15			1.00	44,732,500
a	Block of 4, #1921-24	1.40	1.00	1.50	(4)	2.50	
1925	18¢ International Year of the Disabled, June 29	.32	.15	1.40	(4)	1.00	100,265,000
a	Vertical pair, imperf. horizontally	2,750.00					
1926	18¢ Edna St. Vincent Millay, July 10	.32	.15	1.40	(4)	1.00	99,615,000
a	Black omitted	500.00					
1927	18¢ Alcoholism, Aug. 19	.42	.15	15.00	(6)	1.00	97,535,000
a	Imperf. pair	350.00					

Which law protects individuals with disabilities?

The Americans with Disabilities Act of 1990 goes into full effect July 26, 1994, and provides legislation to eliminate discrimination against individuals with disabilities. It prevents discrimination in hiring, promotion, discharge, compensation, training and other aspects of employment. Employers must also make "reasonable accommodations" to employ people with disabilities. The landmark act is intended to give people with disabilities the same access to the job market as all other applicants. (**#1925**)

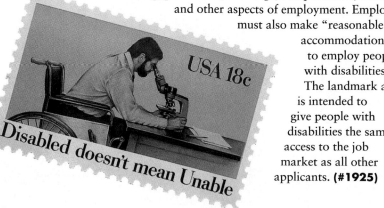

USA 18c

Disabled doesn't mean Unable

1912 1913 1914 1915 1919a
1916 1917 1918 1919

1920

1921 1922 1924a
1923 1924

1925

1927

1926

1928   1929   1931a

1930   1931

1932   1933

1934   1935   1936

1937   1938   1938a

1939   1940

1941

	Issues of 1981 (continued), Perf. 11	Un	U	PB	#	FDC	Q
	American Architecture Issue, Aug. 28						
1928	18¢ NYU Library, by Sanford White	.42	.15			1.00	41,827,000
1929	18¢ Biltmore House, by Richard Morris Hunt	.42	.15			1.00	41,827,000
1930	18¢ Palace of the Arts, by Bernard Maybeck	.42	.15			1.00	41,827,000
1931	18¢ National Farmer's Bank, by Louis Sullivan	.42	.15			1.00	41,827,000
a	Block of 4, #1928-31	1.75	1.00	1.85	(4)	2.50	
	American Sports Issue, Babe Zaharias and Bobby Jones, Sept. 22, Perf. 10½ x 11						
1932	18¢ Babe Zaharias Holding Trophy	.32	.15	1.75	(4)	1.00	101,625,000
1933	18¢ Bobby Jones Teeing off	.32	.15	1.50	(4)	1.00	99,170,000
	Perf. 11						
1934	18¢ Frederic Remington, Oct. 9	.32	.15	1.50	(4)	1.00	101,155,000
a	Vertical pair, imperf. between	250.00					
b	Brown omitted	525.00					
1935	18¢ James Hoban, Oct. 13	.32	.16	1.60	(4)	1.00	101,200,000
1936	20¢ James Hoban, Oct. 13	.35	.15	1.65	(4)	1.00	167,360,000
	American Bicentennial Issue, Yorktown-Virginia Capes, Oct. 16						
1937	18¢ Battle of Yorktown 1781	.35	.15			1.00	81,210,000
1938	18¢ Battle of the Virginia Capes 1781	.35	.15			1.00	81,210,000
a	Attached pair, #1937-38	.80	.15	1.60	(4)	1.50	
b	As "a," black omitted	550.00					
	Christmas Issue, Oct. 28						
1939	20¢ Madonna and Child, by Botticelli	.38	.15	1.60	(4)	1.00	597,720,000
a	Imperf. pair	110.00					
b	Vertical pair, imperf. horizontally	1,650.00					
1940	20¢ Felt Bear on Sleigh	.38	.15	1.60	(4)	1.00	792,600,000
a	Imperf. pair	250.00					
b	Vertical pair, imperf. horizontally	—					
1941	20¢ John Hanson, Nov. 5	.38	.15	1.60	(4)	1.00	167,130,000

How did Babe Zaharias break into golf?

Mildred Ella ("Babe") Didrikson Zaharias (1911-1956) grew up playing baseball with the boys. But it wasn't until a friend convinced Babe to play golf that she picked up the game in 1932. She quickly became a professional. Since there were only two professional tournaments for women at the time, she qualified for a men's tournament, where she met George Zaharias, whom she later married. After Zaharias turned pro in 1947, she helped found the Ladies Professional Golf Association (LPGA).

(#1932)

227

	Issues of 1981 (continued), Perf. 11	Un	U	PB/LP	#	FDC	Q
	Desert Plants Issue, Dec. 11						
1942	20¢ Barrel Cactus	.35	.15			1.00	47,890,000
1943	20¢ Agave	.35	.15			1.00	47,890,000
1944	20¢ Beavertail Cactus	.35	.15			1.00	47,890,000
1945	20¢ Saguaro	.35	.15			1.00	47,890,000
a	Block of 4, #1942-45	1.50	.15	1.60	(4)	2.50	
b	As "a," deep brown omitted	7,500.00					
c	#1945 vertical pair, imperf.	5,250.00					
	Perf. 11 x 10¹/₂						
1946	20¢ C Stamp, Oct. 11	.38	.15	1.85	(4)	1.00	
	Coil Stamp, Perf. 10 Vertically						
1947	20¢ brown Eagle (1946), Oct. 11	.60	.15	1.50	(2)	1.00	
a	Imperf. pair	2,000.00		—	(2)		
	Booklet Stamp, Perf. 11 x 10¹/₂						
1948	20¢ brown Eagle (1946), single from booklet	.38	.15			1.00	
a	Booklet pane of 10, Oct. 11	4.50	—			3.50	
	Issues of 1982, Bighorn Sheep Booklet Issue, Jan. 8, Perf. 11						
1949	20¢ Bighorn Sheep, single from booklet	.50	.15			1.00	
a	Booklet pane of 10	5.00	—			6.00	
b	As "a," imperf. between	100.00					
	#1949 issued only in booklets. All stamps are imperf. at one side or imperf. at one side and bottom.						
1950	20¢ Franklin D. Roosevelt, Jan. 30	.38	.15	1.60	(4)	1.00	163,939,200
	Perf. 11 x 10¹/₂						
1951	20¢ Love, Feb. 1	.38	.15	1.60	(4)	1.00	446,745,000
a	Perf. 11	.48	.15	2.00	(4)		
b	Imperf. pair	275.00					
c	Blue omitted	200.00					
	Perf. 11						
1952	20¢ George Washington, Feb. 22	.38	.15	1.60	(4)	1.00	180,700,000

Why do bighorn sheep ram into each other?

Bighorn sheep, which are native to North America, have huge, curved horns that may be more than four feet long. The males (called rams) weigh up to 300 pounds and are much bigger than the females (called ewes).

Males live together in groups of two to 15, while females live in separate groups with their young. During the mating season, rams often have battles with each other that can last for hours. Two or more rams charge at each other and crash their horns together. One ram finally turns away. By giving up, he recognizes the winner as the stronger animal. Usually, only the strongest rams mate with the ewes. **(#1949)**

1942   1943   1945   1945a

1944

1946

1949

1950   1951

1952

229

Alabama
USA 20c
Yellowhammer &
Camellia

1953

Alaska
USA 20c
Willow Ptarmigan &
Forget-Me-Not

1954

Arizona
USA 20c
Cactus Wren &
Saguaro Cactus Blossom

1955

Arkansas
USA 20c
Mockingbird &
Apple Blossom

1956

California
USA 20c
California Quail &
California Poppy

1957

Colorado
USA 20c
Lark Bunting &
Rocky Mountain Columbine

1958

Connecticut
USA 20c
Robin &
Mountain Laurel

1959

Delaware
USA 20c
Blue Hen Chicken &
Peach Blossom

1960

Florida
USA 20c
Mockingbird &
Orange Blossom

1961

Georgia
USA 20c
Brown Thrasher &
Cherokee Rose

1962

Hawaii
USA 20c
Hawaiian Goose &
Hibiscus

1963

Idaho
USA 20c
Mountain Bluebird &
Syringa

1964

Illinois
USA 20c
Cardinal &
Violet

1965

Indiana
USA 20c
Cardinal &
Peony

1966

Iowa
USA 20c
Eastern Goldfinch &
Wild Rose

1967

Kansas
USA 20c
Western Meadowlark &
Sunflower

1968

Kentucky
USA 20c
Cardinal &
Goldenrod

1969

Louisiana
USA 20c
Brown Pelican &
Magnolia

1970

Maine
USA 20c
Chickadee &
White Pine Cone and Tassel

1971

Maryland
USA 20c
Baltimore Oriole &
Black-Eyed Susan

1972

Massachusetts
USA 20c
Black-Capped Chickadee &
Mayflower

1973

Michigan
USA 20c
Robin &
Apple Blossom

1974

Minnesota
USA 20c
Common Loon &
Showy Lady Slipper

1975

Mississippi
USA 20c
Mockingbird &
Magnolia

1976

Missouri
USA 20c
Eastern Bluebird &
Red Hawthorn

1977

230

	Issues of 1982 (continued), Perf. 10¹/₂ x 11	Un	U	FDC	Q
	State Birds & Flowers Issue, Apr. 14				
1953	20¢ Alabama	.40	.25	1.25	13,339,000
1954	20¢ Alaska	.40	.25	1.25	13,339,000
1955	20¢ Arizona	.40	.25	1.25	13,339,000
1956	20¢ Arkansas	.40	.25	1.25	13,339,000
1957	20¢ California	.40	.25	1.25	13,339,000
1958	20¢ Colorado	.40	.25	1.25	13,339,000
1959	20¢ Connecticut	.40	.25	1.25	13,339,000
1960	20¢ Delaware	.40	.25	1.25	13,339,000
1961	20¢ Florida	.40	.25	1.25	13,339,000
1962	20¢ Georgia	.40	.25	1.25	13,339,000
1963	20¢ Hawaii	.40	.25	1.25	13,339,000
1964	20¢ Idaho	.40	.25	1.25	13,339,000
1965	20¢ Illinois	.40	.25	1.25	13,339,000
1966	20¢ Indiana	.40	.25	1.25	13,339,000
1967	20¢ Iowa	.40	.25	1.25	13,339,000
1968	20¢ Kansas	.40	.25	1.25	13,339,000
1969	20¢ Kentucky	.40	.25	1.25	13,339,000
1970	20¢ Louisiana	.40	.25	1.25	13,339,000
1971	20¢ Maine	.40	.25	1.25	13,339,000
1972	20¢ Maryland	.40	.25	1.25	13,339,000
1973	20¢ Massachusetts	.40	.25	1.25	13,339,000
1974	20¢ Michigan	.40	.25	1.25	13,339,000
1975	20¢ Minnesota	.40	.25	1.25	13,339,000
1976	20¢ Mississippi	.40	.25	1.25	13,339,000
1977	20¢ Missouri	.40	.25	1.25	13,339,000

What do the magnolia and the pelican have in common?

Both the magnolia and the brown pelican are native to the State of Louisiana. The magnolia has been the Louisiana state flower since 1900. Bronze magnolias surround Louisiana's state capitol building.

Louisiana adopted the brown pelican as its state bird in 1966. Early in the century, brown pelicans were quite common along the gulf shore and inland bays of the state. Pesticides and other environmental hazards caused the birds to nearly disappear in the early 1960s.
(#1970)

		Un	U	PB	#	FDC	Q
	Issues of 1982 (continued), Perf. 10¹/₂ x 11						
	State Birds & Flowers Issue (continued), Apr. 14						
1978	20¢ Montana	.40	.25			1.25	13,339,000
1979	20¢ Nebraska	.40	.25			1.25	13,339,000
1980	20¢ Nevada	.40	.25			1.25	13,339,000
1981	20¢ New Hampshire	.40	.25			1.25	13,339,000
1982	20¢ New Jersey	.40	.25			1.25	13,339,000
1983	20¢ New Mexico	.40	.25			1.25	13,339,000
1984	20¢ New York	.40	.25			1.25	13,339,000
1985	20¢ North Carolina	.40	.25			1.25	13,339,000
1986	20¢ North Dakota	.40	.25			1.25	13,339,000
1987	20¢ Ohio	.40	.25			1.25	13,339,000
1988	20¢ Oklahoma	.40	.25			1.25	13,339,000
1989	20¢ Oregon	.40	.25			1.25	13,339,000
1990	20¢ Pennsylvania	.40	.25			1.25	13,339,000
1991	20¢ Rhode Island	.40	.25			1.25	13,339,000
1992	20¢ South Carolina	.40	.25			1.25	13,339,000
1993	20¢ South Dakota	.40	.25			1.25	13,339,000
1994	20¢ Tennessee	.40	.25			1.25	13,339,000
1995	20¢ Texas	.40	.25			1.25	13,339,000
1996	20¢ Utah	.40	.25			1.25	13,339,000
1997	20¢ Vermont	.40	.25			1.25	13,339,000
1998	20¢ Virginia	.40	.25			1.25	13,339,000
1999	20¢ Washington	.40	.25			1.25	13,339,000
2000	20¢ West Virginia	.40	.25			1.25	13,339,000
2001	20¢ Wisconsin	.40	.25			1.25	13,339,000
2002	20¢ Wyoming	.40	.25			1.25	13,339,000
a	Any single, perf. 11	.45	.30				
b	Pane of 50	22.50	—	22.50	(50)	30.00	
c	Pane of 50, perf. 11	25.00	—	25.00	(50)		
d	Pane of 50, imperf.	—					

What is New Hampshire's favorite color?

New Hampshire's favorite color must be purple. Both the state flower and state bird are that color.

The purple lilac, adopted as the state flower in 1919, beat out eight other flowers suggested for the honor. Purple lilacs grow on bushes in the state. The lavender-colored blossoms have a beautiful color and fragrance.

The purple finch, a small songbird, became the state bird in 1957. The purple finch is about 6 inches long and eats mostly weeds and seeds. The bird has reddish-purple feathers and dark brown coloring on its back, wings and tail. **(#1981)**

2003

2004

2005

2006
2008

2007
2009

2009a

2010

2012

2011

2013

2014

2015

2016

2017

2018

2019
2021

2020
2022

2022a

	Issues of 1982 (continued), Perf. 11	Un	U	PB/PNC	#	FDC	Q
2003	20¢ USA/The Netherlands, Apr. 20	.38	.15	3.50	(6)	1.00	109,245,000
a	Imperf. pair	425.00					
2004	20¢ Library of Congress, Apr. 21	.38	.15	1.60	(4)	1.00	112,535,000
	Coil Stamp, Perf. 10 Vertically						
2005	20¢ Consumer Education, Apr. 27	.75	.15	37.50	(3)	1.00	
a	Imperf. pair	125.00		400.00	(2)		

Value for plate no. coil strip of 3 stamps is for most common plate nos. Other plate nos. and strips of 5 stamps may have higher values.

		Un	U	PB/PNC	#	FDC	Q
	Knoxville World's Fair Issue, Apr. 29, Perf. 11						
2006	20¢ Solar Energy	.40	.15			1.00	31,160,000
2007	20¢ Synthetic Fuels	.40	.15				31,160,000
2008	20¢ Breeder Reactor	.40	.15				31,160,000
2009	20¢ Fossil Fuels	.40	.15			1.00	31,160,000
a	Block of 4, #2006-09	1.75	1.00	1.65	(4)	2.50	
2010	20¢ Horatio Alger, Apr. 30	.38	.15	1.60	(4)	1.00	107,605,000
2011	20¢ Aging Together, May 21	.38	.15	1.60	(4)	1.00	173,160,000
	Performing Arts Issue, The Barrymores, June 8						
2012	20¢ Portraits of John, Ethel and Lionel Barrymore	.38	.15	1.60	(4)	1.00	107,285,000
2013	20¢ Dr. Mary Walker, June 10	.38	.15	1.60	(4)	1.00	109,040,000
2014	20¢ International Peace Garden, June 30	.38	.15	1.60	(4)	1.00	183,270,000
a	Black and green omitted	225.00					
2015	20¢ America's Libraries, July 13	.38	.15	1.60	(4)	1.00	169,495,000
a	Vertical pair, imperf. horizontally	300.00					
	Black Heritage Issue, Jackie Robinson, Aug. 2, Perf. 10½ x 11						
2016	20¢ Jackie Robinson Portrait and Robinson Stealing Home Plate	1.00	.15	4.75	(4)	2.00	164,235,000
	Perf. 11						
2017	20¢ Touro Synagogue, Aug. 22	.38	.15	11.50	(20)	1.00	110,130,000
a	Imperf. pair	1,000.00					
2018	20¢ Wolf Trap Farm Park, Sept. 1	.38	.15	1.60	(4)	1.00	110,995,000
	American Architecture Issue, Sept. 30						
2019	20¢ Fallingwater, by Frank Lloyd Wright	.38	.15			1.00	41,335,000
2020	20¢ Illinois Institute of Technology, by Mies van der Rohe	.38	.15			1.00	41,335,000
2021	20¢ Gropius House, by Walter Gropius	.38	.15			1.00	41,335,000
2022	20¢ Dulles Airport by Eeno Saarinen	.38	.15				41,335,000
a	Block of 4, #2019-22	1.90	1.00	1.65	(4)	2.50	

The stamp listings contain a number of "a," "b," "c," etc. additions which include recognized varieties and errors. These listings are as complete as space permits.

235

	Issues of 1982 (continued), Perf. 11	Un	U	PB	#	FDC	Q
2023	20¢ St. Francis of Assisi, Oct. 7	.38	.15	1.60	(4)	1.00	174,180,000
2024	20¢ Ponce de Leon, Oct. 12	.38	.15	3.25	(6)	1.00	110,261,000
a	Imperf. pair	700.00					
	Christmas Issue						
2025	13¢ Puppy and Kitten, Nov. 3	.26	.15	1.05	(4)	1.00	234,010,000
a	Imperf. pair	500.00					
2026	20¢ Madonna and Child, by Tiepolo, Oct. 28	.38	.15	11.00	(20)	1.00	703,295,000
a	Imperf. pair	150.00					
b	Horizontal pair, imperf. vertically	—					
c	Vertical pair, imperf. horizontally	—					
	Seasons Greetings Issue, Oct. 28						
2027	20¢ Children Sledding	.55	.15			1.00	197,220,000
2028	20¢ Children Building a Snowman	.55	.15			1.00	197,220,000
2029	20¢ Children Skating	.55	.15			1.00	197,220,000
2030	20¢ Children Trimming a Tree	.55	.15			1.00	197,220,000
a	Block of 4, #2027-30	2.35	1.00	2.00	(4)	2.50	
b	As "a," imperf.	3,000.00					
c	As "a," imperf. horizontally	—					
	Issues of 1983						
2031	20¢ Science & Industry, Jan. 19	.38	.15	1.60	(4)	1.00	118,555,000
a	Black omitted	1,400.00					
	Balloons Issue, March 31						
2032	20¢ Intrepid, 1861	.38	.15			1.00	56,557,000
2033	20¢ Hot Air Ballooning (wording lower right)	.38	.15			1.00	56,557,000
2034	20¢ Hot Air Ballooning (wording upper left)	.38	.15			1.00	56,557,000
2035	20¢ Explorer II, 1935	.38	.15			1.00	56,557,000
a	Block of 4, #2032-35	1.65	1.00	1.65	(4)	2.50	
b	As "a," imperf.	3,500.00					
2036	20¢ U.S./Sweden Treaty, Mar. 24	.38	.15	1.60	(4)	1.00	118,225,000
2037	20¢ Civilian Conservation Corps, Apr. 5	.38	.15	1.60	(4)	1.00	114,290,000
a	Imperf. pair	2,500.00					
2038	20¢ Joseph Priestley, Apr. 13	.38	.15	1.60	(4)	1.00	165,000,000
2039	20¢ Voluntarism, Apr. 20	.40	.15	3.00	(6)	1.00	120,430,000
a	Imperf. pair	850.00					
2040	20¢ Concord—German Immigration, Apr. 29	.38	.15	1.60	(4)	1.00	117,025,000

What did Ponce de Leon discover?

Ponce de Leon (1474-1521) was a Spanish explorer who tried to find the legendary Fountain of Youth that, according to folklore, was the Water of Life in the Garden of Eden. In 1513, Ponce de Leon landed in Florida, which he claimed for Spain. He named the land Florida for the state's many flowers (*florida* is a Spanish word that means "flowery"). (**#2024**)

2023

2024

2025

2026

2027

2029

2028

2030

2030a

2031

2032

2033

2034

2035

2035a

2036

2037

2038

2039

2040

1983

2041

2042

2043

2044

2045

2046

2047

2048
2050

2049
2051

2051a

2052

2053

2055
2057

2056
2058

2058a

2054

	Issues of 1983 (continued), Perf. 11	Un	U	PB	#	FDC	Q
2041	20¢ Brooklyn Bridge, May 17	.38	.15	1.60	(4)	1.00	181,700,000
2042	20¢ Tennessee Valley Authority, May 18	.40	.15	11.50	(20)	1.00	114,250,000
2043	20¢ Physical Fitness, May 14	.38	.15	3.00	(6)	1.00	111,775,000
	Black Heritage Issue, Scott Joplin, June 9						
2044	20¢ Scott Joplin Portrait and Joplin Playing the Piano	.40	.15	1.60	(4)	1.00	115,200,000
a	Imperf. pair	500.00					
2045	20¢ Medal of Honor, June 7	.40	.15	1.65	(4)	1.00	108,820,000
a	Red omitted	300.00					
	American Sports Issue, Babe Ruth, July 6, Perf. 10½ x 11						
2046	20¢ Babe Ruth Hitting a Home Run	1.00	.15	4.75	(4)	2.50	184,950,000
	Literary Arts Issue, Nathaniel Hawthorne, July 8, Perf. 11						
2047	20¢ Nathaniel Hawthorne, by Cephus Giovanni Thompson	.40	.15	1.60	(4)	1.00	110,925,000
	Olympic Summer Games Issue, July 28 (See also #2082-85, C101-12)						
2048	13¢ Discus Thrower	.28	.15			1.00	98,856,000
2049	13¢ High Jumper	.28	.15			1.00	98,856,000
2050	13¢ Archer	.28	.15			1.00	98,856,000
2051	13¢ Boxers	.28	.15			1.00	98,856,000
a	Block of 4, #2048-51	1.20	.80	1.30	(4)	2.50	
	American Bicentennial Issue, Treaty of Paris, Sept. 2						
2052	20¢ Signing of Treaty of Paris (John Adams, Benjamin Franklin and John Jay observing David Hartley), by Benjamin West	.38	.15	1.60	(4)	1.00	104,340,000
2053	20¢ Civil Service, Sept. 9	.40	.15	3.00	(6)	1.00	114,725,000
2054	20¢ Metropolitan Opera, Sept. 14	.38	.15	1.65	(4)	1.00	112,525,000
	American Inventors Issue, Sept. 21						
2055	20¢ Charles Steinmetz and Curve on Graph	.45	.15			1.00	48,263,750
2056	20¢ Edwin Armstrong and Frequency Modulator	.45	.15			1.00	48,263,750
2057	20¢ Nikola Tesla and Induction Motor	.45	.15			1.00	48,263,750
2058	20¢ Philo T. Farnsworth and First Television Camera	.45	.15			1.00	48,263,750
a	Block of 4, #2055-58	1.60	1.00	1.65	(4)	2.50	
b	As "a," black omitted	450.00					

What type of music did Scott Joplin play?

Scott Joplin (1868-1917) was an African-American pianist and composer who was known for playing ragtime—lively, rhythmic tunes written chiefly for the piano. Ragtime is a distinctly American form of music. Joplin wrote about 50 piano rags and also wrote two operas and a few waltzes and marches.

(#2044)

	Issues of 1983 (continued), Perf. 11	Un	U	PB	#	FDC	Q
	Streetcars Issue, Oct. 8						
2059	20¢ First American Streetcar	.40	.15			1.00	51,931,250
2060	20¢ Early Electric Streetcar	.40	.15			1.00	51,931,250
2061	20¢ "Bobtail" Horsecar	.40	.15			1.00	51,931,250
2062	20¢ St. Charles Streetcar	.40	.15			1.00	51,931,250
a	Block of 4, #2059-62	1.70	1.00	1.65	(4)	2.50	
b	As "a," black omitted	475.00					
c	As "a," black omitted on #2059, 2061	—					
	Christmas Issue, Oct. 28						
2063	20¢ Niccolini-Cowper Madonna, by Raphael	.38	.15	1.65	(4)	1.00	715,975,000
2064	20¢ Santa Claus	.38	.15	3.00	(6)	1.00	848,525,000
a	Imperf. pair	165.00					
2065	20¢ Martin Luther, Nov. 11	.38	.15	1.60	(4)	1.50	165,000,000
	Issues of 1984						
2066	20¢ 25th Anniversary of Alaska Statehood, Jan. 3	.38	.15	1.65	(4)	1.00	120,000,000
	Winter Olympic Games Issue, Jan. 6, Perf. 10½ x 11						
2067	20¢ Ice Dancing	.45	.15			1.00	79,918,750
2068	20¢ Alpine Skiing	.45	.15			1.00	79,918,750
2069	20¢ Nordic Skiing	.45	.15			1.00	79,918,750
2070	20¢ Hockey	.45	.15				79,918,750
a	Block of 4, #2067-70	1.90	1.00	1.95	(4)	2.50	
	Perf. 11						
2071	20¢ Federal Deposit Insurance Corporation, Jan. 12	.38	.15	1.60	(4)	1.00	103,975,000

What does the Federal Deposit Insurance Corporation (FDIC) protect?

In 1933, during the Great Depression, many banks failed and people lost their savings. To make sure that never happened again, the Federal Reserve Act of 1933 created an independent government corporation, the FDIC, to insure bank deposits and regulate certain banking practices. The FDIC insures deposits up to $100,000 at almost all U.S. banks and savings and loan associations.

The funds to support the FDIC come from fees paid by insured institutions and from earnings on U.S. government securities. **(#2071)**

2059   **2060**   **2062a**

2061   **2062**

2064

2063   **2065**

2066   **2071**

2067   **2068**   **2070a**

2072 **2073** **2074** **2075**

2080

2081

2076 **2077** **2079a**
2078 **2079**

2086

2087

2082 **2083** **2085a**
2084 **2085**

	Issues of 1984 (continued), Perf. 11 x 10½	Un	U	PB	#	FDC	Q
2072	20¢ Love, Jan. 31	.38	.15	11.50	(20)	1.00	554,675,000
a	Horizontal pair, imperf. vertically	200.00					
	Black Heritage Issue, Carter G. Woodson, Feb. 1, Perf. 11						
2073	20¢ Carter G. Woodson Holding History Book	.42	.15	1.80	(4)	1.00	120,000,000
a	Horizontal pair, imperf. vertically	1,200.00					
2074	20¢ Soil and Water Conservation, Feb. 6	.38	.15	1.75	(4)	1.00	106,975,000
2075	20¢ 50th Anniversary of Credit Union Act, Feb. 10	.38	.15	1.60	(4)	1.00	107,325,000
	Orchids Issue, Mar. 5						
2076	20¢ Wild Pink	.42	.15			1.00	76,728,000
2077	20¢ Yellow Lady's-Slipper	.42	.15			1.00	76,728,000
2078	20¢ Spreading Pogonia	.42	.15			1.00	76,728,000
2079	20¢ Pacific Calypso	.42	.15			1.00	76,728,000
a	Block of 4, #2076-79	1.80	1.00	1.65	(4)	2.50	
2080	20¢ 25th Anniversary of Hawaii Statehood, Mar. 12	.40	.15	1.60	(4)	1.00	120,000,000
2081	20¢ National Archives, Apr. 16	.40	.15	1.60	(4)	1.00	108,000,000
	Olympic Summer Games Issue, May 4 (See also #2048-52, C101-12)						
2082	20¢ Diving	.62	.15			1.00	78,337,500
2083	20¢ Long Jump	.62	.15			1.00	78,337,500
2084	20¢ Wrestling	.62	.15			1.00	78,337,500
2085	20¢ Kayak	.62	.15			1.00	78,337,500
a	Block of 4, #2082-85	2.75	1.00	3.00	(4)	2.50	
2086	20¢ Louisiana World Exposition, May 11	.38	.15	1.60	(4)	1.00	130,320,000
2087	20¢ Health Research, May 17	.40	.15	1.60	(4)	1.00	120,000,000

How did Carter Woodson influence the study of black history?

A historian and educator, Carter Godwin Woodson (1875-1950) grew up in poverty in Virginia. His formal schooling was postponed until he was almost 20, and his college education was spread over many years as he worked his way through school. Nevertheless, Woodson eventually earned his doctorate from Harvard in 1912. Woodson transformed black studies into an academically respectable field of study and urged other blacks to study their African-American heritage. His work changed the field, freeing it from the traditional interpretations of white historians. In 1915, Woodson founded the Association for the Study of Negro Life. He also wrote many books on black history and organized a publishing group to publish other works on black culture. **(#2073)**

243

	Issues of 1984 (continued), Perf. 11	Un	U	PB	#	FDC	Q
	Performing Arts Issue, Douglas Fairbanks, May 23						
2088	20¢ Douglas Fairbanks Portrait and Fairbanks in Swashbuckling Pirate Role	.38	.15	11.50	(20)	1.00	117,050,000
	American Sports Issue, Jim Thorpe, May 24						
2089	20¢ Jim Thorpe on Football Field	.40	.15	1.75	(4)	1.50	115,725,000
	Performing Arts Issue, John McCormack, June 6						
2090	20¢ John McCormack Portrait and McCormack in Tenor Role	.40	.15	1.75	(4)	1.00	116,600,000
2091	20¢ 25th Anniversary of St. Lawrence Seaway, June 26	.40	.15	1.60	(4)	1.00	120,000,000
2092	20¢ Migratory Bird Hunting and Preservation Act, July 2	.60	.15	1.60	(4)	1.00	123,575,000
a	Horizontal pair, imperf. vertically	500.00					
2093	20¢ Roanoke Voyages, July 13	.40	.15	1.60	(4)	1.00	120,000,000
	Pair with full horizontal gutter between	—					
	Literary Arts Issue, Herman Melville, Aug. 1						
2094	20¢ Herman Melville	.38	.15	1.60	(4)	1.00	117,125,000
2095	20¢ Horace Moses, Aug. 6	.45	.15	3.00	(6)	1.00	117,225,000
2096	20¢ Smokey the Bear, Aug. 13	.38	.15	1.75	(4)	1.00	95,525,000
a	Horizontal pair, imperf. between	300.00					
b	Vertical pair, imperf. between	200.00					
c	Block of 4, imperf. between vertically and horizontally	3,500.00					
	American Sports Issue, Roberto Clemente, Aug. 17						
2097	20¢ Roberto Clemente Wearing Pittsburgh Pirates Cap, Puerto Rican Flag in Background	1.00	.15	5.00	(4)	2.00	119,125,000
a	Horizontal pair, imperf. vertically	1,600.00					
	American Dogs Issue, Sept. 7						
2098	20¢ Beagle and Boston Terrier	.40	.15			1.00	54,065,000
2099	20¢ Chesapeake Bay Retriever and Cocker Spaniel	.40	.15			1.00	54,065,000
2100	20¢ Alaskan Malamute and Collie	.40	.15			1.00	54,065,000
2101	20¢ Black and Tan Coonhound and American Foxhound	.40	.15			1.00	54,065,000
a	Block of 4, #2098-2101	1.75	1.00	1.65	(4)	2.50	

For which team did Roberto Clemente play?

The Pittsburgh Pirates were very lucky when they signed Roberto Walker Clemente (1934-1972), one of the greatest baseball players of all time. During his 18-year career, he won four National League batting titles, won the league's Most Valuable Player award in 1966, and played on 12 National League All-Star teams. Clemente helped lead the Pittsburgh Pirates to World Series victories in 1960 and 1971. In 1972, Clemente became the 11th player in major league history to get 3,000 hits and in 1973, he was named to the National Baseball Hall of Fame. **(#2097)**

2088   2089   2090

2091   2092

2093

2094   2095   2096   2097

2098   2099   2101a
2100   2101

2102

2103

2104

2105

2106

2107

2108

2109

2110

2111

2114

2115b

2116

	Issues of 1984 (continued), Perf. 11	Un	U	PB/PNC	#	FDC	Q
2102	20¢ Crime Prevention, Sept. 26	.38	.15	1.70	(4)	1.00	120,000,000
2103	20¢ Hispanic Americans, Oct. 31	.38	.15	1.60	(4)	1.00	108,140,000
a	Vertical pair, imperf. horizontally	1,500.00					
2104	20¢ Family Unity, Oct. 1	.40	.15	12.00	(20)	1.00	117,625,000
a	Horizontal pair, imperf. vertically	600.00					
2105	20¢ Eleanor Roosevelt, Oct. 11	.38	.15	1.60	(4)	1.00	112,896,000
2106	20¢ A Nation of Readers, Oct. 16	.38	.15	1.60	(4)	1.00	116,500,000
	Christmas Issue, Oct. 30						
2107	20¢ Madonna and Child, by Fra Filippo Lippi	.40	.15	1.70	(4)	1.00	751,300,000
2108	20¢ Santa Claus	.40	.15	1.70	(4)	1.00	786,225,000
a	Horizontal pair, imperf. vertically	1,250.00					
	Perf. 10½						
2109	20¢ Vietnam Veterans' Memorial, Nov. 10	.40	.15	1.60	(4)	1.00	105,300,000
	Issues of 1985, Perf. 11						
	Performing Arts Issue, Jerome Kern, Jan. 23						
2110	22¢ Jerome Kern Portrait and Kern Studying Sheet Music	.40	.15	1.75	(4)	1.00	124,500,000
2111	22¢ D Stamp, Feb. 1	.60	.15	4.50	(6)	1.00	
a	Imperf. pair	75.00					
b	Vertical pair, imperf. horizontally	1,350.00					
	Coil Stamp, Perf. 10 Vertically						
2112	22¢ green Eagle (2111), Feb. 1	.60	.15	6.25	(3)	1.00	
a	Imperf. pair	50.00					
	Booklet Stamp, Perf. 11						
2113	22¢ green Eagle (2111), single from booklet	.80	.15			1.00	
a	Booklet pane of 10, Feb. 1	8.50				7.50	
b	As "a," imperf. between horizontally	—					
	Issues of 1985-87, Flag Over Capitol Issue						
2114	22¢ Flag Over Capitol, Mar. 29, 1985	.40	.15	1.80	(4)	1.00	
	Pair with full horizontal gutter between	—					
	Coil Stamp, Perf. 10 Vertically						
2115	22¢ Flag Over Capitol (2114), Mar. 29, 1985	.40	.15	4.50	(3)	1.00	
a	Imperf. pair	12.50					
b	Inscribed "T" at bottom, May 23, 1987	.48	.15	4.50	(3)	1.00	
c	Black field of stars	—	—				
	#2115b issued for test on prephosphored paper. Paper is whiter and colors are brighter than on #2115.						
	Booklet Stamp, Perf. 10 Horizontally						
2116	22¢ Flag over Capitol, single from booklet	.48	.15			1.00	
a	Booklet pane of 5, Mar. 29, 1985	2.50	—			3.50	
	#2116 issued only in booklets. All stamps are imperf. at both sides or imperf. at both sides and bottom.						

	Issues of 1985 (continued), Perf. 10 vertically	Un	U	PNC	#	FDC
	Seashells Booklet Issue, Apr. 4					
2117	22¢ Frilled Dogwinkle	.40	.15			1.00
2118	22¢ Reticulated Helmet	.40	.15			1.00
2119	22¢ New England Neptune	.40	.15			1.00
2120	22¢ Calico Scallop	.40	.15			1.00
2121	22¢ Lightning Whelk	.40	.15			1.00
a	Booklet pane of 10	4.00	—			7.50
b	As "a," violet omitted	750.00				
c	As "a," imperf. between vertically	650.00				
e	Strip of 5, #2117-21	2.00	—			
	Express Mail Booklet Issue, Apr. 29					
2122	$10.75 Eagle and Moon, booklet single	17.50	6.75			40.00
a	Booklet pane of 3	52.50	—			95.00
	#2122 issued only in booklets. All stamps are imperf. at top and bottom or at top, bottom and one side.					
	Issues of 1985-89, Coil Stamps, Transportation Issue (See also #1897-1908, 2225-26, 2228, 2231, 2252-66, 2452-53A, 2457, 2464, 2468)					
2123	3.4¢ School Bus 1920s, June 8, 1985	.15	.15	1.10	(3)	1.00
a	Untagged (Bureau precanceled)	.15	.15	5.50	(3)	1.00
2124	4.9¢ Buckboard 1880s, June 21, 1985	.15	.15	1.25	(3)	1.00
a	Untagged (Bureau precanceled)	.16	.16	1.75	(3)	
2125	5.5¢ Star Route Truck 1910s, Nov. 1, 1986	.15	.15	1.90	(3)	1.00
a	Untagged (Bureau precanceled)	.15	.15	2.25	(3)	1.00
2126	6¢ Tricycle 1880s, May 6, 1985	.15	.15	1.50	(3)	1.00
a	Untagged (Bureau precanceled)	.15	.15	2.25	(3)	
b	As "a," imperf. pair	200.00				
2127	7.1¢ Tractor 1920s, Feb. 6, 1987	.15	.15	2.75	(3)	1.00
a	Untagged (Bureau precanceled "Nonprofit org.")	.15	.15	2.75	(3)	5.00
a	Untagged (Bureau precanceled "Nonprofit 5-Digit ZIP + 4"), May 26, 1989	.15	.15	2.75	(3)	1.00
2128	8.3¢ Ambulance 1860s, June 21, 1985	.18	.15	1.75	(3)	1.00
a	Untagged (Bureau precanceled)	.18	.18	2.00	(3)	
2129	8.5¢ Tow Truck 1920s, Jan. 24, 1987	.16	.15	2.75	(3)	1.00
a	Untagged (Bureau precanceled)	.16	.16	3.00	(3)	
2130	10.1¢ Oil Wagon 1890s, Apr. 18, 1985	.22	.15	2.75	(3)	1.00
a	Untagged (Bureau precanceled, black)	.22	.22	3.25	(3)	1.00
a	Untagged (Bureau precanceled, red)	.22	.22	2.75	(3)	1.00
b	As "a," black precancel, imperf. pair	15.00				
b	As "a," red precancel, imperf. pair	15.00				
2131	11¢ Stutz Bearcat 1933, June 11, 1985	.22	.15	1.90	(3)	1.00
2132	12¢ Stanley Steamer 1909, Apr. 2, 1985	.24	.15	2.25	(3)	1.00
a	Untagged (Bureau precanceled)	.24	.24	2.75	(3)	
b	As "a," type II	.24	.24	18.00	(3)	
	Type II has "Stanley Steamer 1909" ½mm shorter (17½mm) than #2132 (18mm).					
2133	12.5¢ Pushcart 1880s, Apr. 18, 1985	.25	.15	2.75	(3)	1.25
a	Untagged (Bureau precanceled)	.25	.25	3.50	(3)	
b	As "a," imperf. pair	50.00				
2134	14¢ Iceboat 1880s, Mar. 23, 1985	.28	.15	2.50	(3)	1.25
a	Imperf. pair	80.00				
2135	17¢ Dog Sled 1920s, Aug. 20, 1986	.30	.15	3.00	(3)	1.25
a	Imperf. pair	600.00				
2136	25¢ Bread Wagon 1880s, Nov. 22, 1986	.45	.15	4.25	(3)	1.25
a	Imperf. pair	12.50				

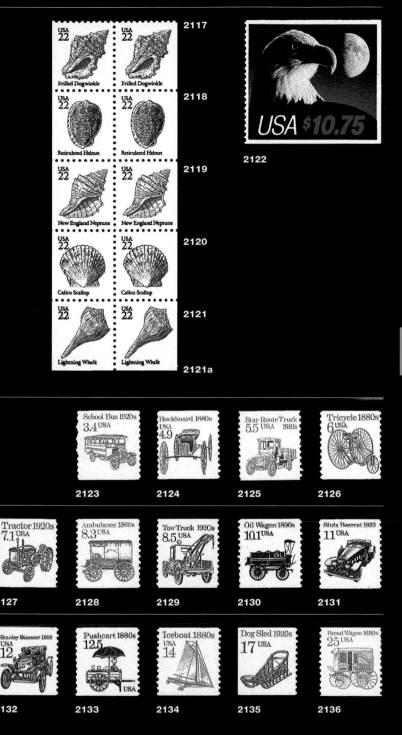

2117 Frilled Dogwinkle

2118 Reticulated Helmet

2119 New England Neptune

2120 Calico Scallop

2121 Lightning Whelk

2121a

2122

School Bus 1920s 3.4 USA — 2123

Buckboard 1880s USA 4.9 — 2124

Star Route Truck 5.5 USA 1910s — 2125

Tricycle 1880s 6 USA — 2126

Tractor 1920s 7.1 USA — 2127

Ambulance 1860s 8.3 USA — 2128

Tow Truck 1920s 8.5 USA — 2129

Oil Wagon 1890s 10.1 USA — 2130

Stutz Bearcat 1933 11 USA — 2131

Stanley Steamer 1909 USA 12 — 2132

Pushcart 1880s 12.5 USA — 2133

Iceboat 1880s USA 14 — 2134

Dog Sled 1920s 17 USA — 2135

Bread Wagon 1880s 25 USA — 2136

2137

2138

2140

2139

2141

2141a

2142

2143

2144

2145

2146

2147

2149

2150

2152

2153

	Issues of 1985 (continued), Perf. 11	Un	U	PB/PNC	#	FDC	Q
	Black Heritage Issue, Mary McLeod Bethune, Mar. 5						
2137	22¢ Mary McLeod Bethune Portrait	.42	.15	1.70	(4)	1.00	120,000,000
	American Folk Art Issue, Duck Decoys, Mar. 22						
2138	22¢ Broadbill Decoy	.60	.15			1.00	75,000,000
2139	22¢ Mallard Decoy	.60	.15			1.00	75,000,000
2140	22¢ Canvasback Decoy	.60	.15			1.00	75,000,000
2141	22¢ Redhead Decoy	.60	.15			1.00	75,000,000
a	Block of 4, #2138-41	2.65	1.00	2.20	(4)	2.75	
2142	22¢ Winter Special Olympics, Mar. 25	.40	.15	1.70	(4)	1.00	120,580,000
a	Vertical pair, imperf. horizontally	750.00					
2143	22¢ Love, Apr. 17	.40	.15	1.70	(4)	1.00	729,700,000
a	Imperf. pair	1,750.00					
2144	22¢ Rural Electrification Administration, May 11	.45	.15	14.00	(20)	1.00	124,750,000
2145	22¢ AMERIPEX '86, May 25	.40	.15	1.70	(4)	1.00	203,496,000
a	Red, black and blue omitted	225.00					
b	Red and black omitted	1,250.00					
2146	22¢ Abigail Adams, June 14	.40	.15	1.80	(4)	1.00	126,325,000
a	Imperf. pair	300.00					
2147	22¢ Frederic A. Bartholdi, July 18	.40	.15	1.80	(4)	1.00	130,000,000
2148	Not assigned						
	Coil Stamps, Perf. 10 Vertically						
2149	18¢ George Washington, Washington Monument, Nov. 6	.32	.15	3.00	(3)	1.25	
a	Untagged (Bureau precanceled)	.35	.35	3.75	(3)		
b	Imperf. pair	950.00					
c	As "a," imperf. pair	700.00		5.00	(3)		
2150	21.1¢ Sealed Envelopes, Oct. 22	.40	.15	3.50	(3)	1.25	
a	Untagged (Bureau precanceled)	.38	.38	4.00	(3)		
2151	Not assigned						
	Perf. 11						
2152	22¢ Korean War Veterans, July 26	.42	.15	1.70	(4)	1.00	119,975,000
2153	22¢ Social Security Act, 50th Anniversary Aug. 14	.42	.15	1.70	(4)	1.00	120,000,000

Whose face is on the Statue of Liberty?

Frederic Auguste Bartholdi (1834-1904) studied architecture, painting and sculpture in Paris. He specialized in creating enormous sculptures glorifying French nationalism and the friendship between France and the United States. When Bartholdi traveled to Egypt in 1856, he was influenced by the colossal monuments of ancient Egypt. The Statue of Liberty was also built on a colossal scale; in fact, it was the largest statue built since ancient times. Bartholdi modeled the stately, kindly face after the face of his mother. (**#2147**)

F.A. Bartholdi, Statue of Liberty Sculptor

USA 22

251

	Issues of 1985 (continued), Perf. 11	Un	U	PB	#	FDC	Q
2154	22¢ World War I Veterans, Aug. 26	.45	.15	1.70	(4)	1.00	119,975,000
	American Horses Issue, Sept. 25						
2155	22¢ Quarter Horse	.75	.15			1.00	36,985,000
2156	22¢ Morgan	.75	.15			1.00	36,985,000
2157	22¢ Saddlebred	.75	.15			1.00	36,985,000
2158	22¢ Appaloosa	.75	.15			1.00	36,985,000
a	Block of 4, #2155-58	3.40	1.00	2.20	(4)	2.50	
2159	22¢ Public Education, Oct. 1	.42	.15	1.70	(4)	1.00	120,000,000
	International Youth Year Issue, Oct. 7						
2160	22¢ YMCA Youth Camping	.50	.15			1.00	32,500,000
2161	22¢ Boy Scouts	.50	.15			1.00	32,500,000
2162	22¢ Big Brothers/Big Sisters	.50	.15			1.00	32,500,000
2163	22¢ Camp Fire	.50	.15			1.00	32,500,000
a	Block of 4, #2160-63	2.35	1.00	2.20	(4)	1.25	
2164	22¢ Help End Hunger, Oct. 15	.42	.15	1.70	(4)	1.00	120,000,000
	Christmas Issue, Oct. 30						
2165	22¢ Genoa Madonna, by Luca Della Robbia	.40	.15	1.70	(4)	1.00	759,200,000
a	Imperf. pair	110.00					
2166	22¢ Poinsettia Plants	.40	.15	1.70	(4)	1.00	757,600,000
a	Imperf. pair	130.00					

How did the appaloosa horse come to America?

Appaloosa horses, also known as "raindrop horses," are known for small round or oval white spots on their rumps or over their whole bodies. These Western riding horses also have white rims around their eyes and black-and-white-striped hoofs.

It is believed that the horses were shipped from Spain to Mexico and North America around the year 1600. The Nez Perce Indians, who lived in the Pacific Northwest, acquired the horses and bred them in the Palouse River region of what is now Idaho and Washington. The name "Appaloosa" comes from the word "Palouse."

(#2158)

2154

2155
2157

2156
2158

2158a

2159

2160
2162

2161
2163

2163a

2164

2165

2166

253

Arkansas Statehood 1836–1986 Old State House Little Rock USA22
2167

Margaret Mitchell USA1
2168

Mary Lyon USA 2
2169

Paul Dudley White MD USA3
2170

Father Flanagan USA 4
2171

Hugo L. Black 5USA
2172

Luis Muñoz Marin Governor, Puerto Rico 05
2173

Red Cloud 10USA
2176

14USA Julia Ward Howe
2177

Buffalo Bill Cody 15
2178

USA 17 Belva Ann Lockwood
2179

Chester Carlson USA 21
2180

USA 23 Mary Cassatt
2182

USA 25 Jack London
2183

Sitting Bull USA 28
2184

Earl Warren Chief Justice of the US USA 29
2184A

Dennis Chavez United States Senator USA 35
2185

Claire Chennault USA40 Flying Tigers, 1940s
2186

Harvey Cushing MD USA 45
2188

Hubert H. Humphrey VICE PRESIDENT USA 52
2190

John Harvard USA56
2191

H.H. "Hap" Arnold USA 65
2192

Wendell Willkie 1892–1944 Statesman 75USA
2193

Bernard Revel USA$1
2194

Johns Hopkins USA$1
2194A

Bryan $2 USA William Jennings
2195

Bret Harte USA $5
2196

	Issues of 1986, Perf. 11	Un	U	PB	#	FDC	Q
2167	22¢ Arkansas Statehood, Jan. 3	.42	.15	1.70	(4)	1.00	130,000,000
a	Vertical pair, imperf. horizontally	—					
	Issues of 1986-91, Great Americans Issue (See also #1844-69)						
2168	1¢ Margaret Mitchell, June 30, 1986	.15	.15	.25	(4)	1.00	
2169	2¢ Mary Lyon, Feb. 28, 1987	.15	.15	.25	(4)	1.00	
2170	3¢ Paul Dudley White, MD, Sept. 15, 1986	.15	.15	.30	(4)	1.00	
2171	4¢ Father Flanagan, July 14, 1986	.15	.15	.35	(4)	1.00	
2172	5¢ Hugo L. Black, Feb. 27, 1986	.15	.15	.40	(4)	1.00	
2173	5¢ Luis Munoz Marin, Feb. 18, 1990	.15	.15	.50	(4)	1.25	
2174-75	Not assigned						
2176	10¢ Red Cloud, Aug. 15, 1987	.18	.15	.85	(4)	1.00	
a	Overall tagging, 1990	—	—				
2177	14¢ Julia Ward Howe, Feb. 12, 1987	.25	.15	1.10	(4)	1.00	
2178	15¢ Buffalo Bill Cody, June 6, 1988	.28	.15	1.20	(4)	1.25	
a	Overall tagging, 1990	—	—				
2179	17¢ Belva Ann Lockwood, June 18, 1986	.30	.15	1.45	(4)	1.00	
2180	21¢ Chester Carlson, Oct. 21, 1988	.38	.15	1.65	(4)	1.25	
2181	Not assigned						
2182	23¢ Mary Cassatt, Nov. 4, 1988	.42	.15	1.75	(4)	1.25	
2183	25¢ Jack London, Jan. 11, 1986	.45	.15	2.00	(4)	1.25	
a	Booklet pane of 10, May 3, 1988	4.50				6.00	
b	Overall tagging, 1990	—	—				
2184	28¢ Sitting Bull, Sept. 28, 1989	.50	.15	2.50	(4)	1.00	
2184A	29¢ Earl Warren, Mar. 9	.58	.15	2.90	(4)		
2185	35¢ Dennis Chavez, Apr. 3, 1991	.65	.15	3.25	(4)		
2186	40¢ Claire Lee Chennault, Sept. 6, 1990	.70	.15	3.25	(4)	1.00	
2187	Not assigned						
2188	45¢ Harvey Cushing, MD, June 17, 1988	.80	.15	3.50	(4)	1.00	
a	Overall tagging, 1990	—	—				
2189	Not assigned						
2190	52¢ Hubert H. Humphrey, June 3, 1991	.90	.15	4.00	(4)	1.25	
2191	56¢ John Harvard, Sept. 3, 1986	.95	.15	4.25	(4)	1.25	
2192	65¢ H.H. 'Hap' Arnold, Nov. 5, 1988	1.20	.18	5.00	(4)	1.50	
2193	75¢ Wendell Willkie	1.50	.20	7.00	(4)		
2194	$1 Bernard Revel, Sept. 23, 1986	2.50	.50	7.25	(4)	2.00	
2194A	$1 Johns Hopkins, June 7, 1989	1.75	.50	7.25	(4)	3.00	
b	Overall tagging, 1990	—	—				
2195	$2 William Jennings Bryan, Mar. 19, 1986	3.00	.50	13.00	(4)	5.00	
2196	$5 Bret Harte, Aug. 25, 1987	7.00	1.00	28.00	(4)	15.00	
	Booklet Stamp, Perf. 10						
2197	25¢ Jack London (2183), single from booklet	.45	.15			1.25	
a	Booklet pane of 6, May 3, 1988	2.65				4.00	

Minimum value listed for a stamp is 15 cents; for a First Day Cover (FDC), $1.00. This minimum represents a fair-market price for having a dealer locate and provide a single stamp or cover from his or her stock. Dealers may charge less per stamp or cover for a group of such stamps or covers, or less for a single stamp or cover.

	Issues of 1986, Perf. 10 Vertically	Un	U	PB	#	FDC	Q
	United States—Sweden Stamp Collecting Booklet Issue, Jan. 23						
2198	22¢ Handstamped Cover	.45	.15			1.00	16,999,200
2199	22¢ Boy Examining Stamp Collection	.45	.15			1.00	16,999,200
2200	22¢ #836 Under Magnifying Glass	.45	.15			1.00	16,999,200
2201	22¢ 1986 Presidents Miniature Sheet	.45	.15			1.00	16,999,200
a	Booklet pane of 4, #2198-2201	2.00				4.00	16,999,200
b	As "a," black omitted on #2198, 2201	45.00					
c	As "a," blue omitted on #2198-2200	—					
d	As "a," buff omitted	—					
	#2198-2201 issued only in booklets. All stamps are imperf. at top and bottom or imperf. at top, bottom and right side.						
	Perf. 11						
2202	22¢ Love, Jan. 30	.40	.15	1.70	(4)	1.00	948,860,000
	Black Heritage Issue, Sojourner Truth, Feb. 4						
2203	22¢ Sojourner Truth Portrait and Truth Lecturing	.40	.15	1.70	(4)	1.00	130,000,000
2204	22¢ Republic of Texas, 150th Anniversary, Mar. 2	.42	.15	1.70	(4)	1.00	136,500,000
a	Horizontal pair, imperf. vertically	1,000.00					
b	Dark red omitted	2,500.00					
	Fish Booklet Issue, Mar. 21, Perf. 10 Horizontally						
2205	22¢ Muskellunge	.50	.15			1.00	43,998,000
2206	22¢ Atlantic Cod	.50	.15			1.00	43,998,000
2207	22¢ Largemouth Bass	.50	.15			1.00	43,998,000
2208	22¢ Bluefin Tuna	.50	.15			1.00	43,998,000
2209	22¢ Catfish	.50	.15			1.00	43,998,000
a	Booklet pane of 5, #2205-09	4.00	—			2.50	43,998,000
	#2205-09 issued only in booklets. All stamps are imperf. at sides or imperf. at sides and bottom.						
	Perf. 11						
2210	22¢ Public Hospitals, Apr. 11	.40	.15	1.70	(4)	1.00	130,000,000
a	Vertical pair, imperf. horizontally	350.00					
b	Horizontal pair, imperf. vertically	1,000.00					
	Performing Arts Issue, Duke Ellington, Apr. 29						
2211	22¢ Duke Ellington Portrait and Piano Keys	.42	.15	1.70	(4)	1.00	130,000,000
a	Vertical pair, imperf. horizontally	1,100.00					
2212-15 Not assigned							

Who made jazz into a big band sound?

"Duke" (Edward Kennedy) Ellington (1899-1974) was a famous African-American pianist, bandleader and composer. In 1923, in New York, Ellington organized a "big band," which revolutionized jazz music. Ellington produced more than 1,000 compositions including *East St. Louis Toodle-Oo* (1927) and *Black, Brown and Beige* (1943), a musical arrangement that presented a panorama of African-American history.
(#2211)

2198 **2199** **2200** **2201** **2201a**

2202 **2203** **2204**

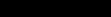

2205 **2210**

2211

2206

2207

2208

2209

2209a

257

George Washington 1789-1797 · John Adams 1797-1801 · Thomas Jefferson 1801-1809 · James Madison 1809-1817 · James Monroe 1817-1825

2216a **2216b** **2216c** **2216d** **2216e**

John Quincy Adams 1825-1829 · Andrew Jackson 1829-1837 · Martin Van Buren 1837-1841 · William Henry Harrison 1841-1841

2216f **2216g** **2216h** **2216i**

John Tyler 1841-1845 · James K. Polk 1845-1849 · Zachary Taylor 1849-1850 · Millard Fillmore 1850-1853 · Franklin Pierce 1853-1857

2217a **2217b** **2217c** **2217d** **2217e**

James Buchanan 1857-1861 · Abraham Lincoln 1861-1865 · Andrew Johnson 1865-1869 · Ulysses S. Grant 1869-1877

2217f **2217g** **2217h** **2217i**

Issues of 1986 (continued), Perf. 11	Un	U	FDC	Q
AMERIPEX '86 Issue, Presidents Miniature Sheets, May 22				
2216 Sheet of 9	3.50		4.00	5,825,050
a 22¢ George Washington	.38	.20	1.00	
b 22¢ John Adams	.38	.20	1.00	
c 22¢ Thomas Jefferson	.38	.20	1.00	
d 22¢ James Madison	.38	.20	1.00	
e 22¢ James Monroe	.38	.20	1.00	
f 22¢ John Quincy Adams	.38	.20	1.00	
g 22¢ Andrew Jackson	.38	.20	1.00	
h 22¢ Martin Van Buren	.38	.20	1.00	
i 22¢ William H. Harrison	.38	.20	1.00	
j Blue omitted	2,400.00			
k Black inscription omitted	2,000.00			
l Imperf.	9,000.00			
2217 Sheet of 9	3.50		4.00	5,825,050
a 22¢ John Tyler	.38	.20	1.00	
b 22¢ James Polk	.38	.20	1.00	
c 22¢ Zachary Taylor	.38	.20	1.00	
d 22¢ Millard Fillmore	.38	.20	1.00	
e 22¢ Franklin Pierce	.38	.20	1.00	
f 22¢ James Buchanan	.38	.20	1.00	
g 22¢ Abraham Lincoln	.38	.20	1.00	
h 22¢ Andrew Johnson	.38	.20	1.00	
i 22¢ Ulysses S. Grant	.38	.20	1.00	

What made James Polk a "dark horse" candidate for President?

Before James Polk (1795-1849) was elected President of the United States in 1844, he was not well known; therefore, he was called a "dark horse" candidate. Formerly, Polk had served in the U.S. House of Representatives and was speaker of the House from 1835 to 1839. He also served one term as governor of Tennessee. He tried twice to run for governor again, but was defeated in both elections. Still, Polk remained interested in politics.

When the Democratic convention met in 1844 to name a candidate for President, the favorite was thought to be Martin Van Buren. But Van Buren only received about half the votes, not the two-thirds required. But, when Andrew Jackson announced his support for Polk, the convention picked Polk as a compromise candidate. **(#2217b)**

	Issues of 1986 (continued), Perf. 11	Un	U	FDC	Q
	AMERIPEX '86 Issue (continued), Presidents Miniature Sheets, May 22				
2218	Sheet of 9	3.50		4.00	5,825,050
a	22¢ Rutherford B. Hayes	.38	.20	1.00	
b	22¢ James A. Garfield	.38	.20	1.00	
c	22¢ Chester A. Arthur	.38	.20	1.00	
d	22¢ Grover Cleveland	.38	.20	1.00	
e	22¢ Benjamin Harrison	.38	.20	1.00	
f	22¢ William McKinley	.38	.20	1.00	
g	22¢ Theodore Roosevelt	.38	.20	1.00	
h	22¢ William H. Taft	.38	.20	1.00	
i	22¢ Woodrow Wilson	.38	.20	1.00	
j	Brown omitted	—			
k	Black inscription omitted	2,600.00			
2219	Sheet of 9	3.50		4.00	5,825,050
a	22¢ Warren G. Harding	.38	.20	1.00	
b	22¢ Calvin Coolidge	.38	.20	1.00	
c	22¢ Herbert Hoover	.38	.20	1.00	
d	22¢ Franklin D. Roosevelt	.38	.20	1.00	
e	22¢ White House	.38	.20	1.00	
f	22¢ Harry S. Truman	.38	.20	1.00	
g	22¢ Dwight D. Eisenhower	.38	.20	1.00	
h	22¢ John F. Kennedy	.38	.20	1.00	
i	22¢ Lyndon B. Johnson	.38	.20	1.00	

Which President was also on the Supreme Court?

William Taft (1857-1930) had a long career in public service. In 1887, he was appointed to the Ohio Supreme Court, and a year later, he won an election for the office of judge. Under President Theodore Roosevelt, Taft served as Civil Governor of the Philippines and as Secretary of War. With Roosevelt's backing, Taft was nominated as the Republican candidate for President in 1908. Taft served one four-year term as President, but lost Roosevelt's support. In the next election, both Roosevelt and Woodrow Wilson ran against Taft. Wilson won. Taft was glad to leave the White House, calling it "the lonesomest place in the world." Taft was appointed Chief Justice of the United States Supreme Court in 1921. **(#2218h)**

USA 22

USA22

Rutherford B. Hayes 1877-1881

2218a

USA22

James A. Garfield 1881-1881

2218b

USA22

Chester A. Arthur 1881-1885

2218c

USA22

Grover Cleveland 1885-89, 1893-97

2218d

USA22

Benjamin Harrison 1889-1893

2218e

USA22

William McKinley 1897-1901

2218f

USA22

Theodore Roosevelt 1901-1909

2218g

USA22

William H. Taft 1909-1913

2218h

USA22

Woodrow Wilson 1913-1921

2218i

USA22

Warren G. Harding 1921-1923

2219a

USA22

Calvin Coolidge 1923-1929

2219b

USA22

Herbert C. Hoover 1929-1933

2219c

USA22

Franklin D. Roosevelt 1933-1945

2219d

USA22

The White House

2219e

USA22

Harry S. Truman 1945-1953

USA22

Dwight D. Eisenhower 1953-1961

USA22

John F. Kennedy 1961-1963

USA22

Lyndon B. Johnson 1963-1969

Elisha Kent Kane — USA 22

Adolphus W. Greely — USA 22

Vilhjalmur Stefansson — USA 22

Robert E. Peary, Matthew Henson — USA 22

Liberty 1886-1986 — USA 22

2224

Omnibus 1880s 1 USA

2225

Locomotive 1870s 2 USA

2220
2222　　**2221**
　　　　2223　　**2223a**

2226

Navajo Art USA 22
Navajo Art USA 22
Navajo Art USA 22
Navajo Art USA 22

T.S. Eliot — 22 USA

2239

Wood Carving: Highlander Figure — Folk Art USA 22
Wood Carving: Ship Figurehead — Folk Art USA 22
Wood Carving: Nautical Figure — Folk Art USA 22
Wood Carving: Cigar-Store Figure — Folk Art USA 22

2235　　**2236**　**2238a**
2237　　**2238**

2240　　**2241**　**2243a**
2242　　**2243**

CHRISTMAS 22 USA
Perugino, National Gallery

2244

22 USA
GREETINGS

2245

USA 22
1837-1987 Michigan Statehood

2246

22 USA
Pan American Games Indianapolis 1987

2247

LOVE
USA 22

2248

Jean Baptiste Pointe Du Sable 22
Black Heritage USA

2249

Enrico Caruso 22 USA

2250

GIRL SCOUTS USA 22

2251

	Issues of 1986 (continued), Perf. 11	Un	U	PB/PNC	#	FDC	Q
	Arctic Explorers Issue, May 28						
2220	22¢ Elisha Kent Kane	.55	.15			1.00	32,500,000
2221	22¢ Adolphus W. Greely	.55	.15			1.00	32,500,000
2222	22¢ Vilhjalmur Stefansson	.55	.15			1.00	32,500,000
2223	22¢ Robert E. Peary, Matthew Henson	.55	.15			1.00	32,500,000
a	Block of 4, #2220-23	2.40	1.00	2.05	(4)	2.50	
b	As "a," black omitted	—					
2224	22¢ Statue of Liberty, July 4	.40	.15	1.80	(4)	1.00	220,725,000
	Issues of 1986-87, Reengraved Transportation Issue, Coil Stamps, Perf. 10 Vertically						
	(See also #1897-1908, 2123-36, 2252-66, 2452-53A, 2457, 2464, 2468)						
2225	1¢ Omnibus, Nov. 26, 1986	.15	.15	.65	(3)	1.00	
2226	2¢ Locomotive, Mar. 6, 1987	.15	.15	.80	(3)	1.00	
2227, 2229-30, 2232-34 Not assigned							
2228	4¢ Stagecoach (1898A), Aug. 1986	.15	.15	1.40	(3)		
2231	8.3¢ Ambulance (Bureau precanceled), Aug. 29, 1986	.16	.16	4.00	(3)		
	On #2228, "Stagecoach 1890s" is 17mm long; on #1898A, it is 19¹/₂mm long. On #2231, "Ambulance 1860s" is 18mm long; on #2128, it is 18¹/₂mm long.						
	American Folk Art Issue, Navajo Blankets, Sept. 4, Perf. 11						
2235	22¢ Navajo Blanket, black and white lines dominate	.42	.15			1.00	60,131,250
2236	22¢ Navajo Blanket, black and white diamonds dominate	.42	.15			1.00	60,131,250
2237	22¢ Navajo Blanket, white diamonds dominate	.42	.15			1.00	60,131,250
2238	22¢ Navajo Blanket, black-and-white bordered patterns dominate	.42	.15			1.00	60,131,250
a	Block of 4, #2235-38	1.75	1.00	1.90	(4)	2.50	
b	As "a," black omitted	350.00					
	Literary Arts Issue, T.S. Eliot, Sept. 26						
2239	22¢ T.S. Eliot Portrait	.40	.15	1.90	(4)	1.00	131,700,000
	American Folk Art Issue, Wood-Carved Figurines, Oct. 1						
2240	22¢ Highlander Figure	.42	.15			1.00	60,000,000
2241	22¢ Ship Figurehead	.42	.15			1.00	60,000,000
2242	22¢ Nautical Figure	.42	.15			1.00	60,000,000
2243	22¢ Cigar Store Figure	.42	.15			1.00	60,000,000
a	Block of 4, #2240-43	1.75	1.00	1.90	(4)	2.50	
b	As "a," imperf. vertically	1,500.00					
	Christmas Issue, Oct. 24						
2244	22¢ Madonna and Child, by Perugino	.40	.15	1.90	(4)	1.00	690,100,000
2245	22¢ Village Scene	.40	.15	1.90	(4)	1.00	882,150,000
	Issues of 1987						
2246	22¢ Michigan Statehood, Jan. 26	.40	.15	1.90	(4)	1.00	167,430,000
	Pair with full vertical gutter between	—					
2247	22¢ Pan American Games, Jan. 29	.40	.15	1.90	(4)	1.00	166,555,000
a	Silver omitted	1,500.00					
	Perf. 11¹/₂ x 11						
2248	22¢ Love, Jan. 30	.40	.15	1.90	(4)	1.00	842,360,000
	Black Heritage Issue, Jean Baptiste Point Du Sable, Feb. 20, Perf. 11						
2249	22¢ Portrait of Du Sable and Chicago Settlement	.40	.15	1.90	(4)	1.00	142,905,000
	Performing Arts Issue, Enrico Caruso, Feb. 27						
2250	22¢ Caruso as the Duke of Mantua in *Rigoletti*	.40	.15	1.90	(4)	1.00	130,000,000
2251	22¢ Girl Scouts, Mar. 12	.40	.15	1.90	(4)	1.00	149,980,000

263

	Issues of 1987-88, Perf. 10 Vertically	Un	U	PNC	#	FDC		Q
	Coil Stamps, Transportation Issue (See also #1897-1908, 2123-36, 2225-26, 2228, 2231, 2452-53A, 2457, 2464, 2468)							
2252	3¢ Conestoga Wagon 1800s, Feb. 29, 1988	.15	.15	.90	(3)	1.25		
2253	5¢ Milk Wagon 1900s, Sept. 25, 1987	.15	.15	1.15	(3)	1.25		
2254	5.3¢ Elevator 1900s, Bureau precanceled, Sept. 16, 1988	.15	.15	1.40	(3)	1.25		
2255	7.6¢ Carreta 1770s, Bureau precanceled, Aug. 30, 1988	.15	.15	2.75	(3)	1.25		
2256	8.4¢ Wheel Chair 1920s, Bureau precanceled, Aug. 12, 1988	.15	.15	2.75	(3)	1.25		
a	Imperf. pair	750.00						
2257	10¢ Canal Boat 1880s, Apr. 11, 1987	.18	.15	1.65	(3)	1.00		
2258	13¢ Patrol Wagon 1880s, Bureau precanceled, Oct. 29, 1988	.22	.22	3.00	(3)	1.25		
2259	13.2¢ Coal Car 1870s, Bureau precanceled, July 19, 1988	.22	.22	3.25	(3)	1.25		
a	Imperf. pair	160.00						
2260	15¢ Tugboat 1900s, July 12, 1988	.24	.15	3.25	(3)	1.25		
2261	16.7¢ Popcorn Wagon 1902, Bureau precanceled, July 7, 1988	.28	.28	4.00	(3)	1.25		
a	Imperf. pair	225.00						
2262	17.5¢ Racing Car 1911, Sept. 25, 1987	.30	.15	3.75	(3)	1.00		
a	Untagged (Bureau precanceled)	.30	.30	3.75	(3)	1.00		
b	Imperf. pair	1,500.00						
2263	20¢ Cable Car 1880s, Oct. 28, 1988	.35	.15	3.75	(3)	1.25		
a	Imperf. pair	90.00						
2264	20.5¢ Fire Engine 1920s, Bureau precanceled, Sept. 28, 1988	.38	.38	4.00	(3)	1.25		
2265	21¢ Railroad Mail Car 1920s, Bureau precanceled, Aug. 16, 1988	.38	.38	4.00	(3)	1.25		
a	Imperf. pair	75.00						
2266	24.1¢ Tandem Bicycle 1890s, Bureau precanceled, Oct. 26, 1988	.42	.42	4.75	(3)	1.25		
	Issues of 1987 (continued), Special Occasions Booklet Issue, Apr. 20, Perf. 10							
2267	22¢ Congratulations!	.55	.15			1.00		1,222,140,000
2268	22¢ Get Well!	.55	.15			1.00		611,070,000
2269	22¢ Thank you!	.55	.15			1.00		611,070,000
2270	22¢ Love You, Dad!	.55	.15			1.00		611,070,000
2271	22¢ Best Wishes!	.55	.15			1.00		611,070,000
2272	22¢ Happy Birthday!	.55	.15			1.00		1,222,140,000
2273	22¢ Love You, Mother!	.55	.15			1.00		611,070,000
2274	22¢ Keep In Touch!	.55	.15			1.00		611,070,000
a	Booklet pane of 10, #2268-71, 2273-74 and 2 each of #2267, 2272	6.75	—			4.00		611,070,000

#2267-74 issued only in booklets. All stamps are imperf. at one or two sides or imperf. at sides and bottom.

Conestoga Wagon 1800s
3 USA

2252

Milk Wagon 1900s
5 USA

2253

Elevator 1900s
5.3 USA
Nonprofit Carrier Route Sort

2254

Carreta 1770s
7.6 USA
Nonprofit

2255

Wheel Chair 1920s
8.4 USA
Nonprofit

2256

Canal Boat 1880s
10 USA

2257

Patrol Wagon 1880s
USA 13 Presorted First-Class

2258

Coal Car 1870s
13.2 Bulk Rate
USA

2259

Tugboat 1900s
USA 15

2260

Popcorn Wagon
16.7 USA 1902
Bulk Rate

2261

Racing Car 1911
USA
17.5

2262

USA 20
Cable Car 1880s

2263

Fire Engine 1900s
20.5 USA
ZIP+4 Presort

2264

Railroad Mail Car 1920s
Presorted First-Class
21 USA

2265

Tandem Bicycle
1890s 24.1 USA
ZIP+4

2266

Congratulations! 22 USA

Get Well! USA 22

USA 22
Thank You!

Love You, Dad! USA 22

Best Wishes! USA 22

Happy Birthday! USA 22

USA 22
Love You, Mother!

Keep In Touch! USA 22

Happy Birthday! USA 22

Congratulations! 22 USA

2274a

2267
2268   2269
2270
2271   2272
2273
2274

2275

2276

2277

2278

2280

2281

2283

2283a

2285b

2284

2285

	Issues of 1987 (continued), Perf. 11	Un	U	PB/PNC	#	FDC	Q
2275	United Way, Apr. 28	.40	.15	1.90	(4)	1.00	156,995,000
2276	Flag with Fireworks, May 9	.40	.15	1.90	(4)	1.00	
a	Booklet pane of 20, Nov. 30	8.50	—			18.00	
	Issues of 1988-89 (All issued in 1988 except #2280 on prephosphored paper)						
2277	25¢ E Stamp, Mar. 22	.45	.15	1.90	(4)	1.00	
2278	25¢ Flag with Clouds, May 6	.40	.15	1.90	(4)	1.00	
	Pair with full vertical gutter between	—					
	Coil Stamps, Perf. 10 Vertically						
2279	25¢ E Stamp (2277), Mar. 22	.45	.15	3.25	(3)	1.00	
a	Imperf. pair	120.00					
2280	25¢ Flag over Yosemite, May 20	.45	.15	4.50	(3)	1.00	
	Prephosphored paper, Feb. 14, 1989	.45	.15	4.50	(3)		
a	Imperf. pair	20.00					
b	Black trees	—	—				
2281	25¢ Honeybee, Sept. 2	.45	.15	3.75	(3)	1.00	
a	Imperf. pair	45.00					
b	Black omitted	70.00					
d	Pair, imperf. between	—					
	Booklet Stamp, Perf. 10						
2282	25¢ E Stamp (2277), single from booklet	.45	.15			1.00	
a	Booklet pane of 10, Mar. 22	4.75	—			6.00	
	Pheasant Booklet Issue, Perf. 11						
2283	25¢ Pheasant, single from booklet	.50	.15			1.25	
a	Booklet pane of 10, Apr. 29	4.75	—			6.00	
c	As "a," red removed from sky	50.00	—				
d	As "a," imperf. horizontally between	—					
	#2283 issued only in booklets. All stamps have one or two imperf. edges. Imperf. and part perf. pairs and panes exist from printer's waste.						
	Owl and Grosbeak Booklet Issue, Perf. 10						
2284	25¢ Owl, single from booklet	.45	.15			1.25	
2285	25¢ Grosbeak, single from booklet	.45	.15			1.25	
b	Booklet pane of 10, 5 each of #2284, 2285, May 28	4.50	—			6.00	
	#2284 and 2285 issued only in booklets. All stamps are imperf. at one side or imperf. at one side and bottom.						
2285A	25¢ Flag with Clouds (2278), single from booklet	.45	.15			1.25	
c	Booklet pane of 6, July 5	2.75	—			4.00	

How was the Yosemite Valley formed?

The waterfalls, rock formations, canyons and gorges of Yosemite National Park were geologically created over many millions of years. A large sea once covered the land in the area that is now the Sierra Nevada. At that time, different geological processes occurred. The result was a great mountain range with a granite core. Rivers and glaciers carved deep gouges into the area and a great glacial lake filled with silt, sand and rock. This eventually became the floor of the Yosemite Valley. (**#2280**)

	Issues of 1987 (continued), Perf. 11	Un	U	FDC	Q
	American Wildlife Issue, June 13				
2286	22¢ Barn Swallow	.85	.15	1.00	12,952,500
2287	22¢ Monarch Butterfly	.85	.15	1.00	12,952,500
2288	22¢ Bighorn Sheep	.85	.15	1.00	12,952,500
2289	22¢ Broad-tailed Hummingbird	.85	.15	1.00	12,952,500
2290	22¢ Cottontail	.85	.15	1.00	12,952,500
2291	22¢ Osprey	.85	.15	1.00	12,952,500
2292	22¢ Mountain Lion	.85	.15	1.00	12,952,500
2293	22¢ Luna Moth	.85	.15	1.00	12,952,500
2294	22¢ Mule Deer	.85	.15	1.00	12,952,500
2295	22¢ Gray Squirrel	.85	.15	1.00	12,952,500
2296	22¢ Armadillo	.85	.15	1.00	12,952,500
2297	22¢ Eastern Chipmunk	.85	.15	1.00	12,952,500
2298	22¢ Moose	.85	.15	1.00	12,952,500
2299	22¢ Black Bear	.85	.15	1.00	12,952,500
2300	22¢ Tiger Swallowtail	.85	.15	1.00	12,952,500
2301	22¢ Bobwhite	.85	.15	1.00	12,952,500
2302	22¢ Ringtail	.85	.15	1.00	12,952,500
2303	22¢ Red-winged Blackbird	.85	.15	1.00	12,952,500
2304	22¢ American Lobster	.85	.15	1.00	12,952,500
2305	22¢ Black-tailed Jack Rabbit	.85	.15	1.00	12,952,500
2306	22¢ Scarlet Tanager	.85	.15	1.00	12,952,500
2307	22¢ Woodchuck	.85	.15	1.00	12,952,500
2308	22¢ Roseate Spoonbill	.85	.15	1.00	12,952,500
2309	22¢ Bald Eagle	.85	.15	1.00	12,952,500
2310	22¢ Alaskan Brown Bear	.85	.15	1.00	12,952,500

22 USA
Armadillo

Which animal wears armor?

The armadillo is a small mammal that has a protective shell of nine narrow, bony plates. This bony "armor" is jointed so the armadillo can curl up and protect itself when in danger. This is the armadillo's best defense since it only has a few small teeth in the back of its mouth and cannot bite.

When danger occurs, an armadillo's first choice for protection is to hide in its burrow. When it is too far from home, it digs itself quickly into the ground with its strong claws. If that won't work, then it curls up into a hard ball within its shell.

Armadillos are usually found in the area between the southern U.S. and Argentina. The animal uses its long tongue to lick up such things as insects, earthworms, spiders and land snails. (**#2296**)

2286 2287 2288 2289 2290

2291 2292 2293 2294 2295

2296 2297 2298 2299 2300

2301 2302 2303 2304 2305

2306 2307 2308 2309 2310

2311	2312	2313	2314	2315
2316	2317	2318	2319	2320
2321	2322	2323	2324	2325
2326	2327	2328	2329	2330
2331	2332	2333	2334	2335

	Issues of 1987 (continued), Perf. 11	Un	U	PB	#	FDC	Q
	American Wildlife Issue (continued), June 13						
2311	22¢ Iiwi	.85	.15			1.00	12,952,500
2312	22¢ Badger	.85	.15			1.00	12,952,500
2313	22¢ Pronghorn	.85	.15			1.00	12,952,500
2314	22¢ River Otter	.85	.15			1.00	12,952,500
2315	22¢ Ladybug	.85	.15			1.00	12,952,500
2316	22¢ Beaver	.85	.15			1.00	12,952,500
2317	22¢ White-tailed Deer	.85	.15			1.00	12,952,500
2318	22¢ Blue Jay	.85	.15			1.00	12,952,500
2319	22¢ Pika	.85	.15			1.00	12,952,500
2320	22¢ Bison	.85	.15			1.00	12,952,500
2321	22¢ Snowy Egret	.85	.15			1.00	12,952,500
2322	22¢ Gray Wolf	.85	.15			1.00	12,952,500
2323	22¢ Mountain Goat	.85	.15			1.00	12,952,500
2324	22¢ Deer Mouse	.85	.15			1.00	12,952,500
2325	22¢ Black-tailed Prairie Dog	.85	.15			1.00	12,952,500
2326	22¢ Box Turtle	.85	.15			1.00	12,952,500
2327	22¢ Wolverine	.85	.15			1.00	12,952,500
2328	22¢ American Elk	.85	.15			1.00	12,952,500
2329	22¢ California Sea Lion	.85	.15			1.00	12,952,500
2330	22¢ Mockingbird	.85	.15			1.00	12,952,500
2331	22¢ Raccoon	.85	.15			1.00	12,952,500
2332	22¢ Bobcat	.85	.15			1.00	12,952,500
2333	22¢ Black-footed Ferret	.85	.15			1.00	12,952,500
2334	22¢ Canada Goose	.85	.15			1.00	12,952,500
2335	22¢ Red Fox	.85	.15			1.00	12,952,500
a	Pane of 50, #2286-2335	46.50		46.50	(50)	30.00	
	Any single, red omitted	—					

What looks like a bear and smells like a skunk?

Wolverines are ferocious animals that resemble miniature bears, and, when threatened, they smell like skunks. These extremely powerful creatures belong to the weasel family, and are short and stocky with thick, long fur. The wolverine has a huge appetite and a tendency to steal anything in sight, including axes, knives, dishes and blankets. Wolverines are about three feet long and weigh up to 55 pounds. They feed on small- and medium-sized animals, birds and plants. Wolverines will even attack large animals like reindeer or caribou. **(#2327)**

271

	Issues of 1987-90, Perf. 11	Un	U	PB	#	FDC	Q
	Constitution Bicentennial Issue, Ratification of the Constitution						
2336	22¢ Delaware, July 4, 1987	.40	.15	1.70	(4)	1.00	168,000,000
2337	22¢ Pennsylvania, Aug. 26, 1987	.40	.15	1.70	(4)	1.00	186,575,000
2338	22¢ New Jersey, Sept. 11, 1987	.42	.15	1.70	(4)	1.00	184,325,000
a	Black omitted	5,000.00					
2339	22¢ Georgia, Jan. 6, 1988	.40	.15	1.70	(4)	1.00	168,845,000
2340	22¢ Connecticut, Jan. 9, 1988	.40	.15	1.70	(4)	1.00	155,170,000
2341	22¢ Massachusetts, Feb. 6, 1988	.40	.15	1.70	(4)	1.00	102,100,000
2342	22¢ Maryland, Feb. 15, 1988	.40	.15	1.70	(4)	1.00	103,325,000
2343	25¢ South Carolina, May 23, 1988	.45	.15	1.90	(4)	1.25	162,045,000
2344	25¢ New Hampshire, June 21, 1988	.45	.15	1.90	(4)	1.25	153,295,000
2345	25¢ Virginia, June 25, 1988	.45	.15	1.90	(4)	1.25	160,245,000
2346	25¢ New York, July 26, 1988	.45	.15	1.90	(4)	1.25	183,290,000
2347	25¢ North Carolina, Aug. 22, 1989	.45	.15	1.90	(4)	1.25	
2348	25¢ Rhode Island, May 29, 1990	.45	.15	1.90	(4)	1.25	164,130,000
2349	22¢ Friendship with Morocco, July 17	.40	.15	1.70	(4)	1.00	157,475,000
a	Black omitted	300.00					
	Issues of 1987, Literary Arts Issue, William Faulkner, Aug. 3						
2350	22¢ Portrait of Faulkner	.40	.15	1.70	(4)	1.00	156,225,000
	American Folk Art Issue, Lacemaking, Aug. 14						
2351	22¢ Squash Blossoms	.42	.15			1.00	40,995,000
2352	22¢ Floral Piece	.42	.15			1.00	40,995,000
2353	22¢ Floral Piece	.42	.15			1.00	40,995,000
2354	22¢ Dogwood Blossoms	.42	.15			1.00	40,995,000
a	Block of 4, #2351-54	1.75	1.00	1.75	(4)	2.75	
b	As "a," white omitted	1,250.00					

Lacemaking USA 22

How is lace made?

Most lace today is made by machine, but handmade lace is created using the needle method or the bobbin method. To make needle lace, the lacemaker draws a pattern on a thick piece of paper backed by linen. He or she stitches the outline of the pattern, then takes a single thread and builds up the pattern with looped stitches. When the pattern is complete, the framework stitches are clipped from the linen and paper and the lace is lifted off. This process is called "tatting."

Bobbin lace is made with many different threads, each fastened to a bobbin (spool). The pattern is drawn on paper, which is attached to a cushion. Pins are stuck in the cushion as the pattern indicates. The lacemaker moves pairs of bobbins from side to side, working around the pins to create the design. **(#2352)**

Dec 7, 1787 USA
Delaware 22
2336

Dec 12, 1787
Pennsylvania 22 USA
2337

Dec 18, 1787 USA
New Jersey 22
2338

January 2, 1788
Georgia 22 USA
2339

January 9, 1788
Connecticut 22 USA
2340

Feb 6, 1788
Massachusetts 22 USA
2341

April 28, 1788 USA
Maryland 22
2342

July 26, 1788 USA
New York 25
2343

June 21, 1788
New Hampshire 25 USA
2344

June 25, 1788 USA
Virginia 25
2345

July 26, 1788 USA
New York 25
2346

November 21, 1789 25 USA
North Carolina
2347

May 29, 1790 25 USA
Rhode Island
2348

Friendship with Morocco 1787-1987
USA 22
2349

William Faulkner
USA 22
2350

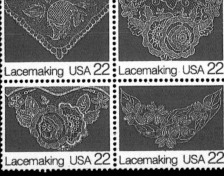

Lacemaking USA 22
Lacemaking USA 22
Lacemaking USA 22
Lacemaking USA 22

2351   **2352**   **2354a**
2353   **2354**

273

The Bicentennial
of the Constitution of
the United States
of America
1787-1987   USA 22

2355

We the people
of the United States,
in order to form
a more perfect Union...
Preamble, U.S. Constitution   USA 22

2356

Establish justice,
insure domestic tranquility,
provide for the common defense,
promote the general welfare...
Preamble, U.S. Constitution   USA 22

2357

And secure
the blessings of liberty
to ourselves
and our posterity...
Preamble, U.S. Constitution   USA 22

2358

Do ordain
and establish this
Constitution for the
United States of America.
Preamble, U.S. Constitution   USA 22

2359

2359a

2360   **2361**

Stourbridge Lion
1829   USA 22

2362

Best Friend
of Charleston
1830   USA 22

2363

John Bull
1831   USA 22

2364

Brother Jonathan
1832   USA 22

2365

Gowan & Marx
1839   USA 22

2366

2366a

CHRISTMAS   22 USA

Moroni, National Gallery

2367

USA 22 GREETINGS

2368

	Issues of 1987 (continued), Perf. 10 Horizontally	Un	U	PB	#	FDC	Q
	Constitution Bicentennial Issue, Drafting of the Constitution Booklet Issue, Aug. 28						
2355	22¢ "The Bicentennial..."	.50	.15			1.00	121,944,000
2356	22¢ "We the people..."	.50	.15			1.00	121,944,000
2357	22¢ "Establish justice..."	.50	.15			1.00	121,944,000
2358	22¢ "And secure..."	.50	.15			1.00	121,944,000
2359	22¢ "Do ordain..."	.50	.15			1.00	121,944,000
a	Booklet pane of 5, #2355-59	2.75	—			3.00	121,944,000
	#2355-59 issued only in booklets. All stamps are imperf. at sides or imperf. at sides and bottom.						
	Signing of the Constitution, Sept. 17, Perf. 11						
2360	22¢ Constitution and Signer's Hand Holding Quill Pen, Sept. 17	.40	.15	1.70	(4)	1.00	168,995,000
2361	22¢ Certified Public Accountants, Sept. 21	1.90	.15	1.70	(4)	2.00	163,145,000
a	Black omitted	850.00					
	Locomotives Booklet Issue, Oct. 1, Perf. 10 Horizontally						
2362	22¢ Stourbridge Lion, 1829	.50	.15			1.00	142,501,200
2363	22¢ Best Friend of Charleston, 1830	.50	.15			1.00	142,501,200
2364	22¢ John Bull, 1831	.50	.15			1.00	142,501,200
2365	22¢ Brother Jonathan, 1832	.50	.15			1.00	142,501,200
2366	22¢ Gowan & Marx, 1839	.50	.15			1.00	142,501,200
a	Booklet pane of 5, #2362-66	2.75	—			3.00	142,501,200
b	As "a," black omitted on #2366	—					
	#2362-66 issued only in booklets. All stamps are imperf. at sides or imperf. at sides and bottom.						
	Christmas Issue, Oct. 23, Perf. 11						
2367	22¢ Madonna and Child, by Moroni	.40	.15	1.70	(4)	1.00	528,790,000
2368	22¢ Christmas Ornaments	.40	.15	1.70	(4)	1.00	978,340,000
	Pair with full vertical gutter between						

What does the Constitution mean?

The original U.S. government, established by the Articles of Confederation in 1781, was weak. It did not define how individual states would work together to solve national problems. Each state acted like a small country, with its own currency and laws. The states paid little regard to the interest of the larger national republic, and also refused to pay their war debts. Individuals began to take up arms to solve their problems.

The Constitution, ratified in 1788, changed everything. It established a federal government with a legislative branch to make laws, a judicial branch to interpret laws and an executive branch to administer laws. It also gave the federal government the power to collect taxes, declare war and regulate trade. **(#2359a)**

275

	Issues of 1988, Perf. 11	Un	U	PB	#	FDC	Q
	Winter Olympic Games Issue, Jan. 10						
2369	22¢ Skier and Olympic Rings	.40	.15	1.70	(4)	1.00	158,870,000
2370	22¢ Australia Bicentennial, Jan. 26	.40	.15	1.70	(4)	1.00	145,560,000
	Black Heritage Issue, James Weldon Johnson, Feb. 2						
2371	22¢ Portrait of Johnson and Music from "Lift Ev'ry Voice and Sing"	.40	.15	1.70	(4)	1.00	97,300,000
	American Cats Issue, Feb. 5						
2372	22¢ Siamese and Exotic Shorthair	.42	.15			1.00	39,639,000
2373	22¢ Abyssinian and Himalayan	.42	.15			1.00	39,639,000
2374	22¢ Maine Coon and Burmese	.42	.15			1.00	39,639,000
2375	22¢ American Shorthair and Persian	.42	.15			1.00	39,639,000
a	Block of 4, #2372-75	2.00	1.00	1.75	(4)	3.50	
	American Sports Issue, Knute Rockne, Mar. 9						
2376	22¢ Rockne Holding Football on Field	.40	.15	1.70	(4)	1.50	97,300,000
	Francis Ouimet, June 13						
2377	25¢ Portrait of Ouimet and Ouimet Hitting Fairway Shot	.45	.15	1.90	(4)	1.50	153,045,000
2378	25¢ Love, July 4	.45	.15	1.90	(4)	1.25	841,240,000
2379	45¢ Love, Aug. 8	.65	.20	3.00	(4)	1.25	179,553,550
	Summer Olympic Games Issue, Aug. 19						
2380	25¢ Gymnast on Rings	.45	.15	1.90	(4)	1.25	157,215,000

What song was called the "Negro National Anthem"?

Lift Ev'ry Voice and Sing (1900), written by James Weldon Johnson (1871-1938) and his brother, composer John Rosamond Johnson, was called the "Negro National Anthem."

James Johnson was an African-American of many talents. He studied literature at Atlanta University and also passed the Florida bar examination to practice law. Johnson was also a poet and a playwright.

Johnson became active as a diplomat from 1906 to 1914, serving as consul to Venezuela and Nicaragua. He also published several books, including *The Autobiography of an Ex-Colored Man*, which describes the ragtime era in New York, and *Black Manhattan*, a history of blacks in New York. In addition, he compiled two books of African-American spirituals with his brother. **(#2371)**

2369

2370

2371

Siamese Cat, Exotic Shorthair Cat

Abyssinian Cat, Himalayan Cat

Maine Coon Cat, Burmese Cat

American Shorthair Cat, Persian Cat

2372   **2373**   **2375a**

2374   **2375**

2378

2376   **2377**   **2379**

2380

1928 Locomobile

1929 Pierce-Arrow

1931 Cord

1932 Packard

1935 Duesenberg

2381

2382

2383

2384

2385

2385a

Nathaniel Palmer

Lt. Charles Wilkes

Richard E. Byrd

Lincoln Ellsworth

2386   **2387**   **2389a**

2388   **2389**

2390   **2391**   **2393a**

2392   **2393**

	Issues of 1988 (continued), Perf. 10 Horizontally	Un	U	PB	#	FDC	Q
	Classic Cars Booklet Issue, Aug. 25						
2381	25¢ 1928 Locomobile	.45	.15			1.25	127,047,600
2382	25¢ 1929 Pierce-Arrow	.45	.15			1.25	127,047,600
2383	25¢ 1931 Cord	.45	.15			1.25	127,047,600
2384	25¢ 1932 Packard	.45	.15			1.25	127,047,600
2385	25¢ 1935 Duesenberg	.45	.15			1.25	127,047,600
a	Booklet pane of 5, #2381-85	2.50	—			3.00	127,047,600
	#2381-85 issued only in booklets. All stamps are imperf. at sides or imperf. at sides and bottom.						
	Antarctic Explorers Issue, Sept. 14, Perf. 11						
2386	25¢ Nathaniel Palmer	.50	.15			1.25	40,535,625
2387	25¢ Lt. Charles Wilkes	.50	.15			1.25	40,535,625
2388	25¢ Richard E. Byrd	.50	.15			1.25	40,535,625
2389	25¢ Lincoln Ellsworth	.50	.15			1.25	40,535,625
a	Block of 4, #2386-89	2.25	1.00	2.00	(4)	3.00	
b	As "a," black omitted	1,500.00					
c	As "a," imperf. horizontally	2,500.00					
	American Folk Art Issue, Carousel Animals, Oct. 1						
2390	25¢ Deer	.55	.15			1.50	76,253,750
2391	25¢ Horse	.55	.15			1.50	76,253,750
2392	25¢ Camel	.55	.15			1.50	76,253,750
2393	25¢ Goat	.55	.15			1.50	76,253,750
a	Block of 4, #2390-93	2.45	1.00	2.50	(4)	3.50	

Why did knights ride on carousels?

In the late 17th century, young noblemen trained for jousting on a device resembling the merry-go-round. A nobleman would sit on a wooden horse and aim his lance at a hanging ring. The device was pulled around in a circle while the knight tried to spear the ring with his lance.

The word *carousel* comes from the old Italian and Spanish words *garosello* and *carosella*, which mean "little war."

(#2391)

	Issues of 1988 (continued), Perf. 11	Un	U	PB	#	FDC	Q
2394	$8.75 Express Mail, Oct. 4	14.50	8.00	55.00	(4)	25.00	
	Special Occasions Booklet Issue, Oct. 22						
2395	25¢ Happy Birthday	.45	.15			1.25	120,000,000
2396	25¢ Best Wishes	.45	.15			1.25	120,000,000
a	Booklet pane of 6, 3 #2395 and 3 #2396 with gutter between	3.00	—				
2397	25¢ Thinking of You	.45	.15			1.25	120,000,000
2398	25¢ Love You	.45	.15			1.25	120,000,000
a	Booklet pane of 6, 3 #2397 and 3 #2398 with gutter between	3.00	—				
b	As "a," imperf. horizontally	—					
	#2395-98a issued only in booklets. All stamps are imperf. on one side or on one side and top or bottom.						
	Christmas Issue, Oct. 20, Perf. 11						
2399	25¢ Madonna and Child, by Botticelli	.45	.15	1.90	(4)	1.25	843,835,000
a	Gold omitted	40.00					
2400	25¢ One-Horse Open Sleigh and Village Scene	.45	.15	1.90	(4)	1.25	1,037,610,000
	Pair with full vertical gutter between	—					

Who did Botticelli paint?

Allesandro Botticelli (c1444-1510) was an Italian Renaissance painter who lived and worked in Florence. His pictures are distinctive for their clear, rhythmic lines, delicate color, lavish decoration and poetic feeling. Botticelli's work is of two kinds. The first is of worldly splendor, complex moral allegory, and beautiful mythological subjects. The second resembles restraint and serious feeling, as in his Madonna and Child.

Paintings of the Madonna are usually divided into five classes according to style and treatment. The style Bottecelli chose was painting the Madonna in a pastoral setting. **(#2399)**

2394

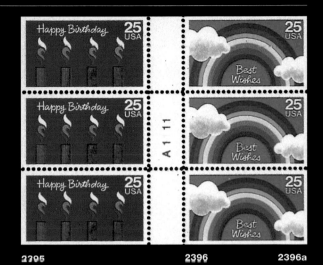

2395   2396   2396a

2397   2398   2398a

2400

2399

2401

2402

2403

2404

2405
2406
2407
2408
2409

2409a

2410

2411

2412

2413

2414

2415

2416

2417

2418

	Issues of 1989, Perf. 11	Un	U	PB	#	FDC	Q
2401	25¢ Montana Statehood, Jan. 15	.45	.15	1.90	(4)	1.25	165,495,000
	Black Heritage Issue, A. Philip Randolph, Feb. 3						
2402	25¢ Portrait of Randolph, Pullman Porters and Railroad Cars	.45	.15	1.90	(4)	1.25	151,675,000
2403	25¢ North Dakota Statehood, Feb. 21	.45	.15	1.90	(4)	1.25	163,000,000
2404	25¢ Washington Statehood, Feb. 22	.45	.15	1.90	(4)	1.25	264,625,000
	Steamboats Booklet Issue, Mar. 3, Perf. 10 Horizontally						
2405	25¢ Experiment 1788-90	.45	.15			1.25	159,154,200
2406	25¢ Phoenix 1809	.45	.15			1.25	159,154,200
2407	25¢ New Orleans 1812	.45	.15			1.25	159,154,200
2408	25¢ Washington 1816	.45	.15			1.25	159,154,200
2409	25¢ Walk in the Water 1818	.45	.15			1.25	159,154,200
a	Booklet pane of 5, #2405-09	2.25	—			4.00	159,154,200
	#2405-09 issued only in booklets. All stamps are imperf. at sides or imperf. at sides and bottom.						
	Perf. 11						
2410	25¢ World Stamp Expo '89, Mar. 16	.45	.15	1.90	(4)	1.25	163,984,000
	Performing Arts Issue, Arturo Toscanini, Mar. 25						
2411	25¢ Portrait of Toscanini Conducting with Baton	.45	.15	1.90	(4)	1.25	152,250,000
	Issues of 1989-90, Constitution Bicentennial Issue						
2412	25¢ U.S. House of Representatives, Apr. 4, 1989	.45	.15	1.90	(4)	1.25	138,760,000
2413	25¢ U.S. Senate, Apr. 6, 1989	.45	.15	1.90	(4)	1.25	137,985,000
2414	25¢ Executive Branch, Apr. 16, 1989	.45	.15	1.90	(4)	1.25	138,580,000
2415	25¢ Supreme Court, Feb. 2, 1990	.45	.15	1.90	(4)	1.25	150,545,000
	Issues of 1989 (continued)						
2416	25¢ South Dakota Statehood, May 3	.45	.15	1.90	(4)	1.25	164,680,000
	American Sports Issue, Lou Gehrig, June 10						
2417	25¢ Portrait of Gehrig, Gehrig Swinging Bat	.60	.15	2.50	(4)	2.50	262,755,000
	Literary Arts Issue, Ernest Hemingway, July 17						
2418	25¢ Portrait of Hemingway, African Landscape in Background	.45	.15	1.90	(4)	1.25	191,755,000

Who helped African-Americans get fair wages?

In 1925, Asa Philip Randolph (1889-1979) founded The Brotherhood of Sleeping Car Porters, the first successful black trade union. Randolph believed that organized labor unions offered the best chance for African-Americans to receive fair wages. He proved his point by winning a major contract with the Pullman Company in 1937, and by making the American Federation of Labor question and change its policies of discrimination. **(#2402)**

283

	Issues of 1989 (continued), Perf. 11 x 11½	Un	U	PB	#	FDC	Q
	Priority Mail Issue, July 20						
2419	$2.40 Moon Landing	4.25	2.00	17.00	(4)	7.00	
a	Black omitted	3,500.00					
b	Imperf. pair	1,500.00					
	Perf. 11						
2420	25¢ Letter Carriers, Aug. 30	.45	.15	1.90	(4)	1.25	188,400,000
	Constitution Bicentennial Issue, Drafting of the Bill of Rights, Sept. 25						
2421	25¢ Stylized U.S. Flag, Eagle With Quill Pen in Mouth	.45	.15	1.90	(4)	1.25	191,860,000
a	Black omitted	275.00					
	Prehistoric Animals Issue, Oct. 1						
2422	25¢ Tryannosaurus	.45	.15			1.25	101,747,000
2423	25¢ Pteranodon	.45	.15			1.25	101,747,000
2424	25¢ Stegosaurus	.45	.15			1.25	101,747,000
2425	25¢ Brontosaurus	.45	.15			1.25	101,747,000
a	Block of 4, #2422-25	2.00	1.00	1.90	(4)	3.00	
b	As "a," black omitted	1,100.00					
	America/PUAS Issue, Oct. 12 (See also #C121)						
2426	25¢ Southwest Carved Figure (A.D. 1150-1350), Emblem of the Postal Union of the Americas	.45	.15	1.90	(4)	1.25	137,410,000
	Christmas Issue, Oct. 19, Perf. 11½						
2427	25¢ Madonna and Child, by Caracci	.45	.15	1.90	(4)	1.25	913,335,000
a	Booklet pane of 10	4.50	—			6.00	
	Perf. 11						
2428	25¢ Sleigh Full of Presents	.45	.15	1.90	(4)	1.25	900,000,000
a	Vertical pair, imperf. horizontally	—					
	Booklet Stamp Issue, Perf. 11½						
2429	25¢ Single from booklet pane (#2428)	.45	.15				399,243,000
a	Booklet pane of 10	4.50	—			6.00	39,924,300
b	As "a," imperf. horiz. between	—					
c	As "a," red omitted	—					
	In #2429, runners on sleigh are twice as thick as in #2428; bow on package at rear of sleigh is same color as package; board running underneath sleigh is pink.						
2430	Not assigned						
	Self-Adhesive, Die-Cut						
2431	25¢ Eagle and Shield, Nov. 10	.50	.20			1.00	75,441,000
a	Booklet pane of 18	9.00					
b	Vertical pair, no die-cutting between	850.00					
2432	Not assigned						
	World Stamp Expo '89 Issue Souvenir Sheet, Nov. 17, Imperf.						
2433	Reproduction of #122, 90¢ Lincoln, and three essays of #122	10.00	9.00			7.00	2,227,600
a-d	Single stamp from sheet	1.85	1.75				

2420

2421

2419

2426

2422

2424

2423

2425

2425a

2427

2428

2431

2433

285

2434   2435   2437a

2436   2437

20th Universal Postal Congress

A review of historical methods of delivering the mail in the United States is the theme of these four stamps issued in commemoration of the convening of the 20th Universal Postal Congress in Washington, D.C. from November 13 through December 15, 1989. The United States, as host nation to the Congress for the first time in ninety-two years, welcomed more than 1,000 delegates from most of the member nations of the Universal Postal Union to the major international event.

2438

2440

2443

2439

2442

	Issues of 1989 (continued), Perf. 11	Un	U	PB	#	FDC	Q
	20th UPU Congress Issues, Classic Mail Transportation, Nov. 19 (See also #C122-26)						
2434	25¢ Stagecoach	.45	.15			1.25	40,956,000
2435	25¢ Paddlewheel Steamer	.45	.15			1.25	40,956,000
2436	25¢ Biplane	.45	.15			1.25	40,956,000
2437	25¢ Depot-hack Type Automobile	.45	.15			1.25	40,956,000
a	Block of 4, #2434-37	3.00	2.00	2.25	(4)	3.00	
b	As "a," dark blue omitted	1,100.00					
	Souvenir Sheet, Nov. 27, Imperf. (See also #C122-26)						
2438	Designs of #2434-37	4.00	1.75			2.00	2,047,200
a-d	Single stamp from sheet	.60	.25				
	Issues of 1990, Perf. 11						
2439	25¢ Idaho Statehood, Jan. 6	.45	.15	2.00	(4)	1.25	173,000,000
	Perf. 12½ x 13						
2440	25¢ Love, January 18	.45	.15	2.00	(4)	1.25	886,220,000
a	Imperf. pair	850.00					
	Booklet Stamp, Perf. 11½						
2441	25¢ Love, single from booklet	.45	.15			1.25	995,178,000
a	Booklet pane of 10, Jan. 18	4.50	—			6.00	
b	As "a," bright pink omitted	1,800.00					
	Black Heritage Issue, Ida B. Wells, Feb. 1, Perf. 11						
2442	25¢ Portrait of Ida B. Wells, Marchers in Background	.45	.15	2.00	(4)	1.25	153,125,000
	Beach Umbrella Booklet Issue, Perf. 11½ x 11						
2443	15¢ Beach Umbrella, single from booklet	.28	.15			1.25	
a	Booklet pane of 10, Feb. 3	2.80				4.25	
b	As "a," blue omitted	2,000.00					

#2443 issued only in booklets. All stamps are imperf. at one side or imperf. at one side and bottom.

How did most people travel in the late 1700s?

Stagecoaches, or horse-drawn carriages, were established in colonial America around 1756, and were the preferred method of travel during the late 1700s. The stagecoaches carried passengers and mail on regular routes, usually between Boston, New York and Philadelphia. The coaches traveled slowly, covering about 100 miles in 24 hours, and horses were changed at relay stations along the way. Later, stagecoach lines took passengers out West, but the railroads gradually replaced them. **(#2434)**

	Issues of 1990 (continued), Perf. 11	Un	U	PB	#	FDC	Q
2444	25¢ Wyoming Statehood, Feb. 23	.45	.15	2.00	(4)	1.25	169,495,000
	Classic Films Issue, Mar. 23						
2445	25¢ The Wizard of Oz	.70	.15			1.25	44,202,000
2446	25¢ Gone With the Wind	.70	.15			1.25	44,202,000
2447	25¢ Beau Geste	.70	.15			1.25	44,202,000
2448	25¢ Stagecoach	.70	.15			1.25	44,202,000
a	Block of 4, #2445-48	3.25	1.00	2.25	(4)	3.00	
	Literary Arts Issue, Marianne Moore, Apr. 18						
2449	25¢ Portrait of Marianne Moore	.45	.15	2.00	(4)	1.25	150,000,000
2450	Not assigned						
	Issues of 1990-92, Transportation Issue, Coil Stamps, Perf. 10 Vertically						
2451	4¢ Steam Carriage 1866, Jan. 25, 1991	.15	.15	1.40	(3)	1.25	
a	Imperf. pair	600.00					
2452	5¢ Circus Wagon 1900s, Aug. 31	.15	.15	1.10	(3)	1.25	
2453	5¢ Canoe 1800s, Bureau precanceled, intaglio printing, May 25, 1991	.15	.15	1.10	(3)	1.25	
2453A	5¢ Canoe 1800s, precanceled, gravure printing, Oct. 22, 1991	.15	.15	1.10	(3)	1.25	
2454-56	Not assigned						
2457	10¢ Tractor Trailer, Bureau precanceled, May 25, 1991	.18	.18	2.00	(3)	1.25	
2458-63	Not assigned						
2464	23¢ Lunch Wagon 1890s, Apr. 12, 1991	.42	.15	4.00	(3)	1.25	
a	Imperf. pair	400.00					
2465-67	Not assigned						
2468	$1 Seaplane 1914, Apr. 20	1.75	.50	7.00	(3)	2.00	
	1990 continued, Lighthouses Booklet Issue, Apr. 26, Perf. 10 Vertically						
2470	25¢ Admiralty Head, WA	.45	.15			1.25	146,721,600
2471	25¢ Cape Hatteras, NC	.45	.15			1.25	146,721,600
2472	25¢ West Quoddy Head, ME	.45	.15			1.25	146,721,600
2473	25¢ American Shoals, FL	.45	.15			1.25	146,721,600
2474	25¢ Sandy Hook, NJ	.45	.15			1.25	146,721,600
a	Booklet pane of 5, #2470-74	2.50	—			4.00	146,721,600
b	As "a," white (USA 25) omitted	90.00					

#2470-74 issued only in booklets. All stamps are imperf. top and bottom or top, bottom and right edge.

What influenced poet Marianne Moore?

Many of the poems written by Marianne Moore (1887-1972) addressed moral issues, but the images she used often came from nature. Moore grew up among books, and she also liked to sketch items found outdoors, such as milkweed pods and stalks of grass. Whether at home, in a college biology lab, or traveling in Europe, Moore liked to sketch scenes and later used those observations in her poems. (**#2449**)

2444

2449

2445   **2446**   **2448a**

2447   **2448**

2451   **2452**   **2453**   **2453A**

2457   **2464**   **2468**

2474a

2475

2476

2481

2482

2487

2489

2493

2494

2496   **2497**   **2498**   **2499**   **2500**   **2500a**

2501   **2502**   **2503**   **2504**   **2505**   **2505a**

2506   **2507**   **2507a**

2511a

2508   **2509**

	Issues of 1990 (continued), Die-Cut, Self-Adhesive	Un	U	PB	#	FDC	Q
2475	25¢ Flag, single from pane	.50	.25			1.25	36,168,000
a	Pane of 12, May 18	6.00					3,140,000
	Wildlife Issue, Perf. 11						
2476	$2 Bobcat, June 1	3.50	1.25	16.50	(4)	5.00	
2477-80	Not assigned						
	Issues of 1991-92						
2481	1¢ American Kestrel, June 22	.15	.15	.15	(4)	1.25	
2482	3¢ Eastern Bluebird, June 22	.15	.15	.30	(4)	1.25	
2483-86	Not assigned						
	Perf. 11½ x 11						
2487	19¢ Fawn, Mar. 11	.35	.15	1.90	(4)	1.25	
2488	Not assigned						
2489	30¢ Cardinal, June 22	.50	.15	2.25	(4)	1.25	
2490-92	Not assigned						
	Wood Duck Booklet Issue, April 12, Perf. 10						
2493	29¢ Black and multicolored	.50	.15			1.25	
a	Booklet pane of 10	5.00				7.25	
	Perf. 11						
2494	29¢ Red and multicolored	.50	.15			1.25	
a	Booklet pane of 10	5.00				7.25	
	#2493-94a issued only in bklts. All stamps are imperf. top or bottom, or top or bottom and right edge.						
2495	Not assigned						
	Issues of 1990 (continued), Olympians Issue, July 6, Perf. 11						
2496	25¢ Jesse Owens	.45	.15			1.25	35,717,500
2497	25¢ Ray Ewry	.45	.15			1.25	35,717,500
2498	25¢ Hazel Wightman	.45	.15			1.25	35,717,500
2499	25¢ Eddie Eagan	.45	.15			1.25	35,717,500
2500	25¢ Helene Madison	.45	.15			1.25	35,717,500
a	Strip of 5, #2496-2500	2.50	—	5.00	(10)	3.00	7,143,500
	Indian Headdresses Booklet Issue, Aug. 17						
2501	25¢ Assiniboin Headdress	.45	.15			1.25	123,825,600
2502	25¢ Cheyenne Headdress	.45	.15			1.25	123,825,600
2503	25¢ Comanche Headdress	.45	.15			1.25	123,825,600
2504	25¢ Flathead Headdress	.45	.15			1.25	123,825,600
2505	25¢ Shoshone Headdress	.45	.15			1.25	123,825,600
a	Booklet pane of 10, 2 each of #2501-05	5.00	—			6.00	61,912,800
b	As "a," black omitted	—					
	#2501-05 issued only in booklets. All stamps imperf. top or bottom, or top or bottom and right edge.						
	Micronesia/Marshall Islands Issue, Sept. 28						
2506	25¢ Canoe and Flag of the Federated States of Micronesia	.45	.15			1.25	76,250,000
a	Black omitted	—					
2507	25¢ Stick Chart, Canoe and Flag of the Marshall Islands	.45	.15			1.25	76,250,000
a	Pair, #2506-07	1.00	.16	2.50	(4)	2.00	61,000,000
	Creatures of the Sea Issue, Oct. 1						
2508	25¢ Killer Whales	.45	.15			1.25	69,566,000
2509	25¢ Northern Sea Lions	.45	.15			1.25	69,566,000
2510	25¢ Sea Otter	.45	.15			1.25	69,566,000
2511	25¢ Common Dolphin	.45	.15			1.25	69,566,000
a	Block of 4, #2508-11	2.00	—	2.00	(4)	3.00	69,566,000
b	As "a," black omitted	1,250.00					

291

	Issues of 1990 (continued), Perf. 11	Un	U	PB	#	FDC	Q
	America/PUAS Issue, Oct. 12 (See also #C127)						
2512	25¢ Grand Canyon	.45	.15	2.00	(4)	1.25	150,760,000
2513	25¢ Dwight D. Eisenhower	.45	.15	2.00	(4)	1.25	142,692,000
a	Imperf. pair	1,750.00					
	Christmas Issue, Oct. 18, Perf. 11½						
2514	25¢ Madonna and Child, by Antonello	.45	.15	2.00	(4)	1.25	499,995,000
a	Booklet pane of 10	4.50				6.00	22,892,400
	Perf. 11						
2515	25¢ Christmas Tree	.45	.15	2.00	(4)	1.25	599,400,000
	Booklet Stamp, Perf. 11½ x 11 on two or three sides						
2516	Single (2515) from booklet pane	.45	.15			1.25	
a	Booklet pane of 10	4.50				6.00	32,030,400
	Issues of 1991, Perf. 13						
2517	29¢ F Stamp, Jan. 22	.50	.15	2.50	(4)	1.25	
	Coil Stamp, Perf. 10 Vertically						
2518	29¢ Tulip (2517), Jan. 22	.50	.15	4.25	(3)	1.25	
	Booklet Stamps, Perf. 11 on two or three sides						
2519	F Stamp, single from booklet	.50	.15			1.25	
a	Booklet pane of 10, Jan. 22	5.00				7.25	
2520	F Stamp, single from booklet	.50	.15			1.25	
a	Booklet pane of 10, Jan. 22	5.50				7.25	

#2519 has bull's-eye perforations that measure approximately 11.2. #2520 has less-pronounced black lines in the leaf, which is a much brighter green than on #2519.

		Un	U	PB	#	FDC	Q
	Perf. 11						
2521	4¢ Makeup Rate, Jan. 22	.15	.15	.40	(4)	1.25	
	Self-Adhesive, Die-Cut, Imperf.						
2522	29¢ F Flag, single from pane	.50	.25			1.25	
a	Pane of 12	6.00				8.25	
	Coil Stamps, Perf. 10 Vertically						
2523	29¢ Flag Over Mt. Rushmore, intaglio printing, Mar. 29	.50	.15	5.00	(3)	1.25	
b	Imperf. pair	35.00					
2523A	29¢ Flag Over Mt. Rushmore, gravure printing, July 4	.50	.15	5.00	(3)	1.25	
	Perf. 11						
2524	29¢ Tulip, Apr. 5	.50	.15	2.25	(4)	1.25	
a	Perf. 13	.50	.15				
	Coil Stamps, Roulette 10 Vertically						
2525	29¢ Tulip, Aug. 16	.50	.15	4.75	(3)	1.25	
	Perf. 10 Vertically						
2526	29¢ Tulip, Mar. 3	.50	.15	4.75	(3)		
	Booklet Stamp, Perf. 11 on two or three sides						
2527	29¢ Tulip (2524), single from bklt.	.50	.15			1.25	
a	Booklet pane of 10, Apr. 5	5.00				7.25	
b	As "a," vertically imperf. between —						
	Flag With Olympic Rings Booklet Issue, Apr. 21						
2528	29¢ U.S. Flag, Olympic Rings, single from booklet	.50	.15			1.25	
a	Booklet pane of 10	5.00				7.25	
	Perf. 10 Vertically						
2529	19¢ Fishing Boat, Aug. 8	.35	.15	3.75	(3)	1.25	
a	New printing	.35	.15	3.75	(3)		

2512

2513

2514

2515

2517

2519

2520

2521

2522

2523

2523A

2524

2525

2526

2528

2529

2530

2531

2531A

2532

2533

2534

2535

2537

2538

2539

2540

2541

2545

2546

2547

2548

2549

2549a

2550

2551

294

	Issues of 1991 (continued), Perf. 10	Un	U	PB	#	FDC	Q
	Ballooning Booklet Issue, May 17, Perf. 10						
2530	19¢ Overhead View of Balloon, single from booklet	.35	.15			1.25	
a	Booklet pane of 10	3.50				4.75	
	#2530 was issued only in booklets. All stamps are imperf. on one side or on one side and bottom.						
	Perf. 11						
2531	29¢ Flags on Parade, May 30	.50	.15	2.25	(4)	1.25	
	Self-Adhesive, Die-Cut, Imperf.						
2531A	29¢ Liberty Torch, single stamp from pane	.58	.25			1.25	
a	Pane of 18, June 25	10.50				12.00	
	Perf. 11						
2532	50¢ Founding of Switzerland, Feb. 22	1.00	.25	4.50	(4)	2.00	100,000,000
2533	29¢ Vermont Statehood, Mar. 1	.50	.15	2.50	(4)	1.25	181,438,000
2534	29¢ Savings Bonds, Apr. 30	.50	.15	2.50	(4)	1.25	150,560,000
	Perf. 12½ x 13						
2535	29¢ Love, May 9	.50	.15	2.50	(4)	1.25	631,330,000
	Booklet Stamp, Perf. 11 on two or three sides						
2536	29¢ (2535), single from booklet	.50	.15			1.25	
a	Booklet pane of 10, May 9	5.00				7.25	
	Perf. 11						
2537	52¢ Love, May 9	.90	.20	4.50	(4)	2.00	200,000,000
	Literary Arts Issue, William Saroyan, May 22						
2538	29¢ Portrait of Saroyan	.50	.15	2.50	(4)	1.25	161,498,000
2539	$1 USPS Logo/Olympic Rings, Sept. 20	1.75	.50	8.75	(4)	1.25	
2540	$2.90 Priority Mail, July 7	5.00	—	25.00	(4)	6.00	
2541	$9.95 Domestic Express Mail, June 16	17.50	—	85.00	(4)	20.00	
2542	$14 International Express Mail, Aug. 31	25.00	—	110.00	(4)	28.00	
	Fishing Flies Booklet Issue, May 31, Perf. 11 Horizontally						
2545	29¢ Royal Wulff	.50	.15			1.25	148,983,600
2546	29¢ Jock Scott	.50	.15			1.25	148,983,600
2547	29¢ Apte Tarpon Fly	.50	.15			1.25	148,983,600
2548	29¢ Lefty's Deceiver	.50	.15			1.25	148,983,600
2549	29¢ Muddler Minnow	.50	.15			1.25	148,983,600
a	Booklet pane of 5, #2545-49	2.90				4.50	148,983,600
	#2545-49 were issued only in booklets. All stamps are imperf. at sides or imperf. at sides and bottom.						
	Performing Arts Issue, Cole Porter, June 8, Perf. 11						
2550	29¢ Portrait of Porter at Piano, Sheet Music	.50	.15	2.50	(4)	1.25	149,848,000
a	Vertical pair, imperf. horizontally	550.00					
2551	29¢ Operations Desert Shield/ Desert Storm, July 2	.50	.15	2.50	(4)	1.25	200,003,000
	Booklet Stamp, Perf. 11 on one or two sides						
2552	29¢ Operations Desert Shield/ Desert Storm (2551), July 2, single from booklet	.50	.15			1.25	200,000,000
a	Booklet pane of 5	2.50				4.50	40,000,000

	Issues of 1991 (continued), Perf. 11	Un	U	PB	#	FDC	Q
	Summer Olympic Games Issue, July 12						
2553	29¢ Pole Vaulter	.50	.15			1.25	34,005,120
2554	29¢ Discus Thrower	.50	.15			1.25	34,005,120
2555	29¢ Women Sprinters	.50	.15			1.25	34,005,120
2556	29¢ Javelin Thrower	.50	.15			1.25	34,005,120
2557	29¢ Women Hurdlers	.50	.15			1.25	34,005,120
a	Strip of 5, #2553-57	2.90		5.50	(10)	3.25	34,005,120
2558	29¢ Numismatics, Aug. 13	.50	.15	2.50	(4)	1.25	150,310,000
	World War II Miniature Sheet, Sept. 3						
2559	Sheet of 10 and central label	5.80	—	5.80	(10)	6.00	15,218,000
a	29¢ Burma Road	.58	.29			1.25	15,218,000
b	29¢ America's First Peacetime Draft	.58	.29			1.25	15,218,000
c	29¢ Lend-Lease Act	.58	.29			1.25	15,218,000
d	29¢ Atlantic Charter	.58	.29			1.25	15,218,000
e	29¢ Arsenal of Democracy	.58	.29			1.25	15,218,000
f	29¢ Destroyer *Reuben James*	.58	.29			1.25	15,218,000
g	29¢ Civil Defense	.58	.29			1.25	15,218,000
h	29¢ Liberty Ship	.58	.29			1.25	15,218,000
i	29¢ Pearl Harbor	.58	.29			1.25	15,218,000
j	29¢ U.S. Declaration of War	.58	.29			1.25	15,218,000
2560	29¢ Basketball, Aug. 28	.50	.15	2.90	(4)	1.25	149,810,000
2561	29¢ District of Columbia, Sept. 7	.50	.15	2.90	(4)	1.25	149,260,000
	Comedians Booklet Issue, Aug. 29, Perf. 11 on two or three sides						
2562	29¢ Stan Laurel and Oliver Hardy	.58	.15			1.25	139,995,600
2563	29¢ Edgar Bergen and Dummy Charlie McCarthy	.58	.15			1.25	139,995,600
2564	29¢ Jack Benny	.58	.15			1.25	139,995,600
2565	29¢ Fanny Brice	.58	.15			1.25	139,995,600
2566	29¢ Bud Abbott and Lou Costello	.58	.15			1.25	139,995,600
a	Booklet pane of 10, 2 each of #2562-66	6.00	—			7.25	69,997,800
b	As "a," scarlet and bright violet omitted	650.00					
	#2562-66 issued only in booklets. All stamps are imperf. at top or bottom, or at top or bottom and right side.						
	Black Heritage Issue, Jan Matzeliger, Sept. 15, Perf. 11						
2567	29¢ Portrait of Matzeliger and Shoe-Lasting Machine Diagram	.50	.15	2.90	(4)	1.25	148,973,000

Which comedienne was called "Baby Snooks"?

Fanny Brice (1891-1951) performed in vaudeville, musicals, dramas, movies and radio, and was well-known for her performances in the *Ziegfeld Follies.* One of her most famous characters was "Baby Snooks," a mischievous infant. Brice's humor was based on parodying characters, not on exploiting herself or other women. **(#2565)**

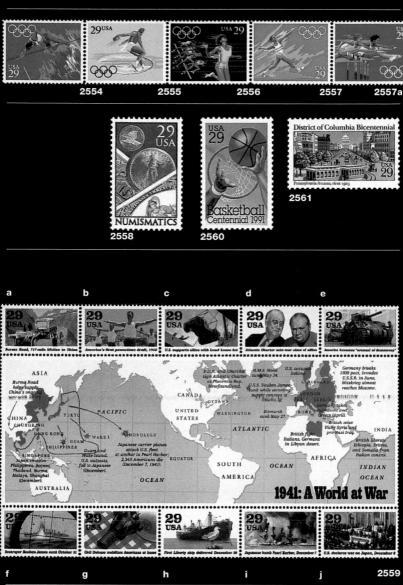

2554   **2555**   **2556**   **2557**   **2557a**

2558   **2560**

2561

a   b   c   d   e

1941: A World at War

f   g   h   i   j   **2559**

2562   **2563**   **2564**   **2565**   **2566**   **2566a**

2567

2568   2569   2570   2571   2572

2573   2574   2575   2576   2577   2577a

2579

2581

2578

2582

2583

2584

2585

2594   2604   2607   2608   2608A

2609

	Issues of 1991 (continued), Perf. 11	Un	U	PB	#	FDC	Q
	Space Exploration Booklet Issue, Oct. 1						
2568	29¢ Mercury, Mariner 10	.50	.15			1.25	33,394,800
2569	29¢ Venus, Mariner 2	.50	.15			1.25	33,394,800
2570	29¢ Earth, Landsat	.50	.15			1.25	33,394,800
2571	29¢ Moon, Lunar Orbiter	.50	.15			1.25	33,394,800
2572	29¢ Mars, Viking Orbiter	.50	.15			1.25	33,394,800
2573	29¢ Jupiter, Pioneer 11	.50	.15			1.25	33,394,800
2574	29¢ Saturn, Voyager 2	.50	.15			1.25	33,394,800
2575	29¢ Uranus, Voyager 2	.50	.15			1.25	33,394,800
2576	29¢ Neptune, Voyager 2	.50	.15			1.25	33,394,800
2577	29¢ Pluto	.50	.15			1.25	33,394,800
a	Booklet pane of 10, #2568-77	6.00	—			7.25	33,394,800
	#2568-77 issued only in booklets. All stamps are imperf. at top or bottom, or at top or bottom and right side.						
	Christmas Issue, Oct. 17, Perf. 11						
2578	29¢ Madonna and Child, by Antoniazzo Romano	.58	.15	2.90	(4)	1.25	401,000,000
a	Booklet pane of 10	5.80					30,000,000
2579	29¢ Santa Claus Sliding Down Chimney	.58	.15	2.90	(4)	1.25	900,000,000
	Booklet Stamps						
2580	29¢ Santa Claus (2579), Type I, single from booklet	.58	.15			1.25	
2581	29¢ Santa Claus (2579), Type II, single from booklet	.58	.15			1.25	
a	Pair, #2580, 2581	1.16	.25			3.50	28,000,000
	The extreme left brick in top row of chimney is missing from Type II, #2581.						
2582	29¢ Santa Claus Checking List, single from booklet	.58	.15			1.25	
a	Booklet pane of 4	2.40	—			3.50	28,000,000
2583	29¢ Santa Claus Leaving Present Under Tree, single from booklet	.58	.15			1.25	
a	Booklet pane of 4	2.40	—			3.50	28,000,000
2584	29¢ Santa Claus Going Up Chimney, single from booklet	.58	.15			1.25	
a	Booklet pane of 4	2.40	—			3.50	28,000,000
2585	29¢ Santa Claus Flying Away in Sleigh, single from booklet	.58	.15			1.25	
a	Booklet pane of 4	2.40	—			3.50	28,000,000
	#2582-85 issued only in booklets. All stamps are imperf. at top or bottom, or at top or bottom and right side.						
	Issues of 1992						
	Coil Stamps, Perf. 10 Vertically						
2594	29¢ Pledge of Allegiance	.50	.15			1.25	
a	Booklet of 10	5.00	—				
2595	29¢ Eagle and Shield	.50	.25				
a	Pane of 17 + label	8.50					
	Issues of 1991 (continued)						
2604	10¢ Eagle and Shield, Dec. 13	.20	.15	3.25	(3)		
2607	23¢ Flag	.46	.46	4.50	(3)		
	Issues of 1992 (continued)						
2608	23¢ USA, July 21	.40	.15	1.50	(3)		
2608A	23¢ USA (Bureau)	.40	.15	1.50	(3)		
2609	29¢ Flag Over White House, April 23	.50	.15	5.25	(3)	1.25	

	Issues of 1992 (continued), Perf. 11	Un	U	PB	#	FDC	Q
	Winter Olympic Games Issue						
2611	29¢ Hockey	.50	.15			1.25	32,000,000
2612	29¢ Figure Skating	.50	.15			1.25	32,000,000
2613	29¢ Speed Skating	.50	.15			1.25	32,000,000
2614	29¢ Skiing	.50	.15			1.25	32,000,000
2615	29¢ Bobsledding	.50	.15			1.25	32,000,000
a	Strip of 5, #2611-15	2.90	—	5.50	(10)		
2616	29¢ World Columbian Stamp Expo, Jan. 24	.50	.15	2.50	(4)	1.25	148,665,000
	Black Heritage Issue						
2617	29¢ W.E.B. DuBois, Jan. 31	.50	.15	2.50	(4)	1.25	149,990,000
2618	29¢ Love, Feb. 6	.50	.15	2.50	(4)	1.25	835,000,000
2619	29¢ Olympic Baseball, April 3	.50	.15	2.50	(4)	1.25	160,000,000
	First Voyage of Christopher Columbus Issue, April 24						
2620	29¢ Seeking Queen Isabella's Support	.50	.15			1.25	40,005,000
2621	29¢ Crossing The Atlantic	.50	.15			1.25	40,005,000
2622	29¢ Approaching Land	.50	.15			1.25	40,005,000
2623	29¢ Coming Ashore	.50	.15			1.25	40,005,000
a	Block of 4, #2620-23	2.00	1.00	2.50	(4)	3.00	

2611 **2612** **2613** **2614** **2615** **2615a**

2616 **2617** **2618** **2619**

2620 **2621** **2623a**
2622 **2623**

2624

2625

2626

2627

2628

2629

Issues of 1992 (continued), Perf. 10½		Un	U		Q
The Voyages of Columbus Souvenir Sheets, May 22					
2624	Seeking Royal Support, sheet of 3	2.10	—		2,000,000
a	1¢ deep blue	.15	.15		
b	4¢ ultramarine	.15	.15		
c	$1 salmon	2.00	1.00		
2625	First Sighting Of Land, sheet of 3	8.10	—		2,000,000
a	2¢ brown violet	.15	.15		
b	3¢ green	.15	.15		
c	$4 crimson lake	8.00	4.00		
2626	Reporting Discoveries, sheet of 3	1.70	—		2,000,000
a	5¢ chocolate	.15	.15		
b	30¢ orange brown	.60	.30		
c	50¢ slate blue	1.00	.50		
2627	Royal Favor Restored, sheet of 3	6.28	—		2,000,000
a	6¢ purple	.15	.15		
b	8¢ magenta	.16	.15		
c	$3 yellow green	6.00	3.00		
2628	Claiming A New World, sheet of 3	4.50	—		2,000,000
a	10¢ black brown	.20	.15		
b	15¢ dark green	.30	.15		
c	$2 brown red	4.00	2.00		
2629	$5 Christopher Columbus, sheet of 1	10.00	—		2,000,000

	Issues of 1992 (continued), Perf. 11	Un	U	PB	#	FDC	Q
2630	29¢ New York Stock Exchange Bicentennial, May 17	.50	.15	2.50	(4)	1.25	148,000,000
	Space Adventures Issue, May 29						
2631	29¢ Cosmonaut, US Space Shuttle	.50	.15			1.25	37,315,000
2632	29¢ Astronaut, Russian Space Station	.50	.15			1.25	37,315,000
2633	29¢ Sputnik, Vostok, Apollo Command and Lunar Modules	.50	.15			1.25	37,315,000
2634	29¢ Soyuz, Mercury and Gemini Spacecraft	.50	.15			1.25	37,315,000
a	Block of 4, #2631-34	2.00		2.50	(4)	3.00	
2635	29¢ Alaska Highway, 50th Anniversary, May 30	.50	.15	2.50	(4)	1.25	146,610,000
a	Black (engr.) omitted	—					
2636	29¢ Kentucky Statehood Bicentennial, June 11	.50	.15	2.50	(4)	1.25	160,000,000
	Summer Olympic Games Issue, June 1						
2637	29¢ Soccer	.50	.15			1.25	32,000,000
2638	29¢ Gymnastics	.50	.15			1.25	32,000,000
2639	29¢ Volleyball	.50	.15			1.25	32,000,000
2640	29¢ Boxing	.50	.15			1.25	32,000,000
2641	29¢ Swimming	.50	.15			1.25	32,000,000
a	Strip of 5, #2637-41	2.90	—	5.50	(10)	4.00	
	Hummingbirds Issue, June 15						
2642	29¢ Ruby-throated	.50	.15			1.25	87,728,000
2643	29¢ Broad-billed	.50	.15			1.25	87,728,000
2644	29¢ Costa's	.50	.15			1.25	87,728,000
2645	29¢ Rufous	.50	.15			1.25	87,728,000
2646	29¢ Calliope	.50	.15			1.25	87,728,000
a	Booklet pane of 5, #2642-46	2.50	—	2.50	(5)	4.00	

2630

2631   2632   2634a

2633   2634

2636

2635

2637   2638   2639   2640   2641   2641a

2642   2643   2644   2645   2646   2646a

2647 Indian Paintbrush
2648 Fragrant Water Lily
2649 Meadow Beauty
2650 Jack-in-the-Pulpit
2651 California Poppy

2652 Large-flowered Trillium
2653 Tickseed
2654 Shooting Star
2655 Stream Violet
2656 Bluets

2657 Herb Robert
2658 Marsh Marigold
2659 Sweet White Violet
2660 Claret Cup Cactus
2661 White Mountain Avens

2662 Sessile Bellwort
2663 Blue Flag
2664 Harlequin Lupine
2665 Twinflower
2666 Common Sunflower

2667 Sego Lily
2668 Virginia Bluebells
2669 Ohi'a Lehua
2670 Rosebud Orchid
2671 Showy Evening Primrose

Issues of 1992 (continued), Perf. 11	Un	U	FDC	Q
Wildflowers Issue, July 24				
2647 29¢ Indian Paintbrush	.50	.15	1.25	11,000,000
2648 29¢ Fragrant Water Lily	.50	.15	1.25	11,000,000
2649 29¢ Meadow Beauty	.50	.15	1.25	11,000,000
2650 29¢ Jack-in-the-Pulpit	.50	.15	1.25	11,000,000
2651 29¢ California Poppy	.50	.15	1.25	11,000,000
2652 29¢ Large-Flowered Trillium	.50	.15	1.25	11,000,000
2653 29¢ Tickseed	.50	.15	1.25	11,000,000
2654 29¢ Shooting Star	.50	.15	1.25	11,000,000
2655 29¢ Stream Violet	.50	.15	1.25	11,000,000
2656 29¢ Bluets	.50	.15	1.25	11,000,000
2657 29¢ Herb Robert	.50	.15	1.25	11,000,000
2658 29¢ Marsh Marigold	.50	.15	1.25	11,000,000
2659 29¢ Sweet White Violet	.50	.15	1.25	11,000,000
2660 29¢ Claret Cup Cactus	.50	.15	1.25	11,000,000
2661 29¢ White Mountain Avens	.50	.15	1.25	11,000,000
2662 29¢ Sessile Bellwort	.50	.15	1.25	11,000,000
2663 29¢ Blue Flag	.50	.15	1.25	11,000,000
2664 29¢ Harlequin Lupine	.50	.15	1.25	11,000,000
2665 29¢ Twinflower	.50	.15	1.25	11,000,000
2666 29¢ Common Sunflower	.50	.15	1.25	11,000,000
2667 29¢ Sego Lily	.50	.15	1.25	11,000,000
2668 29¢ Virginia Bluebells	.50	.15	1.25	11,000,000
2669 29¢ Ohi'a Lehua	.50	.15	1.25	11,000,000
2670 29¢ Rosebud Orchid	.50	.15	1.25	11,000,000
2671 29¢ Showy Evening Primrose	.50	.15	1.25	11,000,000

	Issues of 1992 (continued), Perf. 11	Un	U	PB	#	FDC	Q
	Wildflowers Issue (continued)						
2672	29¢ Fringed Gentian	.50	.15			1.25	11,000,000
2673	29¢ Yellow Lady's Slipper	.50	.15			1.25	11,000,000
2674	29¢ Passionflower	.50	.15			1.25	11,000,000
2675	29¢ Bunchberry	.50	.15			1.25	11,000,000
2676	29¢ Pasqueflower	.50	.15			1.25	11,000,000
2677	29¢ Round-lobed Hepatica	.50	.15			1.25	11,000,000
2678	29¢ Wild Columbine	.50	.15			1.25	11,000,000
2679	29¢ Fireweed	.50	.15			1.25	11,000,000
2680	29¢ Indian Pond Lily	.50	.15			1.25	11,000,000
2681	29¢ Turk's Cap Lily	.50	.15			1.25	11,000,000
2682	29¢ Dutchman's Breeches	.50	.15			1.25	11,000,000
2683	29¢ Trumpet Honeysuckle	.50	.15			1.25	11,000,000
2684	29¢ Jacob's Ladder	.50	.15			1.25	11,000,000
2685	29¢ Plains Prickly Pear	.50	.15			1.25	11,000,000
2686	29¢ Moss Campion	.50	.15			1.25	11,000,000
2687	29¢ Bearberry	.50	.15			1.25	11,000,000
2688	29¢ Mexican Hat	.50	.15			1.25	11,000,000
2689	29¢ Harebell	.50	.15			1.25	11,000,000
2690	29¢ Desert Five Spot	.50	.15			1.25	11,000,000
2691	29¢ Smooth Solomon's Seal	.50	.15			1.25	11,000,000
2692	29¢ Red Maids	.50	.15			1.25	11,000,000
2693	29¢ Yellow Skunk Cabbage	.50	.15			1.25	11,000,000
2694	29¢ Rue Anemone	.50	.15			1.25	11,000,000
2695	29¢ Standing Cypress	.50	.15			1.25	11,000,000
2696	29¢ Wild Flax	.50	.15			1.25	11,000,000
a	Pane of 50, #2647-96	25.00	—	25.00	(50)	32.50	11,000,000

2672 2673 2674 2675 2676

2677 2678 2679 2680 2681

2682 2683 2684 2685 2686

2687 2688 2689 2690 2691

2692 2693 2694 2695 2696

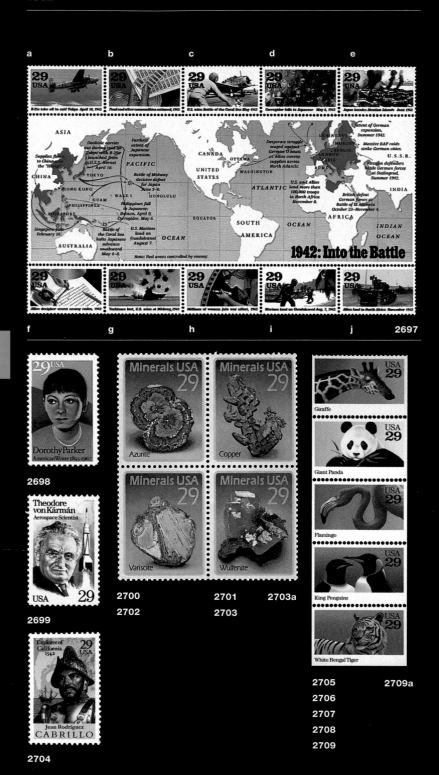

a b c d e

1942: Into the Battle

f g h i j 2697

Dorothy Parker
American Writer 1893-1967

2698

Theodore von Kármán
Aerospace Scientist

2699

Explorer of California 1542
Juan Rodríguez CABRILLO

2704

Minerals USA — Azurite
Minerals USA — Copper
Minerals USA — Variscite
Minerals USA — Wulfenite

2700 2701 2703a
2702 2703

Giraffe
Giant Panda
Flamingo
King Penguins
White Bengal Tiger

2705 2709a
2706
2707
2708
2709

	Issues of 1992 (continued), Perf. 11	Un	U	PB	#	FDC	Q
	World War II Issue Miniature Sheet, Aug. 17						
2697	Sheet of 10 and central label	5.80	2.90				12,000,000
a	29¢ B-25s Take Off to Raid Tokyo	.58	.29			1.25	12,000,000
b	29¢ Food and Other Commodities Rationed	.58	.29			1.25	12,000,000
c	29¢ U.S. Wins Battle of the Coral Sea	.58	.29			1.25	12,000,000
d	29¢ Corregidor Falls to Japanese	.58	.29			1.25	12,000,000
e	29¢ Japan Invades Aleutian Islands	.58	.29			1.25	12,000,000
f	29¢ Allies Decipher Secret Enemy Codes	.58	.29			1.25	12,000,000
g	29¢ Yorktown Lost	.58	.29			1.25	12,000,000
h	29¢ Millions of Women Join War Effort	.58	.29			1.25	12,000,000
i	29¢ Marines Land on Guadalcanal	.58	.29			1.25	12,000,000
j	29¢ Allies Land in North Africa	.58	.29			1.25	12,000,000
2698	29¢ Dorothy Parker, Aug. 22	.50	.15	2.50	(4)	1.25	105,000,000
2699	29¢ Dr. Theodore von Karman, Aug. 31	.50	15	2.50	(4)	1.25	142,500,000
	Minerals Issue, Sept. 17						
2700	29¢ Azurite	.50	15			1.25	36,831,000
2701	29¢ Copper	.50	.15			1.25	36,831,000
2702	29¢ Variscite	.50	.15			1.25	36,831,000
2703	29¢ Wulfenite	.50	.15			1.25	36,831,000
a	Block of 4, #2700-03	2.00	1.10	2.50	(4)	3.00	
2704	29¢ Juan Rodriguez Cabrillo, Sept. 28	.50	.15	2.50	(4)	1.25	85,000,000
	Wild Animals Issue, Oct. 1, Perf. 11 Horizontal						
2705	29¢ Giraffe	.50	.15			1.25	80,000,000
2706	29¢ Giant Panda	.50	.15			1.25	80,000,000
2707	29¢ Flamingo	.50	.15			1.25	80,000,000
2708	29¢ King Penguins	.50	.15			1.25	80,000,000
2709	29¢ White Bengal Tiger	.50	.15			1.25	80,000,000
a	Booklet pane of 5, #2705-09	2.50	—			4.00	

	Issues of 1992 (continued), Perf. 11¹/₂ x 11	Un	U	PB	#	FDC	Q
	Christmas Issue, Oct. 22						
2710	29¢ Madonna and Child by Giovanni Bellini	.50	.15			1.25	300,000,000
a	Booklet pane of 10	5.00					349,254,000
2711	29¢ Horse and Rider	.50	.15			1.25	125,000,000
2712	29¢ Toy Train	.50	.15			1.25	125,000,000
2713	29¢ Toy Steamer	.50	.15			1.25	125,000,000
2714	29¢ Toy Ship	.50	.15			1.25	125,000,000
a	Block of 4, #2711-14	2.00		2.50	(4)	3.00	
	Perf. 11						
2715	29¢ Horse and Rider	.50	.15			1.25	102,137,500
2716	29¢ Toy Train	.50	.15			1.25	102,137,500
2717	29¢ Toy Steamer	.50	.15			1.25	102,137,500
2718	29¢ Toy Ship	.50	.15			1.25	102,137,500
a	Booklet pane of 4, #2715-18	2.00				3.00	
2719	29¢ Toy Train	.58	.15			1.25	21,600,000
a	Booklet pane of 18	10.50	—				
2720	29¢ Happy New Year	.50	.15				

2710

2720

2711   2712   2714a

2713   2714

Elvis Presley (29¢, #2721)
Date of Issue: January 8, 1993
Place of Issue: Memphis, Tennessee
Designer: Mark Stutzman
Printing: Gravure
Elvis Aron Presley changed the face of music worldwide. Justly called the "King of Rock 'n' Roll," he became legendary for his charismatic performing style and unique voice.

Space Fantasy (29¢, #2741-2745 singles, 2745a booklet pane of 5)
Date of Issue: January 25, 1993
Place of Issue: Huntsville, Alabama
Designer: Stephen Hickman
Printing: Gravure
Spaced-themed stamps have long been an American postage staple, but none has ever featured such fun and futuristic designs as these.

Percy Lavon Julian (29¢, #2746)
Date of Issue: January 29, 1993
Place of Issue: Chicago, Illinois
Designer: Higgins Bond
Printing: Offset/Intaglio
This stamp honors a great African-American chemist and scientist. Julian's work paved the way for the treatment of glaucoma.

Oregon Trail (29¢, #2747)
Date of Issue: February 12, 1993
Place of Issue: Salem, Oregon
Designer: Jack Rosenthal
Printing: Offset/Intaglio
This stamp celebrates the 150th anniversary of westward migration along the Oregon Trail.

World University Games (29¢, #2748)
Date of Issue: February 25, 1993
Place of Issue: Buffalo, New York
Designer: David Buck
Printing: Gravure
During July, in Buffalo, New York, 5,000
athletes from 120 countries competed in 12
sports including track and field, baseball,
basketball, swimming and tennis.

Grace Kelly (29¢, #2749)
Date of Issue: March 24, 1993
Place of Issue: Hollywood, California
Designer: Czeslaw Slania
Printing: Intaglio
Loved by millions as one of Hollywood's
greatest actresses, and later as the Princess of
Monaco, she will be forever remembered for
her beauty and dignity.

Oklahoma! (29¢, #2722)
Date of Issue: March 30, 1993
Place of Issue: Oklahoma City, Oklahoma
Designer: Wilson McLean
Printing: Gravure
This stamp commemorates the 50th anniversary
of this famous classic of stage and screen.

Circus (29¢, #2750-2753 singles,
#2753a block of 4)
Date of Issue: April 6, 1993
Place of Issue: Washington, D.C.
Designer: Steve McCracken
Printing: Offset
Celebrating the bicentennial of the
first American circus performance,
these stamps capture the fun and
excitement of the "Greatest Show
on Earth."

315

Cherokee Strip (29¢, #2754)
Date of Issue: April 17, 1993
Place of Issue: Enid, Oklahoma
Designer: Harold Holden
Printing: Offset/Intaglio
This stamp commemorates the 100th anniversary of Oklahoma's Cherokee Strip Land Run.

Dean Acheson (29¢, #2755)
Date of Issue: April 21, 1993
Place of Issue: Washington, D.C.
Designer: Chris Calle
Printing: Intaglio
As Secretary of State under President Truman, Acheson was instrumental in formulating the Marshall Plan to aid war-torn Europe.

Sports Horses (29¢, #2756-2759 singles, #2759a block of 4)
Date of Issue: May 1, 1993
Place of Issue: Louisville, Kentucky
Designer: Michael Dudash
Printing: Offset/Intaglio
The drama and pageantry of polo, steeplechase, harness and track racing are showcased in these action-packed stamps featuring horse and rider.

Garden Flowers (29¢, #2760-2764 singles, #2764a booklet pane of 5)
Date of Issue: May 15, 1993
Place of Issue: Spokane, Washington
Designer: Ned Seidler
Printing: Offset/Intaglio
Both mail users and collectors alike will love these stamps featuring five dazzling spring flowers: iris, tulip, daffodil, hyacinth and lilac.

World War II (1943) (29¢, #2765 miniature sheet of 10, #2765a-j single stamps)
Date of Issue: May 31, 1993
Place of Issue: Washington, D.C.
Designer: Bill Bond
Printing: Offset/Intaglio
This is the third in a set of five sheets to be issued through 1995 to commemorate the 50th anniversary of America's involvement in the second world war.

Hank Williams (29¢, #2723)
Date of Issue: June 9, 1993
Place of Issue: Nashville, Tennessee
Designer: Richard Waldrep
Printing: Gravure
Through songs such as "Your Cheatin' Heart" and "Jambalaya," he popularized Country music years before music videos.

Rock & Roll/Rhythm & Blues
(29¢, #2724-2730 singles from sheets, #2731-2737 singles from booklets, #2737a booklet pane of 4, #2737b booklet pane of 8)
Date of Issue: June 16, 1993
Place of Issue: Cleveland, Ohio and Santa Monica, California
Designer: Mark Stutzman and John Berkey
Printing: Gravure
The Legends of American Music Series continues with these stamps featuring the premier names of early Rock & Roll and Rhythm & Blues. The seven designs were featured in sheets of 35 stamps and in booklets of 20 stamps (containing both panes of 4 and panes of 8 stamps).

Joe Louis (29¢, #2766)
Date of Issue: June 22, 1993
Place of Issue: Detroit, Michigan
Designer: Thomas Blackshear
Printing: Offset/Intaglio
The latest addition to the Sports Series, Joe Louis, also known as the "Brown Bomber," was one of the greatest heavyweight boxers ever to put on the gloves.

Broadway Musicals (29¢, singles, booklet pane of 4)
Date of Issue: July 14, 1993
Place of Issue: New York, New York
Designer: Wilson McLean
Printing: Gravure
Part of the new Legends of American Music Series, these stamps feature four American musical favorites from four different decades.

National Postal Museum (29¢)
Date of Issue: July 30, 1993
Place of Issue: Washington, D.C.
Designer: Richard Schlecht
Printing: Offset/Intaglio
These four stamps helped celebrate the opening of the National Postal Museum in the Old City Post Office building, near Union Station, in Washington, D.C.

Recognizing Deafness/American Sign Language (29¢, singles, set of 2)
Date of Issue: September 20, 1993
Place of Issue: Burbank, California
Designer: Chris Calle
Printing: Gravure
Recognizing deafness at an early age and the use of sign language by those with hearing impairments are two important messages highlighted in these two stamps.

Country & Western (29¢, singles from sheets, singles from booklets, booklet pane of 4)
Date of Issue: September 29, 1993
Place of Issue: Nashville, Tennessee
Designer: Richard Waldrep
Printing: Gravure
These musical pioneers brought Texas Swing, Gospel and traditional music into the homes of millions and laid the groundwork for today's astounding growth of Country music. The four designs were featured in sheets of 20 stamps and in booklets of 20 stamps (5 panes of 4 stamps).

Youth Classics (29¢, singles, block of 4)
Date of Issue: October 1993
Place of Issue: Pending at press time
Designer: Jim Lamb
Printing: Offset/Intaglio
Four of America's most beloved books are honored through stamps featuring: *Rebecca of Sunnybrook Farm*, *Little House on the Prairie*, *The Adventures of Huckleberry Finn* and *Little Women*.

Christmas Contemporary (29¢, singles from booklet, singles from self-adhesive sheet, block of 4, booklet pane of 4)
Date of Issue: October 21, 1993
Place of Issue: Chicago, Illinois
(Self-adhesive versions released October 27, 1993, in New York, New York)
Designer: Peter Good
Printing: Gravure
Four images of Christmas grace the designs of the Contemporary Christmas stamps: a toy soldier, a snowman, a Jack-in-the-box and a red-nosed reindeer.

Christmas Traditional (29¢, singles, singles from booklet)
Date of Issue: October 21, 1993
Place of Issue: Raleigh, North Carolina
Designer: Bradbury Thompson
Printing: Offset/Intaglio
The 1993 art masterpiece stamp features a circa 1515 Cima painting of the Madonna and Child, which now hangs in the North Carolina Museum of Art.

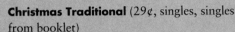

Northern Mariana Islands (29¢)
Date of Issue: November 3, 1993
Place of Issue: Washington, D.C.
Designer: Herb Kane
Printing: Gravure
This stamp recognizes these ocean jewels and their 45-year relationship with the United States as part of the Pacific Trust Territories and now as a Commonwealth.

Columbus Landing in Puerto Rico (29¢)
Date of Issue: November 19, 1993
Place of Issue: Puerto Rico
Designer: Richard Schlecht
Printing: Gravure
In 1493, Christopher Columbus landed in what
is now Puerto Rico during his second voyage to
America. This stamp commemorates the 500th
anniversary of that event.

AIDS Awareness (29¢)
Date of Issue: December 1, 1993
Place of Issue: Pending at press time
Designer: Tom Mann
Printing: Gravure
This stamp recognizes the ongoing battle against
the deadly AIDS virus and the search for a cure.

1993 Issues—Definitive and Airmail

Pledge of Allegiance (29¢)
Date of Issue: March 1993
Designer: Lou Nolan
Printing: Gravure
Printed by a new manufacturer (see original issue, #2594), stamps from these 10-stamp booklets are distinguished by the red (rather than black) "USA 29."

Thomas Jefferson (29¢, #2184B)
Date of Issue: April 13, 1993
Place of Issue: Charlottesville, Virginia
Designer: Chris Calle
Printing: Intaglio
This new stamp in the Great Americans series was issued in conjunction with the 250th birth anniversary of our third President and author of the Declaration of Independence.

USA (23¢, #2608B)
Date of Issue: May 14, 1993
Place of Issue: Denver, Colorado
Designer: Lon Busch
Printing: Gravure
Originally issued in 1992 in two varieties from two different printers (see #2608 and #2608A), a third printer began production in 1993. To distinguish this third variety, the background color was made more purple than the bluish background of the previous two versions.

Eagle (Nondenominated [10¢], #2605 and #2606)
Date of Issue: May 29, 1993
Place of issue: Secaucus, New Jersey
Designer: Chris Calle
Printing: Gravure
The stamp was originally issued in 1991 (see #2604), but two new printers began production in 1993. The new versions are readily distinguished by the inscription "USA Bulk Rate" (rather than the original "Bulk Rate USA"). The new versions are distinguishable from each other because one uses a metallic gold ink, while the other does not.

Space Vehicle ($2.90, #2543)
Date of Issue: June 3, 1993
Place of Issue: Kennedy Space Center, Florida
Designer: Ken Hodges
Printing: Offset/Intaglio
This stamp design of a futuristic spacecraft and other planetary bodies is intended for use on Priority Mail.

Red Squirrel (29¢, #2478)
Date of Issue: June 25, 1993
Place of Issue: Milwaukee, Wisconsin
Designer: Michael Matherly
Printing: Gravure
This stamp was issued in self-adhesive format, with 18 stamps per sheet.

Rose (29¢)
Date of Issue: August 19, 1993
Place of Issue: Houston, Texas
Designer: Gyo Fujikawa
Printing: Gravure
This stamp was issued in self-adhesive format,
with 18 stamps per sheet.

African Violet (29¢)
Date of Issue: October 8, 1993
Place of Issue: Beaumont, Texas
Designer: Ned Seidler
Printing: Gravure
Issued in booklets of 20 stamps, with two
10-stamp panes per booklet.

Pine Cone (29¢)
Date of Issue: November 4, 1993
Place of Issue: Kansas City, Missouri
Designer: Paul Breeden
Printing: Intaglio
This stamp was issued in self-adhesive format,
with 18 stamps per sheet.

1993 Issues—New Printings

Hubert Humphrey (52¢, see #2190)
New printing corrects selvage inscription listing his term as Vice-President
("1965" and "1969" rather than the original 1964 and 1968). Originally
issued in 1991.

Harriet Quimby (50¢, see airmail #C128)
New printing has new selvage inscriptions **without** Olympic sponsorship
message. Originally issued in 1991.

William Piper (40¢, see airmail #C129)
New printing has new selvage inscriptions **without** Olympic sponsorship
message. Originally issued in 1991.

1993 Issues—Postal Stationery

National Cathedral (19¢, #UX166)	January 6, 1993	Postal Card
Wren Building (19¢, #UX167)	February 8, 1993	Postal Card
Holocaust Memorial (19¢, #UX168)	March 23, 1993	Postal Card
Fort Recovery (19¢, #UX169)	June 13, 1993	Postal Card
Playmakers Theatre (19¢, #UX170)	September 14, 1993	Postal Card
O'Kane Hall (19¢, #UX171)	September 17, 1993	Postal Card
Kitten (29¢)	October 2, 1993	Envelope
Beecher Hall (19¢, #UX172)	October 9, 1993	Postal Card
Massachusetts Hall (19¢, #UX173)	October 14, 1993	Postal Card

Share the Excitement of Stamp Ceremonies

- Programs feature biography or background of the stamp's subject
- Comes complete with stamp, postal card or other philatelic item issued

Some of the best moments in philatelic history happen when the Postal Service dedicates the issuance of a new stamp at one of its exciting stamp ceremonies. First Day Ceremonies are held at well-known sites such as the White House, Graceland or the Kentucky Derby.

Share the Moment

You can share the excitement of ceremonies in 1993 and the future! Subscribe to the First Day Ceremony Program now. The price for these limited-edition programs averages approximately $6.00 per program, available by subscription service only.

Subscription Benefits

Colorful, top-quality programs include a list of participants in the ceremonies, a biography or background on the stamp subject and the actual stamp, postal card, stamped envelope or aerogramme affixed and postmarked right in the program.

For More Information

Send in the postage paid request card in this book or write to:

**USPS GUIDE
CEREMONY PROGRAMS
SUBSCRIPTION SERVICE
PHILATELIC FULFILLMENT
SERVICE CENTER
UNITED STATES
POSTAL SERVICE
BOX 449980
KANSAS CITY MO
64144-9980**

American Beauties One and All

- U.S. commemorative stamps issued during the year
- Large-format, informative booklet for displaying stamps
- Clear acetate mounts to protect stamps

A Tribute to America's Best

Whether it's people, places, ideals or events, you'll meet America's winners through U.S. commemorative stamps.

Fun, Informative and Valuable

Commemorative Stamp Collections gather the year's honorees in one convenient, collectible and colorful package. The upcoming Collection will contain 1993 commemoratives, including the following: Circus, National Postal Museum and Christmas Contemporary (blocks of four); the third World War II set (miniature sheet of 10); Garden Flowers (booklet pane of five); American Sign Language pair; Broadway Musicals and Country Music (booklet panes of four); Rock & Roll/Rhythm & Blues (booklet pane of eight); and single stamps featuring Elvis, Grace Kelly, Joe Louis, Percy Lavon Julian, Cherokee Strip, Northern Mariana Islands and Christmas Traditional.

The 1993 Commemorative Stamp Collection is available for $24.95.

To Obtain a Commemorative Stamp Collection

The 1993 Collection and one or two earlier sets may be obtained at your local post office or Philatelic Center. You may also fill out the postage-paid request card in this book or write directly to:

**USPS GUIDE
COMMEMORATIVE
STAMP COLLECTIONS
PHILATELIC FULFILLMENT
SERVICE CENTER
UNITED STATES
POSTAL SERVICE
BOX 449997
KANSAS CITY MO
64144-9997**

1992 Collection Includes:

Space and Columbus (blocks of four); the second World War II set (miniature sheet of 10); Winter and Summer Olympics (strips of five); and Wild Animals (booklet pane of five). ($22.95)

328

Add Stamps Automatically

- Automatic shipment of new stamps, stationery and/or philatelic products you want via mail order
- Quality guaranteed

Convenient and Complete

Armchair collectors need never leave the comfort of home to use the U.S. Postal Service's Standing Order Service subscription program. Sign up once, make an advance deposit, and all postal items you desire will be shipped to you automatically each quarter.

Guaranteed Quality

Subscribers to the Standing Order Service receive mint-condition postal items of exceptional quality—the best available centering, color and printing registration. If you are not completely satisfied, return the item within 30 days for a full refund or replacement.

All products are sold at face value— there are no markups, extra fees or shipping and handling charges. Just make an advance deposit based on the items and quantities you plan to select. You will be notified when you need to replenish your deposit account.

For Information

Send in the postage-paid request card in this book or write to:

**USPS GUIDE
STANDING ORDER
SUBSCRIPTION SERVICE
PHILATELIC FULFILLMENT
SERVICE CENTER
UNITED STATES
POSTAL SERVICE
BOX 449980
KANSAS CITY MO
64144-9980**

330

Join the Club for Collecting Adventure

- A Commemorative Stamp Club Album
- Custom-printed album pages featuring illustrations and mounting areas for individual stamp issues
- Stamps and mounts mailed conveniently to your home

The Commemorative Stamp Club provides a convenient, comprehensive and attractive method for collecting and saving U.S. stamps. Your membership means the start of an exciting adventure, one that will introduce you to America's best—the places, people, events and ideals honored through commemorative stamps.

And if you're looking for further excitement, you can expand your horizons by choosing to receive definitive stamps, other special issues (such as the Music series and the World War II sheets) and album pages. These are offered at the end of each year.

Other Membership Benefits

You'll receive clear acetate mounts to hold and protect your stamps and a free one-year subscription to *Stamps etc.*, a publication mailed four times a year with full-color illustrations of all stamps, postal cards, aerogrammes, stamped envelopes and other collectibles available through mail order.

A no-risk, money-back guarantee assures your satisfaction. If you discontinue your membership within 30 days, simply return the album pages and stamps with a label from one of your shipments, and we'll send you a complete refund; the album is yours to keep.

To Join

For more detailed information, use the postage-paid request card in this book or write to:

**USPS GUIDE
COMMEMORATIVE
STAMP CLUB
PHILATELIC
FULFILLMENT SERVICE
CENTER
UNITED STATES
POSTAL SERVICE
BOX 449980
KANSAS CITY MO
64144-9980**

Issue Date
January 8, 1993

First Day City
Memphis, Tennessee

Designer
Mark Stutzman

Elvis Presley

In the history of popular culture, only a handful of musicians have defined the spirit of an era. Elvis Presley was among those few. Although he did not invent rock & roll, he broadened its appeal by developing a style that brought together elements from country, rhythm & blues, and ballads. Before Elvis, rock & roll had been only one form of pop music among many; after he burst onto the national consciousness in 1956, it dominated the airwaves and sales charts.

Several of rock & roll's early stars died prematurely; others faded after a hit or two; but Elvis turned out one "gold" record after another and retained his hold over a huge audience for the rest of his life.

This stamp, in the Legends of American Music Series, was the first ever selected by a vote of the public. They chose the young Elvis pictured on this issue over an alternative showing an older Elvis later in his career.

Issue Date
January 25, 1993

First Day City
Huntsville, Alabama

Designer
Stephen Hickman

Space Fantasy

Rockets, space stations, and travel to the moon are now accomplished facts. But long before they were achieved, such exploits fired the imaginations of writers and readers. This booklet of five Space Fantasy stamps, comprising a single panoramic view, suggests the past's vision of the future. The stamps' design is reminiscent of the cover art of such pioneering science fiction and fantasy magazines as *Amazing Stories* and *Astounding Science Fiction*.

Futuristic fiction developed into a publishing genre in the 1920s and '30s, spurred by the gathering impact of science on daily life. Although science fiction was not taken seriously at first, the work of such able writers as Isaac Asimov, Arthur C. Clarke, Clifford Simak, and Robert A. Heinlein eventually won it literary respectability.

UNITED STATES
POSTAL SERVICE
(9301)

The Thrill of Favorite Topics on Stamps

- Comprehensive stamp collections devoted to special subjects
- Interesting, informative text in colorfully illustrated books
- Artistic display arrangements complete with protective stamp mounts

There's a Topical Collection Just For You

Whether it's the pure visual appeal of some of America's best stamp designs, the psychological appeal of subjects that evoke fond memories or stir emotions, or the educational appeal of interesting background material on intriguing topics, Topical Stamp Collections contain something for everyone.

Topical Stamp Collections still available include the following:

World War II

Designed for all those whose lives have been affected by the war, these 44-page deluxe, hardbound books are the first three of five annual editions. They focus on the years 1941, 1942 and 1943, and each features two of the striking World War II miniature sheets of 10 stamps—one to grace the front of the book, the other to be broken up and mounted in sections devoted to such subjects as the Battle of Midway, the North Africa landing, Corregidor, the Burma Road, the Atlantic Charter, the bombing of Pearl Harbor and the contributions of medics. ($15.95 each)

To Obtain Topical Collections

Topical Stamp Collections are available at many local post offices and Philatelic Centers. You can also fill out the postage-paid request card in this book or write to:

**USPS GUIDE
TOPICAL STAMP
COLLECTIONS
PHILATELIC FULFILLMENT
SERVICE CENTER
UNITED STATES
POSTAL SERVICE
BOX 449997
KANSAS CITY MO
64144-9980**

334

NOVEMBER 1943

TARAWA TEACHES ATOLL WARFARE

Compared to the battles of Bataan or Guadalcanal, which lasted months and ranged over considerable territory, Tarawa might seem small—a four-day affair fought over a mere 291 acres of sand and palm. But deadly attention in both sides anointed time and place. Tarawa is revered for lives lost there—and lessons taught there.

Lesson one was found in the bravery of young Americans who joined a near defeat into victory, with their blood redeeming errors in planning.

The first problem had to do with tides, which failed to provide the hoped-for five-foot depth needed to float landing craft across vast coral reefs. The first wave, amphibious "amtracs," climbed over reefs like tractors, but the second wave consisted of landing boats that grounded a half mile from shore. Entrenched Japanese had converted the enclave into one of the war's strongest bastions and aimed a murderous fire across the shallows.

The 291 acres comprised the Tarawan island of Betio. It contained the atoll's only airfield. It remained in the defense chain that kept Americans at bay from Japan itself. So the defenders had built 300-plus reinforced concrete casemates and gun emplacements...

seawall of coconut logs. Offshore, mines and barbed wire would funnel attackers into lethal fields of fire.

Unfazed, Rear Adm. Howard Kingman predicted that bombardment would win the battle before Marines landed. He commanded the ships whose guns would deliver 3,000 tons of shells, 10 tons per acre. B-24s had been bombing Betio daily, and hundreds of carrier planes would bomb and strafe it before the assault. "Gentlemen, we will not neutralize Betio," Kingman told 2nd Marine officers, "we will obliterate it."

Once ashore, the Americans would number some 18,000, against less than third as many Japanese. But Betio's defenses caused Rear Adm. Keiji Shibasaki to boast, "A million men cannot take Tarawa in a hundred years." Kingman's prediction died with hundreds of Marines. As landing boats eased up before the reefs, the unthinkable fact emerged that the troops would have to wade in.

And wade they did, arms high to keep weapons dry, as they were cut down by artillery, machine guns and snipers. Those who reached the narrow beach hunkered beneath the seawall, dreading night and the banzai attack that would surely overwhelm them.

But the attack never came. U.S. bombardment had "obliterate the" Betio anese comma...

Marines behind sandbags (above) in the battle for Tarawa. Riflemen (left) take a bead on a sniper in a struggle of shocking ferocity. The U.S. suffered 4,110 casualties, including 1,009 dead. Japanese deaths totaled 4,690. The victors were hard put to find space... tered beach temporary site. The home cost haunted... errors of future land assault. Tarawa became synonym for... and dying.

THE ATLANTA CONSTITUTION
POWERFUL U.S. FORCES GRIP JAPS
...H FIERCE STRUGGLE ON GILBERTS

WORLD WAR II REMEMBERED

1943: TURNING THE TIDE

Collect Every First Day Issue

- Features every stamp issued each year
- Complete with First Day cancellation and informative text
- A convenient, affordable way to collect

The U.S. Postal Service's Souvenir Pages Subscription Program is your ticket to all the year's stamp issues. It's a great way to collect and learn about the stamps and stamp subjects honored during the year.

Fun and Attractive

A Souvenir Page is issued for every stamp—all definitives and commemoratives, as well as airmails, coil stamps and booklet panes. Each Souvenir Page includes the featured stamp(s), postmarked with a First Day of Issue cancellation, mounted on an 8" x 10½" page. Information on relevant philatelic specifications and a lively narrative about the history of the stamp's subject are included.

Affordable Collectibles

Souvenir Pages are printed in a limited quantity each year. The cost of a Souvenir Page currently is approximately $1.25 per page. (In the rare event that the face value of the stamp[s] affixed exceeds $1.25, the price will be the face value.)

Money-back Guarantee

If you are ever dissatisfied, return your Souvenir Pages within 30 days for a full refund. For more information and an order form, fill out request card in this book or write to:

**USPS GUIDE
SOUVENIR PAGES
PROGRAM
PHILATELIC
FULFILLMENT SERVICE
CENTER
UNITED STATES
POSTAL SERVICE
BOX 449980
KANSAS CITY MO
64144-9980**

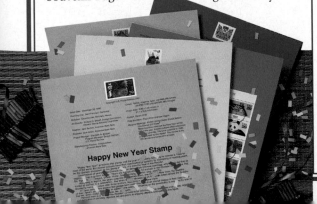

Happy New Year Stamp

Pages in History

- Includes block of four or more mint-condition commemorative stamps mounted on 8½" x 11¼" high-quality paper

Valuable, Elegant Keepsakes

Since the American Commemorative Panel series began in 1972, collectors have recognized these keepsakes as significant milestones in philatelic history. These limited-edition panels are available on an advance subscription basis.

Accompanying the acetate-mounted block of four or more mint stamps are intaglio-printed reproductions of historical steel line engravings and informative articles on the stamp subject.

For Subscription Information

For more information, use the postage-paid request card in this book or write to:

**USPS GUIDE
COMMEMORATIVE
PANEL PROGRAM
PHILATELIC FULFILLMENT
SERVICE CENTER
UNITED STATES
POSTAL SERVICE
BOX 449980
KANSAS CITY MO
64144-9980**

Airmail and Special Delivery Stamps

1918-1938

C1 C2 C3 C4 C5

C6 C7 C10

C11 C12

C13 C14

C15 C18

C20 C21 C23

	Issues of 1918, Perf. 11	Un	U	PB	#	FDC	Q
	For prepayment of postage on all mailable matter sent by airmail. All unwatermarked.						
C1	6¢ Curtiss Jenny, Dec. 10	55.00	25.00	650.00	(6)	*17,500.00*	3,395,900
	Double transfer	80.00	40.00				
C2	16¢ Curtiss Jenny, July 11	80.00	27.50	1,150.00	(6)	*22,500.00*	3,793,900
C3	24¢ Curtiss Jenny, May 13	80.00	32.50	360.00	(4)	*27,500.00*	2,134,900
a	Center Inverted	*135,000.00*		*1,100,000.00*	(4)		
	Issues of 1923						
C4	8¢ Airplane Radiator and Wooden Propeller, Aug. 15	22.50	12.00	250.00	(6)	400.00	6,414,600
C5	16¢ Air Service Emblem, Aug. 17	80.00	27.50	1,900.00	(6)	600.00	5,309,300
C6	24¢ De Havilland Biplane, Aug. 21	80.00	22.50	2,250.00	(6)	750.00	5,285,800
	Issues of 1926-27						
C7	10¢ Map of U.S. and Two Mail Planes, Feb. 13, 1926	2.50	.25	40.00	(6)	55.00	42,092,800
	Double transfer	5.00	1.00				
C8	15¢ olive brown (C7), Sept. 18, 1926	3.00	1.90	45.00	(6)	75.00	15,597,300
C9	20¢ yellow green (C7), Jan. 25, 1927	8.50	1.65	95.00	(6)	100.00	17,616,350
	Issue of 1927-28						
C10	10¢ Lindbergh's "Spirit of St. Louis," June 18, 1927	6.75	1.65	140.00	(6)	20.00	20,379,200
a	Booklet pane of 3, May 26, 1928	82.50	*50.00*			825.00	
	Issue of 1928						
C11	5¢ Beacon on Rocky Mountains, July 25	3.75	.40	175.00	(8)	50.00	106,887,700
	Recut frame line at left	6.00	1.00				
	Issues of 1930						
C12	5¢ Winged Globe, Feb. 10	9.00	.25	160.00	(6)	11.50	97,041,200
a	Horizontal pair, imperf. between	*4,500.00*					
	Graf Zeppelin Issue, Apr. 19						
C13	65¢ Zeppelin over Atlantic Ocean	250.00	150.00	2,000.00	(6)	1,700.00	93,500
C14	$1.30 Zeppelin Between Continents	575.00	350.00	5,000.00	(6)	1,200.00	72,400
C15	$2.60 Zeppelin Passing Globe	900.00	500.00	7,750.00	(6)	1,450.00	61,300
	Issues of 1931-32, Perf. 10½ x 11						
C16	5¢ violet (C12), Aug. 19, 1931	5.00	.35	75.00	(4)	175.00	57,340,050
C17	8¢ olive bister (C12), Sept. 26, 1932	1.90	.20	30.00	(4)	15.00	76,648,800
	Issue of 1933, Century of Progress Issue, Oct. 2, Perf. 11						
C18	50¢ Zeppelin, Federal Building at Chicago Exposition and Hangar at Friedrichshafen	75.00	65.00	800.00	(6)	225.00	324,050
	Beginning with #C19, unused values are for never-hinged stamps.						
	Issue of 1934, Perf. 10½ x 11						
C19	6¢ dull orange (C12), June 30	2.25	.15	25.00	(4)	*175.00*	302,205,100
	Issues of 1935-37, Trans-Pacific Issue, Perf. 11						
C20	25¢ "China Clipper" over the Pacific, Nov. 22, 1935	1.10	.75	25.00	(6)	20.00	10,205,400
C21	20¢ "China Clipper" over the Pacific, Feb. 15, 1937	8.50	1.25	110.00	(6)	20.00	12,794,600
C22	50¢ carmine (C21), Feb. 15, 1937	8.00	4.00	110.00	(6)	20.00	9,285,300
	Issue of 1938						
C23	6¢ Eagle Holding Shield, Olive Branch and Arrows, May 14	.40	.15	8.00	(4)	15.00	349,946,500
a	Vertical pair, imperf. horizontally	300.00					
b	Horizontal pair, imperf. vertically	*10,000.00*					
c	6¢ ultramarine and carmine	150.00					

	Issue of 1939, Perf. 11	Un	U	PB/LP	#	FDC	Q
	Trans Atlantic Issue, May 16						
C24	30¢ Winged Globe	7.50	1.00	165.00	(6)	45.00	19,768,150
	Issues of 1941-44, Perf. 11 x 10½						
C25	6¢ Twin-Motor Transport, June 25, 1941	.15	.15	.80	(4)	2.25	4,476,527,700
a	Booklet pane of 3, Mar. 18, 1943	3.50	*1.00*			25.00	
	Singles of #C25a are imperf. at sides or imperf. at sides and bottom.						
b	Horizontal pair, imperf. between	*1,500.00*					
C26	8¢ olive green (C25), Mar. 21, 1944	.16	.15	1.25	(4)	3.75	1,744,878,650
C27	10¢ violet (C25), Aug. 15, 1941	1.10	.20	8.50	(4)	8.00	67,117,400
C28	15¢ brn. carmine (C25), Aug. 19, 1941	2.25	.35	12.00	(4)	10.00	78,434,800
C29	20¢ bright green (C25), Aug. 27, 1941	1.75	.30	11.00	(4)	12.50	42,359,850
C30	30¢ blue (C25), Sept. 25, 1941	2.00	.30	12.00	(4)	20.00	59,880,850
C31	50¢ orange (C25), Oct. 29, 1941	10.00	3.75	75.00	(4)	40.00	11,160,600
	Issue of 1946						
C32	5¢ DC-4 Skymaster, Sept. 25	.15	.15	.45	(4)	2.00	864,753,100
	Issues of 1947, Perf. 10½ x 11						
C33	5¢ DC-4 Skymaster, Mar. 26	.15	.15	.45	(4)	2.00	971,903,700
	Perf. 11 x 10½						
C34	10¢ Pan American Union Building, Washington, D.C. and Martin 2-0-2, Aug. 30	.25	.15	1.10	(4)	2.00	207,976,550
C35	15¢ Statue of Liberty, N.Y. Skyline and Lockheed Constellation, Aug. 20	.35	.15	1.50	(4)	2.00	756,186,350
a	Horizontal pair, imperf. between	*1,500.00*					
b	Dry printing	.55	.15	2.50	(4)		
C36	25¢ San Francisco-Oakland Bay Bridge and Boeing Stratocruiser, July 30	.85	.15	3.50	(4)	2.75	132,956,100
	Issues of 1948, Coil Stamp, Perf. 10 Horizontally						
C37	5¢ carmine (C33), Jan. 15	.80	.75	8.50	(2)	2.00	33,244,500
	Perf. 11 x 10½						
C38	5¢ New York City, July 31	.15	.15	5.25	(4)	1.75	38,449,100
	Issues of 1949, Perf. 10½ x 11						
C39	6¢ carmine (C33), Jan. 18	.15	.15	.50	(4)	1.50	5,070,095,200
a	Booklet pane of 6, Nov. 18	9.50	*4.00*			9.00	
b	Dry printing	.50	.15	2.25	(4)		
c	As "a," dry printing	15.00	—				
	Perf. 11 x 10½						
C40	6¢ Alexandria, Virginia, May 11	.15	.15	.60	(4)	1.25	75,085,000
	Coil Stamp, Perf. 10 Horizontally						
C41	6¢ carmine (C33), Aug. 25	2.75	.15	12.00	(2)	1.25	260,307,500
	Universal Postal Union Issue, Perf. 11 x 10½						
C42	10¢ Post Office Dept. Bldg., Nov. 18	.20	.18	1.50	(4)	1.75	21,061,300
C43	15¢ Globe and Doves Carrying Messages, Oct. 7	.30	.25	1.50	(4)	2.25	36,613,100
C44	25¢ Boeing Stratocruiser and Globe, Nov. 30	.50	.40	5.75	(4)	3.00	16,217,100
C45	6¢ Wright Brothers, Dec. 17	.15	.15	.65	(4)	3.50	80,405,000
	Issue of 1952						
C46	80¢ Diamond Head, Honolulu, Hawaii, Mar. 26	6.00	1.00	27.50	(4)	17.50	18,876,800
	Issue of 1953						
C47	6¢ Powered Flight, May 29	.15	.15	.55	(4)	1.50	78,415,000
	Issue of 1954						
C48	4¢ Eagle in Flight, Sept. 3	.15	.15	1.75	(4)	1.00	50,484,000

C24

C25

C32

C33

C34

C35

C36

C38

C40

C42

C43

C44

C45

C46

C47

C48

C49

C51

C53

C54

C55

C56

C57

C58

C59

C62

C63

C64

C66

C67

C69

	Issue of 1957, Perf. 11 x 10½	Un	U	PB/LP	#	FDC	Q
C49	6¢ Air Force, Aug. 1	.15	.15	.75	(4)	1.75	63,185,000
	Issues of 1958						
C50	5¢ rose red (C48), July 31	.15	.15	2.00	(4)	1.00	72,480,000
	Perf. 10½ x 11						
C51	7¢ Jet Airliner, July 31	.15	.15	.60	(4)	1.00	1,326,960,000
a	Booklet pane of 6	11.00	6.00			9.50	221,190,000
	Coil Stamp, Perf. 10 Horizontally						
C52	7¢ blue (C51), July 31	2.25	.15	14.00	(2)	1.00	157,035,000
	Issues of 1959, Perf. 11 x 10½						
C53	7¢ Alaska Statehood, Jan. 3	.15	.15	.75	(4)	1.00	90,055,200
	Perf. 11						
C54	7¢ Balloon Jupiter, Aug. 17	.15	.15	.75	(4)	1.10	79,290,000
	Perf. 11 x 10½						
C55	7¢ Hawaii Statehood, Aug. 21	.15	.15	.75	(4)	1.00	84,815,000
	Perf. 11						
C56	10¢ Pan American Games, Aug. 27	.24	.24	1.75	(4)	1.00	38,770,000
	Issues of 1959-60						
C57	10¢ Liberty Bell, June 10, 1960	1.40	.70	6.50	(4)	1.25	39,960,000
C58	15¢ Statue of Liberty, Nov. 20, 1959	.35	.15	1.50	(4)	1.25	98,160,000
C59	25¢ Abraham Lincoln, Apr. 22, 1960	.48	.15	2.00	(4)	1.75	
a	Tagged, Dec. 29, 1966	.60	.25			15.00	
	Issues of 1960, Perf. 10½ x 11						
C60	7¢ Jet Airliner, Aug. 12	.15	.15	.60	(4)	1.00	1,289,460,000
	Pair with full horizontal gutter between	—					
a	Booklet pane of 6, Aug. 19	15.00	7.00			9.50	
	Coil Stamp, Perf. 10 Horizontally						
C61	7¢ carmine (C60), Oct. 22	4.00	.25	32.50	(2)	1.00	87,140,000
	Issues of 1961-67, Perf. 11						
C62	13¢ Liberty Bell, June 28, 1961	.40	.15	1.65	(4)	1.00	
a	Tagged, Feb. 15, 1967	.75	.50			10.00	
C63	15¢ Statue of Liberty, Jan. 13, 1961	.30	.15	1.25	(4)	1.00	
a	Tagged, Jan. 11, 1967	.40	.15			15.00	
b	As "a," hor. pair, imperf. vertically 15,000.00						
	#C63 has a gutter between the two parts of the design; #C58 does not.						
	Issues of 1962-65, Perf. 10½ x 11						
C64	8¢ Jetliner over Capitol, Dec. 5, 1962	.15	.15	.65	(4)	1.00	
a	Tagged, Aug. 1, 1963	.20	.15			2.00	
b	Bklt. pane of 5 + label, Dec. 5, 1962	6.75	2.50			2.00	
c	As "b," tagged, 1964	1.75	.50				
	Coil Stamp, Perf. 10 Horizontally						
C65	8¢ carmine (C64), Dec. 5, 1962	.10	.15	3.75	(2)	1.00	
a	Tagged, Jan. 14, 1965	.35	.15			—	
	Issue of 1963, Perf. 11						
C66	15¢ Montgomery Blair, May 3	.60	.55	3.00	(4)	1.10	42,245,000
	Issues of 1963-67, Perf. 11 x 10½						
C67	6¢ Bald Eagle, July 12, 1963	.15	.15	1.80	(4)	1.00	
a	Tagged, Feb. 15, 1967	2.75	.80			15.00	
	1963 continued, Perf. 11						
C68	8¢ Amelia Earhart, July 24	.20	.15	1.25	(4)	1.75	63,890,000
	Issue of 1964						
C69	8¢ Robert H. Goddard, Oct. 5	.45	.15	1.90	(4)	1.75	62,255,000

	Issues of 1967, Perf. 11	Un	U	PB/LP	#	FDC	Q
C70	8¢ Alaska Purchase, Mar. 30	.24	.15	1.40	(4)	1.00	55,710,000
C71	20¢ "Columbia Jays," by Audubon, Apr. 26 (See also #1241)	.80	.15	3.50	(4)	2.00	165,430,000
	Issues of 1968, Unwmk., Perf. 11 x 10¹/₂						
C72	10¢ 50-Star Runway, Jan. 5	.20	.15	1.00	(4)	1.00	
b	Booklet pane of 8	2.00	.75			3.50	
c	Booklet pane of 5 + label, Jan. 6	3.75	.75			125.00	
	Coil Stamp, Perf. 10 Vertically						
C73	10¢ carmine (C72), Jan. 5	.30	.15	1.70	(2)	1.00	
a	Imperf. pair	600.00		900.00	(2)		
	Perf. 11						
C74	10¢ U.S. Air Mail Service, May 15	.25	.15	2.75	(4)	1.50	
a	Red (tail stripe) omitted		—				
C75	20¢ USA and Jet, Nov. 22	.48	.15	2.25	(4)	1.10	
	Issue of 1969						
C76	10¢ Moon Landing, Sept. 9	.20	.15	.95	(4)	4.50	152,364,800
a	Rose red omitted	425.00					
	Issues of 1971-73, Perf. 10¹/₂ x 11						
C77	9¢ Delta Wing Plane, May 15, 1971	.18	.15	.80	(4)	1.00	
	Perf. 11 x 10¹/₂						
C78	11¢ Silhouette of Jet, May 7, 1971	.20	.15	.90	(4)	1.00	
a	Booklet pane of 4 + 2 labels	1.25	.75			1.75	
C79	13¢ Winged Airmail Envelope, Nov. 16, 1973	.22	.15	1.05	(4)	1.00	
a	Booklet pane of 5 + label, Dec. 27, 1973	1.25	.75			1.75	
b	Untagged (Bureau precanceled)		.28				
	Perf. 11						
C80	17¢ Statue of Liberty, July 13, 1971	.35	.15	1.50	(4)	1.00	
C81	21¢ USA and Jet, May 21, 1971	.40	.15	1.70	(4)	1.00	
	Coil Stamps, Perf. 10 Vertically						
C82	11¢ carmine (C78), May 7, 1971	.25	.15	.80	(2)	1.00	
a	Imperf. pair	175.00		300.00	(2)		
C83	13¢ carmine (C79), Dec. 27, 1973	.26	.15	1.00	(2)	1.00	
a	Imperf. pair	80.00		110.00	(2)		
	Issues of 1972, National Parks Centennial Issue, City of Refuge, May 3, Perf. 11 (See also #1448-54)						
C84	11¢ Kii Statue and Temple at City of Refuge Historical National Park, Honaunau, Hawaii	.20	.15	.90	(4)	1.00	78,210,000
a	Blue and green omitted	1,400.00					
	Olympic Games Issue, Aug. 17, Perf. 11 x 10¹/₂ (See also #1460-62)						
C85	11¢ Skiers and Olympic Rings	.22	.15	2.25	(10)	1.00	96,240,000
	Issues of 1973, Progress in Electronics Issue, July 10, Perf. 11 (See also #1500-02)						
C86	11¢ DeForest Audions	.22	.15	.95	(4)	1.00	58,705,000
a	Vermilion and green omitted	1,500.00					
	Issues of 1974						
C87	18¢ Statue of Liberty, Jan. 11	.40	.25	1.70	(4)	1.00	
C88	26¢ Mount Rushmore National Memorial, Jan. 2	.48	.15	2.00	(4)	1.25	
	Issues of 1976						
C89	25¢ Plane and Globes, Jan. 2	.45	.15	2.10	(4)	1.25	
C90	31¢ Plane, Globes and Flag, Jan. 2	.55	.15	2.30	(4)	1.25	

C70

C71

C72

C74

C75

C76

C77

C78

C79

C80

C81

C84

C85

C86

C87

C88

C89

C90

345

C97

C98

C91   C92a   C93   C94a   C95   C96a
C92   C94   C96

C99   **C100**

C105   C106   C108a
C107   C108

C101   C102   C104a
C103   C104

C109   C110   C112a
C111   C112

	Issues of 1978, Perf. 11	Un	U	PB	#	FDC	Q
	Aviation Pioneers Issue, Wright Brothers, Sept. 23 (See also #C93-96, C99-100, C113-14, C118-19, C128-29)						
C91	31¢ Orville and Wilbur Wright, Flyer A	.65	.30			3.00	157,445,000
C92	31¢ Wright Brothers, Flyer A and Shed	.65	.30			3.00	157,445,000
a	Vert. pair, #C91-92	1.30	.85	3.00	(4)	4.00	
b	As "a," ultramarine and black omitted	900.00					
c	As "a," black omitted	—					
d	As "a," black, yellow, magenta, blue and brown omitted	2,250.00					
	Issues of 1979, Aviation Pioneers Issue, Octave Chanute, Mar. 29						
C93	21¢ Chanute and Biplane Hang-Glider	.70	.32			3.00	29,012,500
C94	21¢ Biplane Hang-Glider and Chanute	.70	.32			3.00	29,012,500
a	Attached pair, #C93-94	1.40	.95	3.50	(4)	4.00	
b	As "a," ultramarine and black omitted	4,000.00					
	Aviation Pioneers Issue, Wiley Post, Nov. 20						
C95	25¢ Wiley Post and "Winnie Mae"	1.10	.35			3.00	32,005,000
C96	25¢ NR-105-W, Post in Pressurized Suit and Portrait	1.10	.35			3.00	32,005,000
a	Attached pair, #C95-96	2.25	.95	9.50	(4)	4.00	
	Olympic Summer Games Issue, Nov. 1 (See also #1790-94)						
C97	31¢ High Jumper	.65	.30	9.50	(12)	1.25	47,200,000
	Issues of 1980-82						
C98	40¢ Philip Mazzei, Oct. 13, 1980	.70	.15	8.75	(12)	1.35	80,935,000
a	Perf. 10½ x 11, 1982	3.00	—				
b	Imperf. pair	2,250.00					
	Issues of 1980, Aviation Pioneers Issues, Blanche Stuart Scott, Dec. 30						
C99	28¢ Portrait of Scott and Biplane	.55	.15	6.75	(12)	1.25	20,190,000
	Glenn Curtiss, Dec. 30						
C100	35¢ Portrait of Curtiss and "Pusher" Biplane	.60	.15	8.00	(12)	1.25	22,945,000
	Issues of 1983, Olympic Summer Games Issue, June 17 (See also #2048-51, 2082-85)						
C101	28¢ Gymnast	.60	.28			1.25	42,893,750
C102	28¢ Hurdler	.60	.28			1.25	42,893,750
C103	28¢ Basketball Player	.60	.28			1.25	42,893,750
C104	28¢ Soccer Player	.60	.28			1.25	42,893,750
a	Block of 4, #C101-04	2.50	1.75	3.50	(4)	3.75	
	Olympic Summer Games Issue, Apr. 8 (See also #2048-51 and 2082-85)						
C105	40¢ Shotputter	.90	.40			1.35	66,573,750
C106	40¢ Gymnast	.90	.40			1.35	66,573,750
C107	40¢ Swimmer	.90	.40			1.35	66,573,750
C108	40¢ Weightlifter	.90	.40			1.05	66,573,750
a	Block of 4, #C105-08	3.60	2.00	5.25	(4)	5.00	
b	As "a," Imperf.	1,350.00					
d	As "a," perf. 11 x 10½	4.25	—				
	Olympic Summer Games Issue, Nov. 4 (See also #2048-51 and 2082-85)						
C109	35¢ Fencer	.90	.35			1.25	42,587,500
C110	35¢ Bicyclist	.90	.35			1.25	42,587,500
C111	35¢ Volleyball Players	.90	.35			1.25	42,587,500
C112	35¢ Pole Vaulter	.90	.35			1.25	42,587,500
a	Block of 4, #C109-12	3.60	1.85	6.00	(4)	4.50	

	Issues of 1985, Perf. 11	Un	U	PB	#	FDC	Q
	Aviation Pioneer Issues, Alfred Verville, Feb. 13, Perf. 11						
C113	33¢ Portrait of Verville and Airplane Diagram	.60	.20	3.00	(4)	1.25	168,125,000
a	Imperf. pair	850.00					
	Lawrence and Elmer Sperry, Feb. 13						
C114	39¢ Portrait of Sperrys and Seaplane	.70	.20	3.25	(4)	1.35	167,825,000
a	Imperf, pair	1,250.00					
C115	44¢ Transpacific Airmail, Feb. 15	.80	.20	3.75	(4)	1.35	209,025,000
a	Imperf. pair	800.00					
C116	44¢ Junipero Serra, Aug. 22	.80	.20	6.00	(4)	1.35	164,350,000
a	Imperf. pair	—					
	Issues of 1988						
C117	44¢ New Sweden, Mar. 29	1.00	.20	5.50	(4)	1.35	136,900,000
C118	45¢ Samuel P. Langley, May 14	.80	.20	3.75	(4)	1.40	406,475,000
C119	36¢ Igor Sikorsky, June 23	.65	.20	3.10	(4)	1.25	179,004,000
	Issues of 1989, Perf. 11½ x 11						
C120	45¢ French Revolution, July 14	.80	.22	4.20	(4)	1.40	38,922,000
	America/PUAS Issue, Oct. 12, Perf. 11 (See also #2426)						
C121	45¢ Southeast Carved Wood Figure, Key Marco Cat (A.D. 700-1450), Emblem of the Postal Union of the Americas and Spain	.80	.22	4.50	(4)	1.40	39,325,000
	20th UPU Congress Issue, Future Mail Transportation, Nov. 28 (See also #2434-38)						
C122	45¢ Hypersonic Airliner	.90	.30			1.40	26,590,000
C123	45¢ Air-Cushion Vehicle	.90	.30			1.40	26,590,000
C124	45¢ Surface Rover	.90	.30			1.40	26,590,000
C125	45¢ Shuttle	.90	.30			1.40	26,590,000
a	Block of 4, #C122-25	3.60	2.25	4.50	(4)	5.00	
b	As "a," light blue omitted	1,500.00					

C113

C114

C115

C116

C117

C118

C119

C120

C121

C122	C123	C125a
C124	C125	

20ᵗʰ Universal Postal Congress

A glimpse at several potential mail delivery methods of the future is the theme of these four stamps issued by the U.S. in commemoration of the convening of the 20th Universal Postal Congress in Washington, D.C. from November 13 through December 14, 1989. The United States, as host nation to the Congress for the first time in ninety-two years, welcomed more than 1,000 delegates from most of the member nations of the Universal Postal Union to the major international event.

©USPS 1988

C126

C127   **C128**   **C129**

C130   **C131**

CE1

E1   **E3**   **E4**

	Issues of 1989 (continued), Imperf.	Un	U	PB	#	FDC	Q
	20th UPU Congress Issue Souvenir Sheet, Nov. 24						
C126	Designs of #C122-25	3.60	2.25			3.00	2,182,400
a-d	Single stamp from sheet	.90	.50				
	Issue of 1990, America/PUAS Issue, Oct. 12, Perf. 11 (See also #2512)						
C127	45¢ Tropical Coast	.90	.20	4.50	(4)	1.40	39,350,000
	Issues of 1991, Aviation Pioneers Issues, Harriet Quimby, Apr. 27						
C128	50¢ Portrait of Quimby and Early Plane	1.00	.24	5.00	(4)	2.00	
	William T. Piper, May 17						
C129	40¢ Portrait of Piper and Piper Cub Airplane	.80	.22	4.00	(4)	1.75	
C130	50¢ Antarctic Treaty, June 21	1.00	.24	5.00	(4)	2.00	113,000,000
	America/PUAS Issue, Oct. 12						
C131	50¢ Eskimo and Bering Land Bridge	1.10	.24	5.00	(4)	2.00	15,260,000
	Airmail Special Delivery Stamps						
	Issues of 1934						
CE1	16¢ Great Seal of the United States, Aug. 30	.55	.65			25.00	
	For imperforate variety see #771.						
	Issue of 1936						
CE2	16¢ red and blue (CE1), Feb. 10	.30	.20	6.50	(4)	17.50	
a	Horizontal pair, imperf. vertically	3,750.00					
	Special Delivery Stamps						
	Issue of 1885, Oct. 1, Perf. 12, Unwmkd.						
E1	10¢ Messenger Running	185.00	27.50	10,000.00	(8)	8,000.00	
	Issue of 1888, Sept. 6						
E2	10¢ blue Messenger Running (E3)	176.00	7.50	10,000.00	(8)		
	Issue of 1893, Jan. 24						
E3	10¢ Messenger Running	110.00	15.00	6,000.00	(8)		
	Issue of 1894, Oct. 10, Line under "Ten Cents"						
E4	10¢ Messenger Running	450.00	14.00	12,000.00	(6)		

	Issue of 1895, Aug. 16, Perf. 12, Wmkd. (191)	Un	U	PB	#	FDC
E5	10¢ blue Messenger Running (E4)	90.00	1.90	*4,000.00*	(6)	
	Double transfer	—	15.00			
	Line of color through "POSTAL DELIVERY"	130.00	9.00			
	Dots in curved frame above messenger	115.00	6.00			
	Issue of 1902, Dec. 9					
E6	10¢ Messenger on Bicycle	55.00	1.90	*2,500.00*	(6)	
	Damaged transfer under "N" of "CENTS"	85.00	3.00			
	Issue of 1908, Dec. 12					
E7	10¢ Mercury Helmet and Olive Branch	40.00	24.00	850.00	(6)	
	Issue of 1911, Jan., Wmkd. (190)					
E8	10¢ ultramarine Messenger on Bicycle (E6)	55.00	2.50	*2,250.00*	(6)	
	Top frame line missing	72.50	3.50			
	Issue of 1914, Sept., Perf. 10					
E9	10¢ ultramarine Messenger on Bicycle (E6)	110.00	3.00	*4,250.00*	(6)	
	Issue of 1916, Oct. 19, Unwmkd.					
E10	10¢ ultramarine Messenger on Bicycle (E6)	200.00	15.00	5,550.00	(6)	
	Issue of 1917, May 2, Perf. 11					
E11	10¢ ultramarine Messenger on Bicycle (E6)	10.00	.25	850.00	(6)	
c	Blue	20.00	.60			
d	Perf. 10 at left	—				
	Issue of 1922, July 12					
E12	10¢ Postman and Motorcycle	18.00	.15	275.00	(6)	400.00
a	10¢ deep ultramarine	25.00	.20			
	Double transfer	35.00	1.00			
	Issues of 1925					
E13	15¢ Postman and Motorcycle, Apr. 11	15.00	.50	150.00	(6)	225.00
E14	20¢ Post Office Truck, Apr. 25	1.65	.85	25.00	(6)	90.00
	Issue of 1927, Nov. 29, Perf. 11 x 10½					
E15	10¢ gray violet Postman and Motorcycle (E12)	.60	.15	4.00	(4)	90.00
c	Horizontal pair, imperf. between	275.00				
	Cracked plate	35.00				
	Issue of 1931, Aug. 13					
E16	15¢ or. Postman and Motorcycle (E13)	.70	.15	3.75	(4)	125.00
	Beginning with #E17, unused values are for never-hinged stamps.					
	Issues of 1944, Oct. 30					
E17	13¢ Postman and Motorcycle	.60	.15	3.00	(4)	12.00
E18	17¢ Postman and Motorcycle	2.75	1.75	22.50	(4)	12.00
	Issue of 1951, Nov. 30					
E19	20¢ black Post Office Truck (E14)	1.25	.15	5.00	(4)	5.00
	Issues of 1954-57					
E20	20¢ Delivery of Letter, Oct. 13, 1954	.40	.15	2.00	(4)	3.00
E21	30¢ Delivery of Letter, Sept. 3, 1957	.50	.15	2.40	(4)	2.25
	Issues of 1969-71, Perf. 11					
E22	45¢ Arrows, Nov. 21, 1969	1.25	.15	5.50	(4)	3.50
E23	60¢ Arrows, May 10, 1971	1.10	.15	4.00	(4)	3.50

E6

E7

E12

E13

E14

E18

E20

E21

E22

E23

Registration, Certified Mail and Postage Due Stamps

1879-1959

F1

FA1

J2

J19

J25

J33

J69

J78

J88

J98

J101

	Issue of 1911, Perf. 12, Wmkd. (190)	Un	U	PB	#	FDC	Q

Registration Stamp

Issued for the prepayment of registry; not usable for postage. Sale discontinued May 28, 1913.

F1	10¢ Bald Eagle, Dec. 11	55.00	3.00	1,350.00	(6)	8,000.00	

Certified Mail Stamp

For use on First-Class mail for which no indemnity value was claimed, but for which proof of mailing and proof of delivery were available at less cost than registered mail.

Issues of 1955, Perf. 10½ x 11

FA1	15¢ Letter Carrier, June 6	.30	.20	4.00	(4)	3.25	54,460,300

Issues of 1879, Printed by American Bank Note Co., Design of J2, Perf. 12, Unwmkd.

Postage Due Stamps

For affixing by a postal clerk to any mail to denote amount to be collected from addressee because of insufficient prepayment of postage.

		Un	U				
J1	1¢ brown	30.00	5.00				
J2	2¢ Figure of Value	200.00	4.00				
J3	3¢ brown	25.00	2.50				
J4	5¢ brown	300.00	30.00				
J5	10¢ brown, Sept. 19	350.00	15.00				
a	Imperf. pair	1,600.00					
J6	30¢ brown, Sept. 19	175.00	35.00				
J7	50¢ brown, Sept. 19	225.00	40.00				
	Special Printing, Soft, Porous Paper						
J8	1¢ deep brown	6,250.00	—				
J9	2¢ deep brown	4,250.00	—				
J10	3¢ deep brown	3,900.00					
J11	5¢ deep brown	3,250.00	—				
J12	10¢ deep brown	2,250.00	—				
J13	30¢ deep brown	2,250.00	—				
J14	50¢ deep brown	2,400.00	—				
J15	1¢ red brown	30.00	2.50				
	Issues of 1884, Design of J19						
J16	2¢ red brown	40.00	2.50				
J17	3¢ red brown	500.00	100.00				
J18	5¢ red brown	250.00	15.00				
J19	10¢ Figure of Value	225.00	10.00				
J20	30¢ red brown	110.00	30.00				
J21	50¢ red brown	1,000.00	125.00				
	Issues of 1891, Design of J25						
J22	1¢ bright claret	14.00	.50				
J23	2¢ bright claret	15.00	.45				
J24	3¢ bright claret	32.50	5.00				
J25	5¢ Figure of Value	35.00	5.00				
J26	10¢ bright claret	70.00	11.00				
J27	30¢ bright claret	250.00	90.00				
J28	50¢ bright claret	275.00	90.00				
	Issues of 1894, Printed by the Bureau of Engraving and Printing, Design of J33, Perf. 12						
J29	1¢ vermilion	650.00	200.00	5,250.00	(6)		
J30	2¢ vermilion	300.00	60.00	2,400.00	(6)		

	Issues of 1894-95, Design of J33, Unwmkd., Perf. 12	Un	U	PB	#
J31	1¢ deep claret, Aug. 14, 1894	22.50	3.00	375.00	(6)
J32	2¢ deep claret, July 20, 1894	17.50	1.75	325.00	(6)
J33	3¢ Figure of Value, Apr. 27, 1895	75.00	20.00	850.00	(6)
J34	5¢ deep claret, Apr. 27, 1895	100.00	22.50	950.00	(6)
J35	10¢ deep claret, Sept. 24, 1894	100.00	17.50	950.00	(6)
J36	30¢ deep claret, Apr. 27, 1895	225.00	60.00		
b	30¢ pale rose	210.00	55.00	2,100.00	(6)
J37	50¢ deep claret, Apr. 27, 1895	500.00	150.00		
a	50¢ pale rose	450.00	135.00	5,000.00	(6)
	Issues of 1895-97, Design of J33, Wmkd. (191)				
J38	1¢ deep claret, Aug. 29, 1895	5.00	.30	190.00	(6)
J39	2¢ deep claret, Sept. 14, 1895	5.00	.20	190.00	(6)
J40	3¢ deep claret, Oct. 30, 1895	35.00	1.00	425.00	(6)
J41	5¢ deep claret, Oct. 15, 1895	37.50	1.00	450.00	(6)
J42	10¢ deep claret, Sept. 14, 1895	40.00	2.00	550.00	(6)
J43	30¢ deep claret, Aug. 21, 1897	300.00	25.00	3,750.00	(6)
J44	50¢ deep claret, Mar. 17, 1896	190.00	20.00	2,250.00	(6)
	Issues of 1910-12, Design of J33, Wmkd. (190)				
J45	1¢ deep claret, Aug. 30, 1910	20.00	2.00		
a	1¢ rose carmine	17.50	1.75	400.00	(6)
J46	2¢ deep claret, Nov. 25, 1910	20.00	.30		
a	2¢ rose carmine	17.50	.30	350.00	(6)
J47	3¢ deep claret, Aug. 31, 1910	350.00	17.50	3,850.00	(6)
J48	5¢ deep claret, Aug. 31, 1910	60.00	3.50		
a	5¢ rose carmine	—	—	600.00	(6)
J49	10¢ deep claret, Aug. 31, 1910	75.00	7.50	1,150.00	(6)
J50	50¢ deep claret, Sept. 23, 1912	600.00	75.00	7,500.00	(6)
	Issues of 1914, Design of J33, Perf. 10				
J52	1¢ carmine lake	40.00	7.50	550.00	(6)
J53	2¢ carmine lake	32.50	.20	350.00	(6)
J54	3¢ carmine lake	425.00	20.00	4,500.00	(6)
J55	5¢ carmine lake	25.00	1.50	285.00	(6)
	5¢ deep claret	—			
J56	10¢ carmine lake	40.00	1.00	600.00	(6)
J57	30¢ carmine lake	145.00	12.00	2,100.00	(6)
J58	50¢ carmine lake	*6,500.00*	375.00	*50,000.00*	(6)
	Issues of 1916, Design of J33, Unwmkd.				
J59	1¢ rose	1,100.00	175.00	8,750.00	(6)
	Experimental Bureau precancel, New Orleans		*125.00*		
J60	2¢ rose	85.00	10.00	800.00	(6)
	Issues of 1917-25, Design of J33, Perf. 11				
J61	1¢ carmine rose	1.75	.15	85.00	(6)
J62	2¢ carmine rose	1.50	.15	35.00	(6)
J63	3¢ carmine rose	8.50	.15	100.00	(6)
J64	5¢ carmine	8.50	.15	100.00	(6)
J65	10¢ carmine rose	12.50	.20	125.00	(6)
	Double transfer	—	—		
J66	30¢ carmine rose	60.00	.40	525.00	(6)
J67	50¢ carmine rose	75.00	.15	750.00	(6)
J68	1/2¢ dull red, Apr. 13, 1925	.70	.15	11.00	(6)

	Issue of 1930-31, Design of J69, Perf. 11	Un	U	PB	#
J69	1/2¢ Figure of Value	3.50	1.00	35.00	(6)
J70	1¢ carmine	2.50	.15	27.50	(6)
J71	2¢ carmine	3.00	.15	40.00	(6)
J72	3¢ carmine	15.00	1.00	250.00	(6)
J73	5¢ carmine	14.00	1.50	225.00	(6)
J74	10¢ carmine	30.00	.50	425.00	(6)
J75	30¢ carmine	85.00	1.00	1,000.00	(6)
J76	50¢ carmine	100.00	.30	1,250.00	(6)
	Design of J78				
J77	$1 carmine	25.00	.15		
a	$1 scarlet	20.00	.15	275.00	(6)
J78	$5 "FIVE" on $	30.00	.15		
a	$5 scarlet	25.00	.15		
b	As "a," wet printing	27.50	.15	375.00	(6)
	Issues of 1931-56, Design of J69, Perf. 11 x 101/2				
J79	1/2¢ dull carmine	.75	.15	22.50	(4)
J80	1¢ dull carmine	.15	.15	1.50	(4)
J81	2¢ dull carmine	.15	.15	1.50	(4)
J82	3¢ dull carmine	.25	.15	2.00	(4)
b	Scarlet, wet printing	.25	.15		
J83	5¢ dull carmine	.35	.15	2.50	(4)
J84	10¢ dull carmine	1.10	.15	6.00	(4)
b	Scarlet, wet printing	1.10	.15		
J85	30¢ dull carmine	8.00	.15	35.00	(4)
J86	50¢ dull carmine	9.50	.15	50.00	(4)
	Design of J78, Perf. 101/2 x 11				
J87	$1 scarlet	35.00	.20	300.00	(4)
	Beginning with #J88, unused values are for never-hinged stamps.				
	Issues of 1959, June 19, Designs of J88, J98 and J101, Perf. 11 x 101/2				
J88	1/2¢ Figure of Value	1.25	.85	165.00	(4)
J89	1¢ carmine rose	.15	.15	.35	(4)
a	"1 CENT" omitted	375.00			
	Pair, one without "1 CENT"	—			
J90	2¢ carmine rose	.15	.15	.45	(4)
J91	3¢ carmine rose	.15	.15	.50	(4)
J92	4¢ carmine rose	.15	.15	.60	(4)
J93	5¢ carmine rose	.15	.15	.65	(4)
J94	6¢ carmine rose	.15	.15	.70	(4)
	Pair, one without "6 CENTS"	800.00			
J95	7¢ carmine rose	.15	.15	.80	(4)
J96	8¢ carmine rose	.15	.15	.90	(4)
J97	10¢ carmine rose	.20	.15	1.00	(4)
J98	30¢ Figure of Value	.55	.15	2.75	(4)
J99	50¢ carmine rose	.90	.15	4.50	(4)
	Design of J101				
J100	$1 carmine rose	1.50	.15	7.50	(4)
J101	$5 Outline Figure of Value	8.00	.15	40.00	(4)
	Issues of 1978-85, Designs of J98				
J102	11¢ carmine rose, Jan. 2, 1978	.25	.15	2.00	(4)
J103	13¢ carmine rose, Jan. 2, 1978	.25	.15	2.00	(4)
J104	17¢ carmine rose, June 10, 1985	.40	.15	25.00	(4)

Official and
Penalty Mail Stamps

1873-1991

O7   O14   O18   O34   O44

O52   O57   O76   O91   O121

O127   O129A   O139   O140   O143

	Issues of 1873, Thin, Hard Paper, Perf. 12, Unwmkd. Department of Agriculture: Yellow	Un	U

Official Stamps

The franking privilege having been abolished as of July 1, 1873, these stamps were provided for each of the departments of government for the prepayment on official matter. These stamps were supplanted on May 1, 1879 by penalty envelopes and on July 5, 1884 were declared obsolete.

		Un	U
O1	1¢ Franklin	90.00	60.00
	Ribbed paper	100.00	50.00
O2	2¢ Jackson	70.00	25.00
O3	3¢ Washington	65.00	3.50
	Double transfer	—	—
O4	6¢ Lincoln	75.00	15.00
O5	10¢ Jefferson	150.00	70.00
	10¢ golden yellow	155.00	62.50
	10¢ olive yellow	165.00	65.00
O6	12¢ Clay	200.00	95.00
	12¢ golden yellow	225.00	90.00
O7	15¢ Webster	150.00	70.00
	15¢ olive yellow	160.00	65.00
O8	24¢ Scott	175.00	70.00
	24¢ golden yellow	190.00	65.00
O9	30¢ Hamilton	225.00	110.00
	30¢ olive yellow	250.00	115.00

Executive Dept. Issue: Carmine

O10	1¢ Franklin	350.00	150.00
O11	2¢ Jackson	225.00	80.00
	Double transfer	—	—
O12	3¢ Washington	275.00	75.00
O13	6¢ Lincoln	400.00	250.00
O14	10¢ Jefferson	375.00	200.00

Dept. of the Interior Issue: Vermilion

O15	1¢ Franklin	20.00	3.50
	Ribbed paper	25.00	4.50
O16	2¢ Jackson	17.50	2.00
O17	3¢ Washington	27.50	2.00
O18	6¢ Lincoln	20.00	2.00
O19	10¢ Jefferson	19.00	4.00
O20	12¢ Clay	30.00	3.00
O21	15¢ Webster	50.00	6.00
	Double transfer of left side	100.00	17.50
O22	24¢ Scott	37.50	5.00
O23	30¢ Hamilton	50.00	6.00
O24	90¢ Perry	110.00	15.00

Dept. of Justice Issue: Purple

O25	1¢ Franklin	60.00	30.00
O26	2¢ Jackson	95.00	30.00
O27	3¢ Washington	95.00	6.00
O28	6¢ Lincoln	90.00	10.00

	Issues of 1873 (continued), Perf. 12	Un	U

Dept. of Justice Issue (continued): Purple

O29	10¢ Jefferson	100.00	27.50
	Double transfer	—	—
O30	12¢ Clay	75.00	15.00
O31	15¢ Webster	165.00	50.00
O32	24¢ Scott	450.00	135.00
O33	30¢ Hamilton	400.00	75.00
	Double transfer at top	420.00	85.00
O34	90¢ Perry	600.00	200.00

Navy Dept. Issue: Ultramarine

O35	1¢ Franklin	45.00	10.00
a	1¢ dull blue	52.50	8.50
O36	2¢ Jackson	32.50	9.00
a	2¢ dull blue	42.50	7.50
	2¢ gray blue	35.00	7.50
O37	3¢ Washington	37.50	4.00
a	3¢ dull blue	42.50	5.50
O38	6¢ Lincoln	32.50	5.00
a	6¢ dull blue	42.50	5.00
	Vertical line through "N" of "NAVY"	65.00	10.00
O39	7¢ Stanton	225.00	70.00
a	7¢ dull blue	250.00	70.00
O40	10¢ Jefferson	45.00	12.50
a	10¢ dull blue	50.00	13.00
	Cracked plate	125.00	—
O41	12¢ Clay	57.50	7.00
	Double transfer of left side	110.00	30.00
O42	15¢ Webster	95.00	20.00
O43	24¢ Scott	95.00	25.00
a	24¢ dull blue	110.00	—
O44	30¢ Hamilton	85.00	10.00
O45	90¢ Perry	400.00	70.00
a	Double impression		3,250.00

Post Office Dept. Issue: Black

O47	1¢ Figure of Value	7.25	3.00
O48	2¢ Figure of Value	7.00	2.50
a	Double impression	300.00	
O49	3¢ Figure of Value	2.50	.55
	Cracked plate	—	—
O50	6¢ Figure of Value	8.00	1.40
	Vertical ribbed paper	—	7.50
O51	10¢ Figure of Value	40.00	15.00
O52	12¢ Figure of Value	22.50	3.50
O53	15¢ Figure of Value	25.00	5.00
a	Imperf. pair	600.00	
	Double transfer	—	—
O54	24¢ Figure of Value	32.50	6.00
O55	30¢ Figure of Value	32.50	5.50
O56	90¢ Figure of Value	47.50	7.50

Issues of 1873 (continued), Perf. 12		
	Un	U
Dept. of State Issue: Green		
O57	1¢ Franklin	60.00	15.00
O58	2¢ Jackson	125.00	25.00
O59	3¢ Washington	50.00	9.00
	Double paper	—	—
O60	6¢ Lincoln	47.50	10.00
O61	7¢ Stanton	90.00	17.50
	Ribbed paper	110.00	19.00
O62	10¢ Jefferson	75.00	13.50
	Short transfer	100.00	27.50
O63	12¢ Clay	110.00	35.00
O64	15¢ Webster	125.00	25.00
O65	24¢ Scott	250.00	75.00
O66	30¢ Hamilton	250.00	45.00
O67	90¢ Perry	400.00	125.00
O68	$2 Seward	550.00	400.00
O69	$5 Seward	4,250.00	2,000.00
O70	$10 Seward	3,000.00	1,500.00
O71	$20 Seward	2,250.00	800.00
Treasury Dept. Issue: Brown		
O72	1¢ Franklin	22.50	1.75
	Double transfer	30.00	3.50
O73	2¢ Jackson	25.00	1.75
	Double transfer	—	5.00
	Cracked plate	40.00	—
O74	3¢ Washington	16.00	.75
	Shaded circle outside right frame line	—	—
O75	6¢ Lincoln	22.50	1.50
	Worn plate	24.00	2.50
O76	7¢ Stanton	57.50	10.00
O77	10¢ Jefferson	57.50	3.00
O78	12¢ Clay	57.50	1.75
O79	15¢ Webster	50.00	2.50
O80	24¢ Scott	250.00	30.00
O81	30¢ Hamilton	82.50	3.00
	Short transfer top right	—	—
O82	90¢ Perry	87.50	3.00
War Dept. Issue: Rose		
O83	1¢ Franklin	82.50	3.25
O84	2¢ Jackson	75.00	4.50
	Ribbed paper	67.50	7.50
O85	3¢ Washington	72.50	1.00
O86	6¢ Lincoln	250.00	2.00
O87	7¢ Stanton	75.00	30.00
O88	10¢ Jefferson	22.50	4.00
O89	12¢ Clay	75.00	2.00
	Ribbed paper	90.00	3.50
O90	15¢ Webster	20.00	2.50
	Ribbed paper	25.00	4.50

Issues of 1873 (continued), Perf. 12		
	Un	U
War Dept. Issue (continued): Rose		
O91	24¢ Scott	20.00	3.00
O92	30¢ Hamilton	22.50	2.50
O93	90¢ Perry	50.00	10.00
Issues of 1879, Soft, Porous Paper		
Dept. of Agriculture: Yellow		
O94	1¢ Franklin, issued without gum	1,500.00	
O95	3¢ Washington	175.00	35.00
Dept. of the Interior Issue: Vermilion		
O96	1¢ Franklin	110.00	85.00
O97	2¢ Jackson	2.50	1.00
O98	3¢ Washington	2.00	.60
O99	6¢ Lincoln	3.00	2.50
O100	10¢ Jefferson	32.50	27.50
O101	12¢ Clay	65.00	40.00
O102	15¢ Webster	150.00	65.00
	Double transfer	200.00	—
O103	24¢ Scott	1,500.00	
O104-05	Not assigned		
Dept. of Justice Issue: Bluish Purple		
O106	3¢ Washington	50.00	22.50
O107	6¢ Lincoln	110.00	80.00
Post Office Dept. Issue: Black		
O108	3¢ Figure of Value	7.50	1.75
Treasury Dept. Issue: Brown		
O109	3¢ Washington	27.50	2.50
O110	6¢ Lincoln	50.00	16.00
O111	10¢ Jefferson	70.00	17.50
O112	30¢ Hamilton	800.00	125.00
O113	90¢ Perry	825.00	125.00
War Dept. Issue: Rose Red		
O114	1¢ Franklin	2.00	1.50
O115	2¢ Jackson	3.00	1.50
O116	3¢ Washington	3.00	.75
a	Imperf. pair	800.00	
b	Double impression	500.00	
	Double transfer	6.00	4.00
O117	6¢ Lincoln	2.50	.80
O118	10¢ Jefferson	20.00	15.00
O119	12¢ Clay	15.00	3.00
O120	30¢ Hamilton	47.50	30.00

Issues of 1910-11, Perf. 12	Un	U

Official Postal Savings Mail

These stamps were used to prepay postage on official correspondence of the Postal Savings Division of the Post Office Department. Discontinued Sept. 23, 1914.

		Un	U
O121	2¢ Postal Savings	9.00	1.10
	Double transfer	12.50	2.00
O122	50¢ dark green Postal Savings	110.00	25.00
O123	$1 ultramarine	100.00	7.00
	Wmkd. (190)		
O124	1¢ dark violet Postal Savings	5.50	1.00
O125	2¢ Postal Savings (O121)	30.00	3.50
O126	10¢ carmine Postal Savings	10.00	1.00

Penalty Mail Stamps

Stamps for use by government departments were reinstituted in 1983. Now known as Penalty Mail stamps, they help provide a better accounting of actual mail costs for official departments and agencies, etc.

Beginning with #O127, unused values are for never-hinged stamps.

Issues of 1983-91, Unwmkd., Perf. 11 x 10½			
O127	1¢, Jan. 12, 1983	.15	.15
O128	4¢, Jan. 12, 1983	.15	.20
O129	13¢, Jan. 12, 1983	.20	.75
O129A	14¢, May 15, 1985	.28	.50
O130	17¢, Jan. 12, 1983	.34	.40

Issues of 1983-91 (continued), Perf. 11 x 10½		Un	U
O131, O134, O137, O142 Not assigned			
O132	$1, Jan. 12, 1983	1.75	1.00
O133	$5, Jan. 12, 1983	9.00	5.00
	Coil Stamps, Perf. 10 Vertically		
O135	20¢, Jan. 12, 1983	2.00	2.00
a	Imperf. pair	1,500.00	
O136	22¢, May 15, 1985	.60	2.00
	Perf. 11		
O138	14¢ D Stamp, Feb. 4, 1985	3.50	5.00
	Coil Stamps, Perf. 10 Vertically		
O138A	15¢, June 11, 1988	.30	.15
O138B	20¢, May 19, 1988	.40	.15
O139	22¢ D Stamp, Feb. 4, 1985	4.50	3.00
O140	25¢ E Stamp, Mar. 22, 1988	.50	2.00
O141	25¢, June 11, 1988	.50	.20
	Perf. 11		
O143	1¢, July 5, 1989	.15	—
	Perf. 10		
O144	29¢ F Stamp, Jan. 22, 1991	.58	.50
O145	29¢, May 24, 1991	.58	.25
	Perf. 11		
O146	4¢, Apr. 6, 1991	.15	.15
O147	19¢, May 24, 1991	.38	.50
O148	23¢, May 24, 1991	.46	.25

Parcel Post and Special Handling Stamps

1912-1955

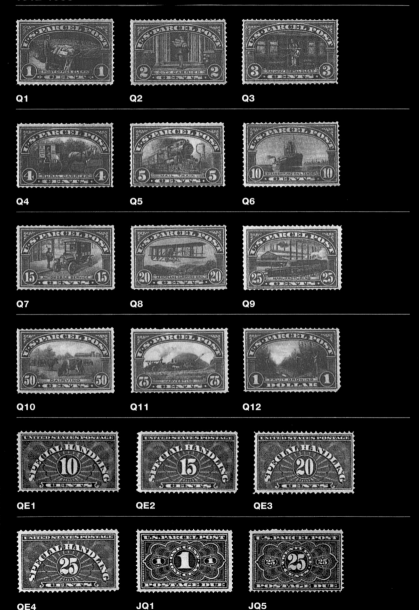

Q1   Q2   Q3

Q4   Q5   Q6

Q7   Q8   Q9

Q10   Q11   Q12

QE1   QE2   QE3

QE4   JQ1   JQ5

Issues of 1913, Wmkd. (190), Perf. 12	Un	U	PB	#	FDC

Parcel Post Stamps

Issued for the prepayment of postage on parcel post packages only. Beginning July 1, 1913 these stamps were valid for all postal purposes.

		Un	U	PB	#	FDC
Q1	1¢ Post Office Clerk, July 1, 1913	2.50	.85	30.00	(4)	*1,500.00*
	Double transfer	5.00	3.00			
Q2	2¢ City Carrier, July 1, 1913	3.00	.60	35.00	(4)	*1,500.00*
	2¢ lake	—				
	Double transfer	—	—			
Q3	3¢ Railway Postal Clerk, Apr. 5, 1913	5.75	4.50	65.00	(4)	*3,000.00*
	Retouched at lower right corner	15.00	12.50			
	Double transfer	15.00	12.50			
Q4	4¢ Rural Carrier, July 1, 1913	16.00	1.90	250.00	(4)	*3,000.00*
	Double transfer	—	—			
Q5	5¢ Mail Train, July 1, 1913	15.00	1.25	250.00	(4)	*3,000.00*
	Double transfer	25.00	5.00			
Q6	10¢ Steamship and Mail Tender	25.00	1.75	300.00	(4)	
	Double transfer	—	—			
Q7	15¢ Automobile Service, July 1, 1913	35.00	7.75	500.00	(4)	
Q8	20¢ Aeroplane Carrying Mail	77.50	15.00	1,050.00	(4)	
Q9	25¢ Manufacturing	35.00	4.00	2,500.00	(6)	
Q10	50¢ Dairying, Mar. 15, 1913	160.00	27.50	1,500.00	(4)	
Q11	75¢ Harvesting	45.00	22.50	3,000.00	(6)	
Q12	$1 Fruit Growing, Jan. 3, 1913	260.00	17.00	*20,000.00*	(6)	

Special Handling Stamps

Issued for use on parcel post packages to secure the same expeditious handling accorded first class mail matter.

Issues of 1925, 1928-29, 1955, Unwmkd., Perf. 11,						
QE1	10¢ Special Handling, 1955	1.00	.80	15.00	(6)	
a	Wet printing, June 25, 1928	2.50	.80			45.00
QE2	15¢ Special Handling, 1955	1.00	.70	27.50	(6)	
a	Wet printing, June 25, 1928	2.50	.70			45.00
QE3	20¢ Special Handling, 1955	1.75	1.00	30.00	(6)	
a	Wet printing, June 25, 1928	3.00	1.00			45.00
QE4	25¢ Special Handling, 1929	13.00	5.50	240.00	(6)	
a	25¢ deep grn., Apr. 11, 1925	22.50	4.50	325.00	(6)	225.00
	"A" and "T" of "STATES" joined at top	37.50	20.00			
	"T" and "A" of "POSTAGE" joined at top	37.50	37.50			

Parcel Post Postage Due Stamps

Issued for affixing by a postal clerk to any parcel post package to denote the amount to be collected from the addressee because of insufficient prepayment of postage. Beginning July 1, 1913 these stamps were valid for use as regular postage due stamps.

Issues of 1912, Wmkd. (190), Perf. 12						
JQ1	1¢ Figure of Value, Nov. 27	5.00	2.75	550.00	(6)	
JQ2	2¢ dark green Parcel Post Postage Due, Dec. 9	45.00	13.00	4,000.00	(6)	
JQ3	5¢ dark green Parcel Post Postage Due, Nov. 27	7.00	3.50	675.00	(6)	
JQ4	10¢ dark green Parcel Post Postage Due, Dec. 12	110.00	30.00	10,000.00	(6)	
JQ5	25¢ Figure of Value, Dec. 16	50.00	3.25	4,500.00	(6)	

Duck Stamps Save Waterfowl

When explorers first set foot on this continent, the skies, lakes and marshes teemed with ducks and geese.

Only 400 years later, America's waterfowl species were in danger of extinction. The Federal Duck Stamp was created to help protect waterfowl and their wetland homes.

As settlers moved across America, enthusiastic hunters depleted a vast number of bird flocks. Millions of acres of marshland were drained to accommodate the country's ever-growing population. To make matters worse, the prolonged drought that created The Dust Bowl had an unfortunate effect on the continent's waterfowl.

But in 1934, one man's concern for wildlife became one of the most successful conservation programs ever. J.N. "Ding" Darling, a famous political cartoonist who had a keen interest in hunting and wildlife, became concerned when he observed the waterfowl habitat in his own state rapidly diminish. Darling developed the concept of a Federal Duck Stamp that every waterfowl hunter would be required to purchase and carry each year. Proceeds from the sale of Duck Stamps would go directly toward the purchase of land to create waterfowl habitats.

Congress passed the Migratory Bird Hunting Stamp Act, making Darling's idea law. In 1934, 635,000 stamps were sold at $1 each. Today each stamp costs approximately $15, and more than 98c of every dollar goes toward the purchase of North American wetlands for waterfowl and many other species of plants and animals. Since 1934, millions of Duck Stamp dollars have contributed to preserving approximately 4 million acres of wetland habitat in the National Wildlife Refuge System.

	Issues of 1934-55	Un	U	PB	#	Q
	Department of Agriculture Duck Stamps					
RW1	1934, $1 Mallards Alighting	400.00	85.00	6,000.00	(6)	635,001
a	Imperf. pair	5,000.00				
b	Vert. pair, imperf. horiz.	—				
RW2	1935, $1 Canvasbacks Taking to Flight	400.00	100.00	7,000.00	(6)	448,204
RW3	1936, $1 Canada Geese in Flight	200.00	50.00	2,500.00	(6)	603,623
RW4	1937, $1 Scaup Ducks Taking to Flight	160.00	27.50	1,750.00	(6)	783,039
RW5	1938, $1 Pintail Drake and Hen Alighting	160.00	35.00	1,800.00	(6)	1,002,715
	Department of the Interior Duck Stamps					
RW6	1939, $1 Green-winged Teal	115.00	15.00	1,200.00	(6)	1,111,561
RW7	1940, $1 Black Mallards	110.00	15.00	1,100.00	(6)	1,260,810
RW8	1941, $1 Family of Ruddy Ducks	110.00	15.00	1,000.00	(6)	1,439,967
RW9	1942, $1 Baldpates	110.00	14.00	1,000.00	(6)	1,383,629
RW10	1943, $1 Wood Ducks	47.50	15.00	425.00	(6)	1,169,352
RW11	1944, $1 White-fronted Geese	40.00	14.00	400.00	(6)	1,487,029
RW12	1945, $1 Shoveller Ducks in Flight	35.00	10.00	225.00	(6)	1,725,505
RW13	1946, $1 Redhead Ducks	32.50	9.00	225.00	(6)	2,016,841
RW14	1947, $1 Snow Geese	35.00	9.00	225.00	(6)	1,722,677
RW15	1948, $1 Buffleheads in Flight	32.50	9.00	225.00	(6)	2,127,603
RW16	1949, $2 Goldeneye Ducks	37.50	8.00	250.00	(6)	1,954,734
RW17	1950, $2 Trumpeter Swans in Flight	45.00	7.00	325.00	(6)	1,903,644
RW18	1951, $2 Gadwall Ducks	45.00	5.00	325.00	(6)	2,167,767
RW19	1952, $2 Harlequin Ducks	45.00	5.00	325.00	(6)	2,296,628
RW20	1953, $2 Blue-winged Teal	45.00	5.00	325.00	(6)	2,268,446
RW21	1954, $2 Ring-necked Ducks	45.00	4.75	325.00	(6)	2,184,550
RW22	1955, $2 Blue Geese	45.00	4.75	325.00	(6)	2,369,940

What does this stamp commemorate?

J.N. "Ding" Darling became concerned when he observed the waterfowl in his own state start to diminish. Darling designed the Duck Stamp, in 1934, to be sold to help create and maintain waterfowl habitats. In 1984, a postage stamp, shown here, was issued to commemorate the 50th anniversary of the design of the original Duck Stamp. **(#2092)**

RW57

RW58

RW59

TAKE PRIDE IN AMERICA
BUY DUCK STAMPS
SAVE WETLANDS

●

SEND IN ALL BIRD BANDS

●

IT IS UNLAWFUL TO HUNT WATERFOWL OR USE THIS STAMP
AS A NATIONAL WILDLIFE REFUGE ENTRANCE PASS UNLESS
YOU SIGN YOUR NAME IN INK ON THE FACE OF THIS STAMP.

back

	Issues of 1956-92	Un	U	PB	#	Q
	Department of the Interior Duck Stamps (continued)					
RW23	1956, $2 American Merganser	45.00	4.75	325.00	(6)	2,332,014
RW24	1957, $2 American Eider	45.00	4.75	325.00	(6)	2,355,190
RW25	1958, $2 Canada Geese	45.00	4.75	325.00	(6)	2,176,425
RW26	1959, $3 Labrador Retriever Carrying Mallard Drake	60.00	4.75	285.00	(4)	1,626,115
RW27	1960, $3 Redhead Ducks	60.00	4.00	285.00	(4)	1,725,634
RW28	1961, $3 Mallard Hen and Ducklings	60.00	4.00	285.00	(4)	1,344,236
RW29	1962, $3 Pintail Drakes Coming in for Landing	70.00	5.50	350.00	(4)	1,147,212
RW30	1963, $3 Pair of Brant Landing	65.00	5.50	350.00	(4)	1,448,191
RW31	1964, $3 Hawaiian Nene Geese	65.00	5.50	2,250.00	(6)	1,573,155
RW32	1965, $3 Three Canvasback Drakes	65.00	5.50	325.00	(4)	1,558,197
RW33	1966, $3 Whistling Swans	65.00	5.00	300.00	(4)	1,805,341
RW34	1967, $3 Old Squaw Ducks	65.00	5.00	300.00	(4)	1,934,697
RW35	1968, $3 Hooded Mergansers	40.00	5.50	200.00	(4)	1,837,139
RW36	1969, $3 White-winged Scoters	40.00	4.50	200.00	(4)	2,072,108
RW37	1970, $3 Ross's Geese	40.00	4.00	200.00	(4)	2,420,244
RW38	1971, $3 Three Cinnamon Teal	27.50	3.75	140.00	(4)	2,441,664
RW39	1972, $5 Emperor Geese	17.00	3.75	75.00	(4)	2,179,628
RW40	1973, $5 Steller's Eiders	17.00	3.75	80.00	(4)	2,113,594
RW41	1974, $5 Wood Ducks	14.00	3.75	62.50	(4)	2,190,268
RW42	1975, $5 Canvasbacks Decoy, 3 Flying Canvasbacks	10.00	3.75	50.00	(4)	2,218,589
RW43	1976, $5 Family of Canada Geese	9.30	0.75	50.00	(4)	2,248,394
RW44	1977, $5 Pair of Ross's Geese	9.50	3.75	50.00	(4)	2,180,625
RW45	1978, $5 Hooded Merganser Drake	9.50	3.75	50.00	(4)	2,196,758
RW46	1979, $7.50 Green-winged Teal	12.00	4.00	55.00	(4)	2,209,572
RW47	1980, $7.50 Mallards	12.00	4.00	55.00	(4)	2,103,021
RW48	1981, $7.50 Ruddy Ducks	12.00	4.00	55.00	(4)	1,907,114
RW49	1982, $7.50 Canvasbacks	12.00	4.00	55.00	(4)	1,926,253
RW50	1983, $7.50 Pintails	12.00	4.00	55.00	(4)	1,867,998
RW51	1984, $7.50 Widgeons	12.00	4.00	55.00	(4)	1,913,509
RW52	1985, $7.50 Cinnamon Teal	12.00	4.00	55.00	(4)	
RW53	1986, $7.50 Fulvous Whistling Duck	12.00	4.00	55.00	(4)	
a	Black omitted	—				
RW54	1987, $10 Redheads	14.00	4.00	65.00	(4)	
RW55	1988, $10 Snow Goose	14.00	4.00	65.00	(4)	
RW56	1989, $12.50 Lesser Scaup	17.00	3.50	80.00	(4)	
RW57	1990, $12.50 Black Bellied Whistling Duck	20.00	3.50	100.00	(4)	
RW58	1991, $15 King Eiders	20.00	4.00	100.00	(4)	
RW59	1992, $15 Spectacled Eider	20.00	4.00	100.00	(4)	

Stamped Envelopes

1875-1893

U172　　　　**U348**

368

Issues of 1853-64	Un	U

Represented below is only a partial listing of stamped envelopes. At least one example is listed for most die types; most die types exist on several colors of envelope paper. Values are for cut squares; prices for entire envelopes are higher. Color in italic is the color of the envelope paper; when no color is specified, envelope paper is white. "W" with catalog number indicates wrapper instead of envelope.

		Un	U
U1	3¢ red Washington (top label 13mm wide), *buff*	185.00	15.00
U4	3¢ red Washington (top label 15mm wide)	185.00	14.00
U5	3¢ red (label has octagonal ends)	3,500.00	350.00
U7	3¢ red (label 20mm wide)	500.00	77.50
U9	3¢ red (label 14½mm)	17.50	2.00
U12	6¢ red Washington, *buff*	85.00	55.00
U14	6¢ green Washington, *buff*	170.00	80.00
U15	10¢ green Washington (label 15½mm wide)	130.00	60.00
U17	10¢ green (label 20mm)	195.00	95.00
a	10¢ pale green	170.00	95.00
U19	1¢ blue Franklin (period after "POSTAGE"), *buff*	27.50	12.50
U23	1¢ blue (bust touches inner frame line), *orange*	400.00	350.00
U24	1¢ blue (no period after "POSTAGE"), *buff*	185.00	90.00
U27	3¢ red, no label, *buff*	15.00	12.50
U28	3¢ + 1¢ (U12 and U9)	325.00	225.00
U30	6¢ red Wash., no label	2,000.00	1,250.00
U33	10¢ green, no label, *buff*	1,000.00	250.00
U34	3¢ pink Washington (outline lettering)	17.50	5.00
U36	3¢ pink, *blue* (letter sheet)	65.00	50.00
U39	6¢ pink Washington, *buff*	60.00	55.00
U40	10¢ yellow green Wash.	27.50	27.50
U42	12¢ red, brn. Wash., *buff*	170.00	150.00
U44	24¢ Washington, *buff*	180.00	140.00
U45	40¢ blk., red Wash., *buff*	275.00	275.00
U46	2¢ black Jackson ("U.S. POSTAGE." downstroke, tail of "2" unite near point)	30.00	15.00
U49	2¢ black ("POSTAGE." downstroke and tail of "2" touch but do not merge), *orange*	975.00	
U50	2¢ blk. Jack. ("U.S. POST." stamp 24-25mm wide), *buff*	9.00	8.50

Issues of 1863-86	Un	U

		Un	U
W51	2¢ blk. Jack. ("U.S. POST." stamp 24-25mm wide), *buff*	150.00	150.00
U54	2¢ blk. Jack. ("U.S. POST." stp. 25½-26½mm), *buff*	11.00	9.00
W55	2¢ blk. Jack. ("U.S. POST." stp. 25½-26½mm), *buff*	75.00	45.00
U58	3¢ pink Washington (solid lettering)	6.00	1.50
U60	3¢ brown Washington	37.50	20.00
U62	6¢ pink Washington	45.00	25.00
U64	6¢ purple Washington	40.00	20.00
U66	9¢ lemon Washington, *buff*	325.00	200.00
U67	9¢ orange Washington, *buff*	90.00	72.50
U68	12¢ brn. Wash., *buff*	325.00	195.00
U69	12¢ red brown Wash., *buff*	85.00	50.00
U70	18¢ red Washington, *buff*	85.00	80.00
U71	24¢ bl. Washington, *buff*	90.00	72.50
U72	30¢ green Washington, *buff*	60.00	50.00
U73	40¢ rose Washington, *buff*	75.00	*200.00*
U75	1¢ blue Franklin (bust points to end of "N" of "ONE"), *amber*	27.50	22.50
U78	2¢ brown Jackson (bust narrow at back, small, thick numerals)	35.00	12.50
U84	3¢ grn. Washington ("ponytail" projects below bust), *cream*	7.50	3.00
U85	6¢ dark red Lincoln (neck very long at back)	16.00	12.50
a	6¢ vermilion	12.50	12.50
U88	7¢ verm. Stanton (figures 7 normal), *amber*	37.50	*165.00*
U89	10¢ olive blk. Jefferson	375.00	375.00
U92	10¢ brown Jefferson, *amber*	65.00	45.00
U93	12¢ plum Clay (chin prominent)	95.00	60.00
U97	15¢ red orange Webster (has side whiskers), *amber*	135.00	165.00
U99	24¢ purple Scott (locks of hair project, top of head)	100.00	90.00
U103	30¢ black Hamilton (back of bust very narrow), *amber*	175.00	200.00
U105	90¢ carmine Perry (front of bust very narrow, pointed)	130.00	185.00
U113	1¢ lt. blue Frank. (lower part of bust points to end of "E" in "ONE")	1.25	.75
a	1¢ dark blue	7.00	5.00

Issues of 1874-86	Un	U
U114	1¢ lt. blue (lower part of bust points to end of "E" in "Postage"), *amber*	3.75	3.00
U122	2¢ brown Jackson (bust narrow at back; numerals thin)	77.50	35.00
U128	2¢ brown Jackson (numerals in long ovals)	37.50	27.50
U132	2¢ brown, die 3 (left numeral touches oval)	50.00	20.00
U134	2¢ brown Jackson (similar to U128-31 but "O" of "TWO" has center netted instead of plain)	600.00	100.00
U139	2¢ brown (bust broad; numerals short, thick)	37.50	30.00
U142	2¢ verm. Jackson (U139)	5.00	2.25
U149	2¢ verm. Jackson (similar to U139-48 but circles around ovals much heavier)	45.00	25.00
W155	2¢ verm. Jackson (like U149 but middle stroke of "N" as thin as verticals), *manila*	15.00	8.00
U156	2¢ verm. Jackson (bottom of bust cut almost semi-circularly)	525.00	100.00
U159	3¢ grn. Wash. (thin letters, long numerals)	17.50	5.00
U163	3¢ grn. Wash. (thick letters, "ponytail" does not project below bust)	1.00	.25
U169	3¢ grn. (top of head egg-shaped; "ponytail" knot projects as point), *amber*	180.00	90.00
U172	5¢ Taylor, die 1 (numerals have thick, curved tops)	9.00	7.00
U177	5¢ blue, die 2 (numerals have long, thin tops)	5.50	5.25
U183	6¢ red Lincoln (neck short at back), *cream*	15.00	9.00
U186	7¢ verm. Stanton (figures turned up at ends), *amber*	85.00	52.50
U187	10¢ brown Jefferson (very large head)	27.50	15.00
U190	10¢ choc. Jeff. (knot of "ponytail" stands out) *amb.*	6.50	5.50
U195	12¢ plum Clay (chin receding)	140.00	72.50
U198	15¢ orange Webster (no side whiskers)	37.50	27.50
U201	24¢ purple Scott (hair does not project)	140.00	100.00
U204	30¢ blk. Hamilton (back of bust rather broad)	50.00	25.00
U212	90¢ carm. Perry (front of bust broad, sloping), *amber*	140.00	185.00
U218	3¢ red Post Rider, Train (1 line under "POSTAGE")	50.00	22.50
U225	5¢ brown Garfield, *blue*	45.00	32.50

Issues of 1883-93	Un	U
U228	2¢ red Washington, *amber*	4.25	1.75
U234	2¢ red, four wavy lines in oval (wavy lines fine, clear), *fawn*	4.00	2.50
U236	2¢ red (wavy lines thick, blurred)	5.00	3.00
U240	2¢ red Washington (3½ links over left "2")	45.00	30.00
U244	2¢ red Wash. (2 links below right "2"), *amber*	110.00	60.00
U249	2¢ red Washington (round "O" in "TWO"), *fawn*	600.00	325.00
U250	4¢ green Jackson, die 1 (left numeral 2¾mm wide)	2.50	2.50
U256	4¢ green, die 2 (left numeral 3¼mm wide)	4.00	3.25
U259	4¢, die 2, *amber manila*	7.75	5.00
U262	2¢ brn. Wash. (U234), *blue*	11.50	8.00
U267	2¢ brn. Wash. (U236)	10.00	5.00
U270	2¢ brown Washington (2 links below right "2")	75.00	32.50
U274	2¢ brown Wash. (round "O" in "TWO"), *amber*	150.00	65.00
U277	2¢ brn. Washington (extremity of bust below "ponytail" forms point)	.35	.15
U288	2¢ brn. Wash. (extremity of bust is rounded)	140.00	30.00
U294	1¢ blue Franklin, no wavy lines	.50	.20
U302	1¢ dark blue, *manila*	19.00	8.00
U307	2¢ grn. Washington ("G" of "POSTAGE" has no bar), *oriental buff*	60.00	25.00
U314	2¢ green ("G" has bar, ear indicated by 1 heavy line), *blue*	.50	.20
U320	2¢ green (like U314 but ear indicated by 2 curved lines), *oriental buff*	145.00	37.50
U327	4¢ carmine Jackson, *blue*	4.00	3.50
U331	5¢ blue Grant (space between beard and collar), *amber*	3.75	1.75
U335	5¢ blue (collar touches beard), *amber*	9.00	5.00
U340	30¢ red brown Hamilton (U204), *manila*	40.00	40.00
U344	90¢ pur. Perry (U212), *oriental buff*	70.00	75.00
U348	1¢ Columbus and Liberty	2.00	1.00
U351	10¢ slate brown	35.00	25.00

Issues of 1899-16		Un	U
U355	1¢ grn. Frank. (U294), *bl.*	9.00	6.00
U358	2¢ carm. Washington (bust points to first notch of inner oval)	2.50	1.50
U362	2¢ carmine (bust points to middle of second notch of inner oval, "ponytail")	.25	.20
U368	2¢ carm. (same as U362 but hair flowing; no ribbon "ponytail"), *amber*	7.50	5.25
U371	4¢ brown Lincoln (bust pointed, undraped)	15.00	10.00
U374	4¢ brown (head larger; inner oval has no notches)	9.00	6.00
U377	5¢ blue Grant (like U331, U335 but smaller)	8.75	8.50
U379	1¢ green Franklin, horizontal oval	.45	.15
U386	2¢ carm. Wash. (1 short, 2 long vertical lines at right of "CENTS", *amber*	1.50	.20
U390	4¢ chocolate Grant	18.00	10.00
U393	5¢ blue Lincoln	16.00	9.50
U398	2¢ carm. Washington, recut die (lines at end of "TWO CENTS" all short), *blue*	3.00	.90
U400	1¢ grn. Frank., oval, die 1 (wide "D" in "UNITED")	.25	.15
U401a	1¢ grn. Frank., die 2 (narrow "D"), *amber*	.85	.70
U402b	1¢, grn. die 3 (wide "S" in "STATES"), *oriental buff*	5.00	1.50
U403c	1¢, die 4 (sharp angle at back of bust, "N," "E" of "ONE" are parallel), *blue*	3.50	1.25
U406	2¢ brn. red Wash., die 1 (oval "O" in "TWO" and "C" in "CENTS")	.70	.15
U407a	2¢, die 2 (like die 1, but hair recut in 2 distinct locks, top of head), *amb.*	100.00	45.00
U408b	2¢, die 3 (round "O" in "TWO" and "C" in "CENTS," coarse letters), *or. buff*	6.00	2.50
U411c	2¢ carmine, die 4 (like die 3 but lettering, hair lines fine, clear)	.35	.15
U412d	2¢ carmine Wash., die 5 (all 3's wide), *amber*	.55	.35
U413e	2¢ carm., die 6 (like die 1 but front of bust narrow), *oriental buff*	.50	.35
U414f	2¢ carm., die 7 (like die 6 but upper corner of front of bust cut away), *blue*	12.50	7.50
U414g	2¢ carm., die 8 (like die 7 but lower stroke of "S" in "CENTS" straight line; hair as in die 2), *blue*	12.50	7.50

Issues of 1907-32		Un	U
U416	4¢ blk. Wash., die 2 ("F" is 13/4mm from left "4")	3.50	2.25
a	4¢, die 1 ("F" is 1mm from left "4")	4.25	3.00
U420	1¢ grn. Frank., round, die 1 ("UNITED" nearer inner circle than outer circle)	.15	.15
U421a	1¢, die 2 (large "U"; "NT" closely spaced), *amber*	300.00	175.00
U423a	1¢ grn. die 3 (knob of hair at back of head; large "NT" widely spaced), *blue*	.75	.45
b	1¢, die 4 ("UNITED" nearer outer circle than inner)	1.25	.65
c	1¢, die 5 (narrow, oval "C")	.65	.35
U429	2¢ carmine Washington, die 1 (letters broad, numerals vertical, "E" closer than "N" to inner circle)	.15	.15
a	2¢, die 2 (like die 1 but "U" far from left circle), *amber*	9.00	6.00
b	2¢, die 3 (like die 2 but inner circles very thin)	30.00	25.00
U430b	2¢, die 4 (like die 1 but "C" very close to left circle), *amber*	20.00	10.00
c	2¢, die 5 (small head, 83/4mm from tip of nose to back of neck; "TS" of "CENTS" close at bottom)	.55	.35
U431d	2¢, die 6 (like die 6 but "TS" of "CENTS" far apart at bottom; left numeral slopes right), *oriental buff*	3.50	2.00
e	2¢, die 7 (large head, both numerals slope right, T's have short top strokes)	3.00	1.75
U432h	2¢, die 8 (like die 7 but all T's have long top strokes), *blue*	.60	.25
i	2¢, die 9 (narrow, oval "C")	.90	.20

	Issues of 1916-62	Un	U
U436	3¢ dk. violet Washington, die 1 (as 2¢)	.50	.15
U440	4¢ black Washington	1.00	.60
U447	2¢ on 3¢ dark violet, rose surcharge	6.00	5.50
U458	Same as U447, black surcharge, bars 2mm apart	.45	.35
U468	Same as U458, bars 1¹/₂mm apart	.60	.45
U481	1¹/₂¢ brown Washington, die 1 (as U429)	.15	.15
W485	1¹/₂¢ brown, *manila*	.75	.15
U490	1¹/₂¢ on 1¢ grn. Franklin, black surcharge	3.75	3.50
U499	1¹/₂¢ on 1¢, *manila*	10.00	6.00
U510	1¹/₂¢ on 1¢ grn., outline numeral in surcharge	1.75	1.25
U522	2¢ carmine Liberty Bell	1.50	.50
a	2¢, center bar of "E" of "Postage" same length as top bar	8.50	6.00
U523	1¢ ol. grn. Mount Vernon	1.75	1.00
U524	1¹/₂¢ choc. Mount Vernon	3.00	1.50
U525	2¢ carmine Mount Vernon	.40	.15
a	2¢, die 2 "S" of "POSTAGE" raised	70.00	16.00
U526	3¢ violet Mount Vernon	4.00	.35
U527	4¢ black Mount Vernon	20.00	15.00
U528	5¢ dark blue Mount Vernon	5.00	3.25
U529	6¢ orange Washington	5.00	2.75
U530	6¢ orange Wash., *amber*	10.00	7.50
U531	6¢ or. Washington, *blue*	10.00	7.50
U532	1¢ green Franklin	5.00	1.75
U533	2¢ carmine Wash. (oval)	.70	.25
U534	3¢ dk. violet Washington, die 4 (short N in UNITED, thin crossbar in A of STATES)	.40	.15
U535	1¹/₂¢ brown Washington	4.50	3.50
U536	4¢ red violet Franklin	.75	.15
U537	2¢ + 2¢ Wash. (U429)	3.00	1.50
U538	2¢ + 2¢ Washington (U533)	.75	.20
U539	3¢ + 1¢ purple, die 1 (4¹/₂mm tall, thick "3")	14.00	10.00
U540	3¢ + 1¢ purple, die 3 (4mm tall, thin "3")	.50	.15
a	Die 2 (4¹/₂mm tall, thin "3" in medium circle), entire	1,000.00	—
U541	1¹/₄¢ turquoise Franklin	.70	.50
a	Die 2 ("4" 3¹/₂mm high), precanceled		2.00
U542	2¹/₂¢ dull blue Washington	.80	.50
U543	4¢ brn. Pony Express Rider	.60	.30
U544	5¢ dark blue Lincoln	.80	.20
c	With albino impression of 4¢ (U536)	50.00	—

	Issues of 1962-78	Un	U
U545	4¢ + 1¢, type 1 (U536)	1.30	.50
U546	5¢ New York World's Fair	.60	.40
U547	1¹/₄¢ brown Liberty Bell		.15
U548	1⁴/₁₀¢ brown Liberty Bell		.15
U548a	1⁶/₁₀¢ orange Liberty Bell		.15
U549	4¢ blue Old Ironsides	.75	.15
U550	5¢ purple Eagle	.75	.15
a	Tagged	1.00	.15
U551	6¢ green Statue of Liberty	.70	.15
U552	4¢ + 2¢ brt. bl. (U549)	3.75	2.00
U553	5¢ + 1¢ brt. pur.(U550)	3.50	2.25
U554	6¢ lt. blue Herman Melville	.50	.15
U555	6¢ Youth Conference	.75	.15
U556	1⁷/₁₀¢ lilac Liberty Bell		.15
U557	8¢ ultramarine Eagle	.40	.15
U561	6¢ + (2¢) lt. grn.	1.00	.30
U562	6¢ + (2¢) lt. blue	2.50	1.00
U563	8¢ rose red Bowling	.50	.15
U564	8¢ Aging Conference	.50	.15
U565	8¢ Transpo '72	.50	.15
U566	8¢ + 2¢ brt. ultra.	.40	.15
U567	10¢ emerald Liberty Bell	.40	.15
U568	1⁸/₁₀¢ Volunteer Yourself		.15
U569	10¢ Tennis Centenary	.30	.16
U571	10¢ Compass Rose	.30	.15
a	Brown "10¢/USA" omitted, entire	110.00	
U572	13¢ Quilt Pattern	.35	.15
U573	13¢ Sheaf of Wheat	.35	.15
U574	13¢ Mortar and Pestle	.35	.15
U575	13¢ Tools	.35	.15
U576	13¢ Liberty Tree	.30	.15
U577	2¢ red Nonprofit		.15
U578	2.1¢ yel. green Nonprofit		.15
U579	2.7¢ green Nonprofit		.15
U580	15¢ orange Eagle, A	.35	.15
U581	15¢ red Uncle Sam	.35	.15
U582	13¢ emerald Centennial	.35	.15
U583	13¢ Golf	.45	.20
U584	13¢ Energy Conservation	.40	.15
d	Blk, red omitted, ent.	200.00	
U585	13¢ Energy Development	.40	.15
U586	15¢ on 16¢ blue USA	.35	.15
U587	15¢ Auto Racing	.35	.15
a	Black omitted, entire	125.00	

U523

U569

U576

U581

U587

U601

U609

U610

U611

U614

U616

U617

UC14

Issues of 1978-92		Un	U
U588	15¢ on 13¢ (U576)	.35	.15
U590	3.5¢ purple Violins		.15
U591	5.9¢ Auth Nonprofit Org		.15
U592	18¢ violet Eagle, B	.45	.18
U593	18¢ dark blue Star	.45	.18
U594	20¢ brown Eagle, C	.45	.15
U595	15¢ Veterinary Medicine	.35	.15
U596	15¢ Summer Oly. Games	.60	.15
a	Red, grn. omitted, ent.	150.00	
U597	15¢ Highwheeler Bicycle	.40	.15
a	Blue "15¢ USA" omitted, entire	100.00	
U598	15¢ America's Cup	.40	.15
U599	Brown 15¢ Honeybee	.35	.15
a	Brown "15¢ USA" omitted, entire	125.00	
U600	18¢ Blind Veterans	.45	.18
U601	20¢ Capitol Dome	.45	.15
U602	20¢ Great Seal of U.S.	.45	.15
U603	20¢ Purple Heart	.45	.15
U604	5.2¢ Auth Nonprofit Org		.15
U605	20¢ Paralyzed Veterans	.45	.15
U606	20¢ Small Business	.50	.15
U607	22¢ Eagle, D	.55	.15
U608	22¢ Bison	.55	.15
U609	6¢ USS Constitution		.15
U610	8.5¢ Mayflower		.15
U611	25¢ Stars	.60	.15
U612	8.4¢ USF Constellation		.15
U613	25¢ Snowflake	.50	.25
U614	25¢ USA, Stars (Philatelic Mail)	.50	.25
U615	25¢ Stars (lined paper)	.50	.25
U616	25¢ Love	.50	.25
U617	25¢ Space hologram	.60	.28
U618	25¢ Football hologram	.50	.25
U619	29¢ Star	.58	.29
U620	11.1¢ Birds		.20
U621	29¢ Love	.58	.29
U622	29¢ Magazine Industry	.58	.29
U623	29¢ Star and Bars	.58	.29
U624	29¢ Country Geese	.58	.58
U625	29¢ Space Shuttle	.58	.29
U626	29¢ Western Americana	.58	.29
U627	29¢ Protect the Environment	.58	.29
U628	19.8¢ Bulk Rate precanceled		.38
U629	29¢ Disabled Americans	.58	.29

Issues of 1929-46, Airmail Envelopes and Aerogrammes		Un	U
UC1	5¢ blue Airplane, die 1 (vertical rudder is not semicircular)	3.50	2.00
	1933 wmk., entire	700.00	700.00
	1937 wmk., entire	—	2000.00
	Bicolored border omitted, entire	600.00	
UC2	5¢ blue, die 2 (vertical rudder is semicircular)	11.00	5.00
	1929 wmk., entire	—	1,500.00
	1933 wmk., entire	600.00	
UC3	6¢ orange Airplane, die 2a ("6" is 6½mm wide)	1.45	.40
a	With #U436a added impression	3,000.00	
UC4	6¢ orange, die 2b ("6" is 6mm wide)	2.75	2.00
UC5	6¢ orange, die 2c ("6" is 5½mm wide)	.75	.30
UC6	6¢ orange, die 3 (vertical rudder leans forward)	1.00	.35
a	6¢ orange, *blue*, entire	3,500.00	2,400.00
UC7	8¢ olive green Airplane	13.00	3.50
UC8	6¢ on 2¢ carm. Washington (U429)	1.25	.65
a	6¢ on 1¢ green (U420)	1,750.00	
c	6¢ on 3¢ purple (U437a)	3,000.00	
UC9	6¢ on 2¢ Wash. (U525)	75.00	40.00
UC10	5¢ on 6¢ orange (UC3)	2.75	1.50
a	Double surcharge	60.00	

Issues of 1946-58		Un	U
UC11	5¢ on 6¢ orange (UC4)	9.00	5.50
UC13	5¢ on 6¢ orange (UC6)	.80	.60
a	Double surcharge	60.00	
UC14	5¢ carm. DC-4, die 1 (end of wing on right is smooth curve)	.75	.20
UC16	10¢ red, DC-4 2-line back inscription, entire, *pale blue*	7.50	6.00
a	"Air Letter" on face, 4-line back inscription	16.00	14.00
	Die-cutting reversed	275.00	
b	10¢ chocolate	400.00	
c	"Air Letter" and "Aerogramme" on face	45.00	12.50
d	3-line back inscription	8.00	8.00
UC17	5¢ Postage Centenary	.40	.25
UC18	6¢ carm. Airplane (UC14), type I (6's lean right)	.35	.15
a	Type II (6's upright)	.75	.25
UC20	6¢ on 5¢ (UC15)	.80	.50
a	6¢ on 6¢ carmine, entire	*1,500.00*	
b	Double surcharge	*250.00*	
UC21	6¢ on 5¢ (UC14)	26.00	17.50
UC22	6¢ on 5¢ (UC14)	3.50	2.50
a	Double surcharge	75.00	
UC23	6¢ on 5¢ (UC17)	1,250.00	
UC25	6¢ red Eagle	.75	.50
UC26	7¢ blue (UC14)	.65	.50

Issues of 1958-73		Un	U
UC27	6¢ + 1¢ orange (UC3)	225.00	225.00
UC28	6¢ + 1¢ orange (UC4)	65.00	75.00
UC29	6¢ + 1¢ (UC5)	37.50	50.00
UC30	6¢ + 1¢ orange (UC5)	1.00	.50
UC32	10¢ Jet Airliner, back inscription in 2 lines	6.00	5.00
a	Type 1, entire	10.00	5.00
UC33	7¢ blue Jet Silhouette	.60	.25
UC34	7¢ carmine (UC33)	.60	.25
UC35	11¢ Jet, Globe, entire	3.00	1.50
a	Red omitted	*875.00*	
a	Die-cutting reversed	35.00	
UC36	8¢ red Jet Airliner	.50	.15
UC37	8¢ red Jet in Triangle	.35	.15
a	Tagged	1.25	.30
UC39	13¢ John Kennedy, entire	3.00	1.50
a	Red omitted	*500.00*	
UC40	10¢ Jet in Triangle	.50	.15
UC41	8¢ + 2¢ (UC37)	.65	.15
UC42	13¢ Human Rights, entire	7.50	4.00
	Die-cutting reversed	75.00	
UC43	11¢ Jet in Circle	.50	.15
UC44	15¢ gray, red, white and blue Birds in Flight	1.50	1.10
UC45	10¢ + (1¢) (UC40)	1.50	.20
UC46	15¢ (UC44) red, white, bl.	.75	.40

Issues of 1973-91		Un	U
UC47	13¢ red Bird in Flight	.30	.15
UC48	18¢ USA, entire	.90	.30
UC50	22¢ red and bl. USA, entire	.90	.40
UC51	22¢ blue USA, entire	.70	.25
	Die-cutting reversed	25.00	
UC52	22¢ Summer Olympic Games	1.50	.22
UC53	30¢ blue, red, brn. Tour the United States, entire	.65	.30
a	Red "30" omitted	75.00	
UC54	30¢ yellow, magenta, blue and black (UC53), entire	.65	.30
	Die-cutting reversed	20.00	
UC55	30¢ Made in USA, entire	.65	.30
UC56	30¢ World Communications Year, entire	.65	.30
	Die-cutting reversed	27.50	
UC57	30¢ Olympic Games, entire	.65	.30
UC58	36¢ Landsat, entire	.72	.36
UC59	36¢ Tourism Week, entire	.72	.36
UC60	36¢ Mark Twain/Halley's Comet, entire	.72	.36
UC61	39¢ Envelope	.78	.40
UC62	39¢ Montgomery Blair	.78	.40
UC63	45¢ Eagle, entire, blue	.90	.45
a	White paper	.90	.45

Issues of 1873-75		Un	U
Official Envelopes			
Post Office Department Numeral 9¹/₂mm high			
UO1	2¢ black, lemon	11.00	6.00
Numeral 10¹/₂mm high			
UO5	2¢ black, lemon	5.00	3.00
UO9	3¢ black, amber	35.00	24.00
Postal Service			
UO16	blue, amber	32.50	22.50
War Department			
UO20	3¢ dk. red Washington	45.00	35.00
UO26	12¢ dark red Clay	95.00	35.00
UO39	10¢ vermilion Jefferson	180.00	
UO48	2¢ red Jackson, amber	22.50	12.50
UO55	3¢ red Washington, fawn	4.00	1.50
Issues of 1983-91 (Entries), Penalty Mail Envelopes			
UO73	20¢ blue Great Seal	.60	30.00
UO74	22¢ (seal embossed)	.65	5.00
UO75	22¢ (seal typographed)	.60	20.00
UO76	25¢ Great Seal, E	.65	20.00
UO77	25¢ black, blue Great Seal (seal embossed)	.65	5.00
UO78	25¢ (seal typographed)	.65	25.00
UO79	45¢ (stars illegible)	1.25	40.00
UO80	65¢ (stars illegible)	1.50	50.00
UO81	45¢ (stars clear)	1.25	40.00
UO82	65¢ (stars clear)	1.50	50.00
UO83	29¢ Great Seal, F	1.00	10.00

Postal Cards

1897-1980

UX14

UX27

UX56

UX70

UX79

UX81

UX83

Issues of 1873-1918		Un	U

Represented below is only a partial listing of postal cards. Values are for entire cards. Color in italic is color of card. Cards preprinted with written address or message usually sell for much less.

		Un	U
UX1	1¢ brown Liberty, wmkd. (90 x 60mm)	300.00	15.00
UX3	1¢ brown Liberty, wmkd. (53 x 36mm)	60.00	2.25
UX4	1¢ blk. Liberty, wmkd USPOD in monogram	2,000.00	300.00
UX5	1¢ blk. Liberty, unwmkd.	50.00	.40
UX6	2¢ blue Liberty, *buff*	20.00	17.50
a	2¢ dark blue, *buff*	26.00	19.00
UX7	1¢ (UX5), inscribed "Nothing But The Address"	50.00	.35
a	23 teeth below "One Cent"	500.00	30.00
b	Printed on both sides	575.00	400.00
UX8	1¢ brown Jefferson, large "one-cent" wreath	35.00	1.25
c	1¢ chocolate	60.00	6.00
UX9	1¢ blk. Jefferson, *buff*	10.00	.55
a	1¢ blk., *dark buff*	16.50	1.25
UX10	1¢ black Grant	25.00	1.40
UX11	1¢ blue Grant	10.00	2.50
UX12	1¢ black Jefferson, wreath smaller than UX14	27.50	.40
UX13	2¢ blue Liberty, *cream*	125.00	75.00
UX14	1¢ Jefferson	22.50	.40
UX15	1¢ black John Adams	30.00	15.00
UX16	2¢ black Liberty	9.00	9.00
UX17	1¢ black McKinley	4,000.00	2,250.00
UX18	1¢ black McKinley, facing left	9.00	.30
UX19	1¢ black McKinley, triangles in top corners	27.50	.50
UX20	1¢ (UX19), correspondence space at left	40.00	5.00
UX21	1¢ blue McKinley, shaded background	90.00	6.50
a	1¢ bronze blue, *bluish*	165.00	12.50
UX22	1¢ blue McKinley, white background	12.50	.25
UX23	1¢ red Lincoln, solid background	6.00	5.50
UX24	1¢ red McKinley	8.00	.25
UX25	2¢ red Grant	1.25	8.50
UX26	1¢ green Lincoln, solid background	7.00	6.00
UX27	1¢ Jefferson, *buff*	.25	.25
a	1¢ green, *cream*	3.50	.60
UX27C	1¢ green Jefferson, *gray*, die I	1,750.00	150.00
UX28	1¢ green Lincoln, *cream*	.60	.30
a	1¢ green, *buff*	1.50	.60
UX29	2¢ red Jefferson, *buff*	35.00	2.00
a	2¢ lake, *cream*	45.00	2.50

Issues of 1917-68		Un	U
c	2¢ vermilion, *buff*	275.00	60.00
UX30	2¢ red Jefferson, *cream*	19.00	1.50
	Surcharged in one line by canceling machine.		
UX31	1¢ on 2¢ red Jefferson	*3,500.00*	*3,500.00*
	Surcharged in two lines by canceling machine.		
UX32	1¢ on 2¢ red Jeff., *buff*	40.00	12.50
a	1¢ on 2¢ vermilion	*95.00*	*60.00*
b	Double surcharge	—	*82.50*
UX33	1¢ on 2¢ red Jefferson, *cream*	7.50	1.75
a	Inverted surcharge	55.00	
b	Double surcharge	55.00	35.00
d	Triple surcharge	350.00	
	Surcharged in two lines by press printing.		
UX34	1¢ on 2¢ red (UX29)	500.00	45.00
UX35	1¢ on 2¢ red Jefferson, *cream*	200.00	30.00
UX36	1¢ on 2¢ red (UX25)		3,500.00
UX37	3¢ red McKinley, *buff*	3.75	*9.00*
UX38	2¢ carmine rose Franklin	.35	.25
a	Double impression	200.00	
	Surcharged by canceling machine in light green.		
UX39	2¢ on 1¢ grn. Jefferson, *buff*	.50	.35
b	Double surcharge	17.50	20.00
UX40	2¢ on 1¢ green (UX28)	.65	.45
	Surcharged typographically in dark green.		
UX41	2¢ on 1¢ green Jefferson, *buff*	3.50	1.50
a	Invrtd surchge lower left	75.00	125.00
UX42	2¢ on 1¢ green (UX29)	5.00	2.00
a	Surcharged on back	80.00	
UX43	2¢ carmine Lincoln	.25	*1.00*
UX44	2¢ FIPEX	.25	*1.00*
b	Dk. vio. blue omitted	450.00	225.00
UX45	4¢ Statue of Liberty	1.50	*40.00*
UX46	3¢ purple Statue of Liberty	.40	.20
a	"N GOD WE TRUST"	12.00	25.00
UX47	2¢ + 1¢ carmine rose Franklin	160.00	250.00
UX48	4¢ red violet Lincoln	.25	.20
UX49	7¢ World Vacationland	3.00	*35.00*
UX50	4¢ U.S. Customs	.40	*1.00*
a	Blue omitted	450.00	
UX51	4¢ Social Security	.40	*1.00*
b	Blue omitted	*700.00*	
UX52	4¢ blue & red Coast Guard	.30	*1.00*
UX53	4¢ Bureau of the Census	.30	*1.00*
UX54	8¢ blue & red (UX49)	3.00	*35.00*
UX55	5¢ emerald Lincoln	.30	.50
UX56	5¢ Women Marines	.35	*1.00*

Issues of 1970-83		Un	U
UX57	5¢ Weather Services	.30	1.00
a	Yellow, black omitted	700.00	
b	Blue omitted	650.00	
c	Black omitted	600.00	
UX58	6¢ brown Paul Revere	.30	1.00
a	Double impression	300.00	
UX59	10¢ blue & red (UX49)	3.00	35.00
UX60	6¢ America's Hospitals	.30	1.00
a	Blue, yellow omitted	700.00	
UX61	6¢ USF Constellation	.30	3.00
a	Address side blank	300.00	
UX62	6¢ black Monument Valley	.35	3.00
UX63	6¢ Gloucester, MA	.35	3.00
UX64	6¢ blue John Hanson	.25	1.00
UX65	6¢ magenta Liberty	.25	1.00
UX66	8¢ orange Samuel Adams	.25	1.00
UX67	12¢ Visit USA/ Ship's Figurehead	.35	30.00
UX68	7¢ Charles Thomson	.30	5.00
UX69	9¢ John Witherspoon	.25	1.00
UX70	9¢ blue Caesar Rodney	.25	1.00
UX71	9¢ Federal Court House	.25	1.00
UX72	9¢ green Nathan Hale	.25	1.00
UX73	10¢ Cincinnati Music Hall	.30	1.00
UX74	10¢ John Hancock	.30	1.00
UX75	10¢ John Hancock	.30	.15
UX76	14¢ Coast Guard Eagle	.40	15.00
UX77	10¢ Molly Pitcher	.30	1.00
UX78	10¢ George Rogers Clark	.30	1.00
UX79	10¢ Casimir Pulaski	.30	1.00
UX80	10¢ Olympic Sprinter	.50	1.00
UX81	10¢ Iolani Palace	.30	1.00
UX82	14¢ Olympic Games	.50	10.00
UX83	10¢ Salt Lake Temple	.25	1.00
UX84	10¢ Landing of Rochambeau	.25	1.00
UX85	10¢ Battle of Kings Mtn.	.25	1.00
UX86	19¢ Drake's Golden Hinde	.55	10.00
UX87	10¢ Battle of Cowpens	.25	2.50
UX88	12¢ violet Eagle, nondenominated	.30	.50
UX89	12¢ lt. bl. Isaiah Thomas	.30	.50
UX90	12¢ Nathanael Greene	.30	1.00
UX91	12¢ Lewis and Clark	.30	3.00
UX92	13¢ buff Robert Morris	.30	.50
UX93	13¢ buff Robert Morris	.30	.75
UX94	13¢ "Swamp Fox" Francis Marion	.30	.75
UX95	13¢ LaSalle Claims Louisiana	.30	.75
UX96	13¢ Academy of Music	.30	.75
UX97	13¢ Old Post Office, St. Louis, Missouri	.30	.75
UX100	13¢ Olympic Yachting	.30	.75

Issues of 1984-90		Un	U
UX101	13¢ *Ark* and *Dove,* Maryland	.30	.75
UX102	13¢ Olympic Torch	.30	.75
UX103	13¢ Frederic Baraga	.30	.75
UX104	13¢ Dominguez Adobe	.30	.75
UX105	14¢ Charles Carroll	.30	.50
UX106	14¢ green Charles Carroll	.30	.15
UX107	25¢ Clipper *Flying Cloud*	.70	5.00
UX108	14¢ brt. grn. George Wythe	.30	.50
UX109	14¢ Settlement of Connecticut	.30	.75
UX110	14¢ Stamp Collecting	.30	.75
UX111	14¢ Francis Vigo	.30	.75
UX112	14¢ Settling of Rhode Island	.30	.75
UX113	14¢ Wisconsin Territory	.30	.75
UX114	14¢ National Guard	.30	.75
UX115	14¢ Self-Scouring Plow	.30	.50
UX116	14¢ Constitutional Convention	.30	.50
UX117	14¢ Stars and Stripes	.30	.50
UX118	14¢ Take Pride in America	.30	.50
UX119	14¢ Timberline Lodge	.30	.50
UX120	15¢ Bison and Prairie	.30	.25
UX121	15¢ Blair House	.30	.30
UX122	28¢ *Yorkshire*	.60	3.00
UX123	15¢ Iowa Territory	.30	.30
UX124	15¢ Ohio, Northwest Terr.	.30	.30
UX125	15¢ Hearst Castle	.30	.30
UX126	15¢ The Federalist Papers	.30	.30
UX127	15¢ Hawk and Desert	.30	.30
UX128	15¢ Healy Hall	.30	.30
UX129	15¢ Blue Heron and Marsh	.30	.30
UX130	15¢ Settling of Oklahoma	.30	.30
UX131	21¢ Geese and Mountains	.42	3.00
UX132	15¢ Seagull and Seashore	.30	.30
UX133	15¢ Deer and Waterfall	.30	.30
UX134	15¢ Hull House, Chicago	.30	.30
UX135	15¢ Ind. Hall, Philadelphia	.30	.30
UX136	15¢ Inner Harbor, Baltimore	.30	.30
UX137	15¢ Bridge, New York	.30	.30
UX138	15¢ Capitol, Washington	.30	.30
	#UX139-42 issued in sheets of 4 plus 2 inscribed labels, rouletted 9 1/2 on 2 or 3 sides.		
UX139	15¢ (UX135)	.30	.90
UX140	15¢ The White House	.30	.90
UX141	15¢ (UX137)	.30	.90
UX142	15¢ (UX138)	.30	.90
a	Sheet of 4, #UX139-42	1.20	
UX143	15¢ The White House	1.00	1.00
UX144	15¢ Jefferson Memorial	1.00	1.00
UX145	15¢ Papermaking	.30	.30
UX146	15¢ World Literacy Year	.30	.30

"Swamp Fox" Francis Marion, 1782

UX94

Settling of Connecticut, 1636

UX109

Settling of Rhode Island, 1636

UX112

Wisconsin Territory, 1836

UX113

Self-scouring steel plow, 1837

UX115

Constitutional Convention, 1787

UX116

Take Pride in America, 14 USA

UX118

UX119

UX131

UX143

UX144

UXC19

UXC20

UXC23

Issues of 1990-92	Un	U
UX147 15¢ George Caleb Bingham	1.00	1.00
UX148 15¢ Isaac Royall House	.30	.30
UX150 15¢ Stanford University	.30	.30
UX151 15¢ Constitution Hall	1.00	1.00
UX152 15¢ Chgo. Orchestra Hall	.30	.30
UX153 19¢ Flag	.38	.19
UX154 19¢ Carnegie Hall	.38	.38
UX155 19¢ Old Red, UT-Galveston	.38	.38
UX156 19¢ Bill of Rights	.38	.38
UX157 19¢ Notre Dame	.38	.38
UX158 30¢ Niagara Falls	.60	.60
UX159 19¢ The Old Mill	.38	.38
UX160 19¢ Wadsworth Atheneum, Hartford, CT	.38	.38
UX161 19¢ Cobb Hall, University of Chicago	.38	.38
UX162 19¢ Waller Hall, Willamette University	.38	.38
UX163 19¢ America's Cup	1.00	1.00
UX164 19¢ Columbia River Gorge	.38	.38
UX165 19¢ Ellis Island Immigration Museum	.38	.38

Issues of 1892-1988, Paid Reply Postal Cards

Prices are: Un=unsevered, U=severed card.

		Un	U
UY1	1¢ + 1¢ black Grant	35.00	7.50
UY6	1¢ + 1¢ green G. and M. Washington, double frame line around instructions	140.00	22.50
UY7	1¢ + 1¢ green G. and M. Washington, single frame line	1.00	.50
UY12	3¢ + 3¢ red McKinley	9.00	25.00
UY18	4¢ + 4¢ Lincoln	2.50	2.50
UY23	6¢ + 6¢ John Adams	.75	2.00
UY31	12¢ + 12¢ Eagle, nondenominated	.75	2.00
UY39	15¢ + 15¢ Bison and Prairie	.75	1.00

Issues of 1949-88	Un	U
Airmail Postal Cards		
UXC1 4¢ orange Eagle	.45	.75
UXC2 5¢ red Eagle (C48)	1.50	.75
UXC3 5¢ UXC2 redrawn—"Air Mail-Postal Card" omitted	6.00	2.00
UXC4 6¢ red Eagle	.45	.75
UXC5 11¢ Visit The USA	.50	12.50
UXC6 6¢ Virgin Islands	.40	6.00
a Red, yellow omitted	1,700.00	
UXC7 6¢ Boy Scout World Jamboree	.40	6.00
UXC8 13¢ blue & red (UXC5)	1.25	8.00
UXC9 8¢ Stylized Eagle	.60	2.00
UXC10 9¢ red & blue (UXC5)	.50	1.00
UXC11 15¢ Commerce Department Travel Service	1.50	12.50
UXC12 9¢ black Grand Canyon	.50	8.00
UXC13 15¢ black Niagara Falls	.65	15.00
UXC14 11¢ Stylized Eagle	.70	2.00
UXC15 18¢ Eagle Weather Vane	.85	7.00
UXC16 21¢ Angel Weather Vane	.80	7.50
UXC17 21¢ Curtiss Jenny	.75	6.00
UXC18 21¢ Olympic Gymnast	.95	10.00
UXC19 28¢ First Transpacific Flight	.90	4.00
UXC20 28¢ Gliders	.90	3.00
UXC21 28¢ Olympic Speed Skater	.90	2.00
UXC22 33¢ China Clipper	.90	2.00
UXC23 33¢ AMERIPEX '86	.65	2.00
UXC24 36¢ DC-3	.70	1.00
UXC25 40¢ Yankee Clipper	.80	1.00
Issues of 1913-91, Official Mail Postal Cards		
UZ1 1¢ black Numeral	325.00	150.00
UZ2 13¢ blue Great Seal	.50	35.00
UZ3 14¢ blue Great Seal	.50	30.00
UZ4 15¢ blue Great Seal	.50	15.00
UZ5 19¢ blue Great Seal	.38	—

Souvenir Pages

With First Day Cancellations

The Postal Service offers Souvenir Pages for new stamps. The series began with a page for the Yellowstone Park Centennial stamp issued March 1, 1972. The Pages feature one or more stamps tied by the first day cancel, along with technical data and information on the subject of the issue. More than just collectors' items, Souvenir Pages make wonderful show and conversation pieces. Souvenir Pages are issued in limited editions. Number in parentheses ( ) indicates number of stamps on page if there are more than one.

	1972	
72-0	Family Planning	750.00
72-1	Yellowstone Park	110.00
72-1a	Yellowstone Park	
	with DC cancel	500.00
72-2	2¢ Cape Hatteras	100.00
72-3	14¢ Fiorello	
	LaGuardia	110.00
72-4	11¢ City of	
	Refuge Park	100.00
72-5	6¢ Wolf Trap	
	Farm Park	40.00
72-6	Colonial Craftsmen (4)	20.00
72-7	11¢ Mount McKinley	30.00
72-8	6¢-11¢	
	Olympic Games (4)	10.00
72-8E	Olympic Games with	
	broken red circle on	
	6¢ stamp	1,000.00
72-9	PTA	7.50
72-10	Wildlife	
	Conservation (4)	10.00
72-11	Mail Order	7.50
72-12	Osteopathic Medicine	7.50
72-13	Tom Sawyer	7.50
72-14	7¢ Benjamin Franklin	7.50
72-15	Christmas (2)	10.00
72-16	Pharmacy	7.50
72-17	Stamp Collecting	7.50
	1973	
73-1	$1 Eugene O'Neill	15.00
73-1E	$1 Eugene O'Neill	
	picture perforation	
	error	750.00
73-2	Love	10.00
73-3	Pamphleteer	6.00
73-4	George Gershwin	7.00
73-5	Broadside	20.00
73-6	Copernicus	6.00
73-7	Postal Employees	8.00
73-8	Harry S. Truman	6.00
73-9	Post Rider	6.00
73-10	21¢ Amadeo Gianninni	6.00
73-11	Boston Tea Party (4)	8.00
73-12	6¢-15¢ Electronics (4)	8.00
73-13	Robinson Jeffers	5.00
73-14	Lyndon B. Johnson	5.00
73-15	Henry O. Tanner	6.00
73-16	Willa Cather	5.00
73-17	Colonial Drummer	5.00
73-18	Angus Cattle	5.00
73-19	Christmas (2)	7.00
73-20	13¢ Winged Envelope	
	airmail	4.00
73-21	10¢ Crossed Flags	4.00
73-22	10¢ Jefferson Memorial	4.00
73-23	13¢ Winged Envelope	
	airmail coil (2)	4.00

	1974	
74-1	26¢ Mount Rushmore	
	airmail	6.00
74-2	ZIP Code	5.00
74-2E	ZIP Code with	
	date error 4/4/74	500.00
74-3	18¢ Statue of Liberty	
	airmail	7.50
74-4	18¢ Elizabeth Blackwell	3.00
74-5	VFW	3.00
74-6	Robert Frost	3.00
74-7	EXPO '74	3.00
74-8	Horse Racing	3.50
74-9	Skylab	7.50
74-10	UPU (8)	6.00
74-11	Mineral Heritage (4)	7.50
74-12	Fort Harrod	3.00
74-13	Continental	
	Congress (4)	5.00
74-14	Chautauqua	3.00
74-15	Kansas Wheat	3.00
74-16	Energy Conservation	3.00
74-17	6.3¢ Liberty Bell coil (2)	5.00
74-18	Sleepy Hollow	4.00
74-19	Retarded Children	3.00
74-20	Christmas (3)	6.00
	1975	
75-1	Benjamin West	3.00
75-2	Pioneer/Jupiter	7.00
75-3	Collective Bargaining	3.00
75-4	8¢ Sybil Ludington	4.00
75-5	Salem Poor	5.00
75-6	Haym Salomon	4.00
75-7	18¢ Peter Francisco	4.00
75-8	Mariner 10	6.00
75-9	Lexington & Concord	3.00
75-10	Paul Dunbar	5.00
75-11	D.W. Griffith	4.00
75-12	Bunker Hill	3.00
75-13	Military Uniforms (4)	7.00
75-14	Apollo Soyuz (2)	7.00
75-15	International	
	Women's Year	3.00
75-16	Postal Service	
	Bicentennial (4)	5.00
75-17	World Peace	
	Through Law	3.00
75-18	Banking	
	& Commerce (2)	3.00
75-19	Christmas (2)	5.00
75-20	3¢ Francis Parkman	4.00
75-21	11¢ Freedom	
	of the Press	3.00
75-22	24¢ Old North Church	3.00
75-23	Flag over	
	Independence Hall (2)	3.00
75-24	9¢ Freedom	
	to Assemble (2)	3.00

75-25	Liberty Bell coil (2)	3.00
75-26	Eagle & Shield	3.00
	1976	
76-1	Spirit of '76 (3)	5.00
76-1E	Spirit of '76 with	
	cancellation error	
	Jan. 2, 1976 (3)	1,000.00
76-2	25¢ and 31¢ Plane	
	and Globes airmails (2)	4.00
76-3	Interphil '76	4.00
76-4	State Flags,	
	DE to VA (10)	10.00
76-5	State Flags,	
	NY to MS (10)	10.00
76-6	State Flags,	
	IL to WI (10)	10.00
76-7	State Flags,	
	CA to SD (10)	10.00
76-8	State Flags,	
	MT to HI (10)	10.00
76-9	9¢ Freedom	
	to Assemble coil (2)	3.00
76-10	Telephone Centennial	3.00
76-11	Commercial Aviation	3.00
76-12	Chemistry	3.00
76-13	7.9¢ Drum coil (2)	3.00
76-14	Benjamin Franklin	3.00
76-15	Bicentennial	
	souvenir sheet	10.00
76-15E	Bicentennial	
	souvenir sheet with	
	perforation and	
	numerical errors	1,000.00
76-16	18¢ Bicentennial	
	souvenir sheet	10.00
76-17	24¢ Bicentennial	
	souvenir sheet	10.00
76-18	31¢ Bicentennial	
	souvenir sheet	10.00
76-19	Declaration	
	of Independence (4)	5.00
76-20	Olympics (4)	5.00
76-21	Clara Maass	3.00
76-22	Adolph S. Ochs	3.00
76-23	Christmas (3)	4.00
76-24	7.7¢ Saxhorns coil (2)	3.00
	1977	
77-1	Washington	
	at Princeton	3.00
77-2	Flag over Capitol booklet	
	pane (9¢ and 13¢)	
	Perf. 10 (8)	20.00
77-3	Sound Recording	3.00
77-4	Pueblo Pottery (4)	4.00
77-5	Lindbergh Flight	4.00
77-6	Colorado Centennial	3.00
77-7	Butterflies (4)	4.00

Please detach at perforation.

Penalty for private
use to avoid payment
of postage: $300

United States Postal Service
Kansas City MO 64144-9997

Official Business

United States Postal Service
Philatelic Fulfillment Service Center
Box 449997
Kansas City MO 64144-9997

Ibilmhmdilmllmlmlmlmdmllmll

Additional Information on Stamp Collecting Products

Item #8893
Price $9.95

You can expand your stamp collection and keep it updated with philatelic products from the USPS. Check the box next to the products you'd like to learn more about.

❏ *American Commemorative Panels*
❏ *Commemorative Stamp Collections*
❏ *Commemorative Stamp Club*
❏ *Souvenir Pages Program*
❏ *Standing Order Service*
❏ *Topical Stamp Collections*

...And a Free Offer!

Let us know if you're interested in receiving:
❏ *A copy of **Stamps, etc.**, our catalog which contains details and mail-order information on all stamps and stamp products currently available from the Postal Service.*

Neatly print your name and address below, and drop this card in the mail—no postage necessary. (Information that you provide is protected and only disclosed in accordance with the Privacy Act of 1974.)

Mr./Mrs./Ms.

Street Address
(Include P.O. Box, Apt. no., R.D. Route, etc., where appropriate)

City   State   ZIP Code

Please detach at perforation.

77-8	Lafayette	3.00
77-9	Skilled Hands (4)	4.00
77-10	Peace Bridge	3.00
77-11	Battle of Oriskany	3.00
77-12	Alta, CA, First Civil Settlement	3.00
77-13	Articles of Confederation	3.00
77-14	Talking Pictures	3.00
77-15	Surrender at Saratoga	3.00
77-16	Energy (2)	3.00
77-17	Christmas, Mailbox and Christmas, Valley Forge, Omaha cancel (2)	3.00
77-18	Same, Valley Forge cancel	3.00
77-19	10¢ Petition for Redress coil (2)	3.00
77-20	10¢ Petition for Redress sheet (2)	3.00
77-21	1¢-4¢ Americana (5)	3.00

1978

78-1	Carl Sandburg	3.00
78-2	Indian Head Penny	3.00
78-3	Captain Cook, Anchorage cancel (2)	4.00
78-4	Captain Cook, Honolulu cancel (2)	4.00
78-5	Harriet Tubman	5.00
78-6	American Quilts (4)	4.00
78-7	16¢ Statue of Liberty sheet and coil (2)	3.00
78-8	29¢ Sandy Hook Lighthouse	3.00
78-9	American Dance (4)	4.00
78-10	French Alliance	3.00
78-11	Early Cancer Detection	3.00
78-12	"A" (15¢) sheet and coil (2)	6.00
78-13	Jimmie Rodgers	5.00
78-14	CAPEX '78 (8)	10.00
78-15	Oliver Wendell Holmes coil	3.00
78-16	Photography	3.00
78-17	Fort McHenry Flag sheet and coil (2)	4.00
78-18	George M. Cohan	3.00
78-19	Rose booklet single	3.00
78-20	8.4¢ Piano coil (2)	4.00
78-21	Viking Missions	6.00
78-22	70¢ Remote Outpost	4.00
78-23	American Owls (4)	4.00
78-24	31¢ Wright Brothers airmails (2)	4.00
78-25	American Trees (4)	4.00
78-26	Christmas, Madonna	3.00
78-27	Christmas, Hobby Horse	3.00
78-28	$2 Kerosene Lamp	7.50

1979

79-1	Robert F. Kennedy	3.00
79-2	Martin Luther King, Jr.	5.00
79-3	International Year of the Child	3.00
79-4	John Steinbeck	3.00
79-5	Albert Einstein	3.00
79-6	21¢ Octave Chanute airmails (2)	4.00
79-7	Pennsylvania Toleware (4)	4.00
79-8	American Architecture (4)	4.00
79-9	Endangered Flora (4)	4.00
79-10	Seeing Eye Dogs	3.00
79-11	$1 Lamp & Candle	6.00
79-12	Special Olympics	3.00
79-13	$5 Lantern	15.00
79-14	30¢ Schoolhouse	4.00
79-15	10¢ Summer Olympics (2)	4.00
79-16	50¢ Whale Oil Lamp	5.00
79-17	John Paul Jones	3.00
79-18	Summer Olympics (4)	5.00
79-19	Christmas, Madonna	4.00
79-20	Christmas, Santa Claus	4.00
79-21	3.1¢ Guitar coil (2)	10.00
79-22	31¢ Summer Olympics airmail	6.00
79-23	Will Rogers	3.00
79-24	Vietnam Veterans	3.00
79-25	25¢ Wiley Post airmails (2)	5.00

1980

80-1	W.C. Fields	3.00
80-2	Winter Olympics (4)	6.00
80-3	Windmills booklet pane (10)	6.00
80-4	Benjamin Banneker	5.00
80-5	Letter Writing (6)	3.00
80-6	1¢ Ability to Write (2)	3.00
80-7	Frances Perkins	3.00
80-8	Dolley Madison	3.00
80-9	Emily Bissell	3.00
80-10	3.5¢ Violins coil (2)	4.00
80-11	Helen Keller/ Anne Sullivan	3.00
80-12	Veterans Administration	3.00
80-13	General Bernardo de Galvez	3.00
80-14	Coral Reefs (4)	4.00
80-15	Organized Labor	5.00
80-16	Edith Wharton	5.00
80-17	Education	5.00
80-18	Indian Masks (4)	4.00
80-19	American Architecture (4)	4.00
80-20	40¢ Philip Mazzei airmail	4.00
80-21	Christmas, Madonna	4.00
80-22	Christmas, Antique Toys	4.00
80-23	Sequoyah	3.00
80-24	28¢ Blanche Scott airmail	3.00
80-25	35¢ Glenn Curtiss airmail	3.00

1981

81-1	Everett Dirksen	3.00
81-2	Whitney M. Young	5.00
81-3	"B" (18¢) sheet and coil (3)	4.00
81-4	"B" (18¢) booklet pane (8)	3.00
81-5	12¢ Freedom of Conscience sheet and coil (3)	4.00
81-6	Flowers block (4)	3.00
81-7	Flag and Anthem sheet and coil (3)	4.00
81-8	Flag and Anthem booklet pane (8 - 6¢ and 18¢)	4.00
81-9	American Red Cross	3.00
81-10	George Mason	3.00
81-11	Savings & Loans	3.00
81-12	Wildlife booklet pane (10)	5.00
81-13	Surrey coil (2)	5.00
81-14	Space Achievement (8)	10.00
81-15	17¢ Rachel Carson (2)	3.00
81-16	35¢ Charles Drew, MD	4.00
81-17	Professional Management	3.00
81-18	17¢ Electric Auto coil (2)	5.00
81-19	Wildlife Habitat (4)	4.00
81-20	International Year of the Disabled	3.00
81-21	Edna St. Vincent Millay	5.00
81-22	Alcoholism	4.00
81-23	American Architecture (4)	4.00
81-24	Babe Zaharias	4.00
81-25	Bobby Jones	4.00
81-26	Frederic Remington	3.00
81-27	"C" (20¢) sheet and coil (3)	5.00
81-28	"C" (18¢) booklet pane (10)	4.00
81-29	18¢ and 20¢ Hoban (2)	3.00
81-30	Yorktown/ Virginia Capes (2)	3.00
81-31	Christmas, Madonna	4.00
81-32	Christmas, Bear on Sleigh	5.00
81-33	John Hanson	3.00
81-34	Fire Pumper coil (2)	7.00
81-35	Desert Plants (4)	4.00
81-36	9.3¢ Mail Wagon coil (3)	6.00
81-37	Flag over Supreme Court sheet and coil (3)	6.00
81-38	Flag over Supreme Court booklet pane (6)	5.00

1982

82-1	Sheep booklet pane (10)	4.00
82-2	Ralph Bunche	7.00
82-3	13¢ Crazy Horse (2)	3.00
82-4	37¢ Robert Millikan	3.00
82-5	Franklin D. Roosevelt	3.00
82-6	Love	3.00
82-7	5.9¢ Bicycle coil (4)	7.00
82-8	George Washington	8.00
82-9	10.9¢ Hansom Cab coil (2)	6.00
82-10	Birds & Flowers, AL-GE (10)	15.00
82-11	Birds & Flowers, HI-MD (10)	15.00
82-12	Birds & Flowers, MA-NJ (10)	15.00
82-13	Birds & Flowers, NM-SC (10)	15.00
82-14	Birds & Flowers, SD-WY (10)	15.00
82-15	USA/Netherlands	3.00
82-16	Library of Congress	3.00
82-17	Consumer Education coil (2)	4.00
82-18	Knoxville World's Fair (4)	3.00
82-19	Horatio Alger	3.00
82-20	2¢ Locomotive coil (2)	4.00
82-21	Aging Together	3.00
82-22	The Barrymores	3.00
82-23	Mary Walker	3.00
82-24	Peace Garden	3.00
82-25	America's Libraries	3.00
82-26	Jackie Robinson	15.00
82-27	4¢ Stagecoach coil (3)	5.00
82-28	Touro Synagogue	3.00
82-29	Wolf Trap Farm Park	3.00
82-30	American Architecture (4)	3.00
82-31	Francis of Assisi	3.00
82-32	Ponce de Leon	3.00
82-33	13¢ Kitten & Puppy (2)	4.00
82-34	Christmas, Madonna	4.00
82-35	Christmas, Seasons Greetings (4)	4.00
82-36	2¢ Igor Stravinsky (2)	3.00

1983

83-1	1¢, 4¢, 13¢ Penalty Mail (5)	3.00
83-2	1¢ and 17¢ Penalty Mail (1)	3.00
83-3	Penalty Mail coil (2)	4.00
83-4	$1 Penalty Mail	5.00
83-5	$5 Penalty Mail	10.00
83-6	Science & Industry	3.00
83-7	5.2¢ Antique Sleigh coil (4)	6.00
83-8	Sweden/USA Treaty	3.00
83-9	3¢ Handcar coil (3)	5.00
83-10	Balloons (4)	3.00
83-11	Civilian Conservation Corps	3.00
83-12	40¢ Olympics airmails (4)	4.00
83-13	Joseph Priestley	3.00
83-14	Volunteerism	3.00
83-15	Concord/German Immigration	3.00
83-16	Physical Fitness	3.00
83-17	Brooklyn Bridge	3.00
83-18	TVA	3.00
83-19	4¢ Carl Schurz (5)	3.00
83-20	Medal of Honor	3.00
83-21	Scott Joplin	5.00
83-22	Thomas H. Gallaudet	3.00
83-23	28¢ Olympics (4)	5.00
83-24	5¢ Pearl S. Buck (4)	3.00
83-25	Babe Ruth	12.50
83-26	Nathaniel Hawthorne	3.00
83-27	3¢ Henry Clay (7)	3.00
83-28	13¢ Olympics (4)	5.00
83-29	$9.35 Eagle booklet single	125.00
83-30	$9.35 Eagle booklet pane (3)	200.00
83-31	1¢ Omnibus coil (3)	5.00
83-32	Treaty of Paris	3.00
83-33	Civil Service	3.00
83-34	Metropolitan Opera	3.00
83-35	Inventors (4)	4.00
83-36	1¢ Dorothea Dix (3)	3.00
83-37	Streetcars (4)	4.00
83-38	5¢ Motorcycle coil (4)	5.00
83-39	Christmas, Madonna	3.00
83-40	Christmas, Santa Claus	3.00
83-41	35¢ Olympics airmails (4)	5.00

83-42	Martin Luther	4.00		
83-43	Flag over Supreme Court booklet pane (10)	4.00		

1984

84-1	Alaska Statehood	3.00
84-2	Winter Olympics (4)	5.00
84-3	FDIC	3.00
84-4	Harry S. Truman	3.00
84-5	Love	3.00
84-6	Carter G. Woodson	5.00
84-7	11¢ RR Caboose coil (2)	5.00
84-8	Soil & Water Conservation	3.00
84-9	Credit Union Act	3.00
84-11	40¢ Lillian M. Gilbreth	3.00
84-11	Orchids (4)	4.00
84-12	Hawaii Statehood	3.00
84-13	7.4¢ Baby Buggy coil (3)	5.00
84-14	National Archives	3.00
84-15	20¢ Summer Olympics (4)	5.00
84-16	New Orleans World's Fair	3.00
84-17	Health Research	3.00
84-18	Douglas Fairbanks	3.00
84-19	Jim Thorpe	10.00
84-20	10¢ Richard Russell (2)	10.00
84-21	John McCormack	3.00
84-22	St. Lawrence Seaway	3.00
84-23	Migratory Bird Hunting and Conservation Stamp Act	6.00
84-24	Roanoke Voyages	3.00
84-25	Herman Melville	3.00
84-26	Horace Moses	3.00
84-27	Smokey Bear	8.00
84-28	Roberto Clemente	10.00
84-29	30¢ Frank C. Laubach	3.00
84-30	Dogs (4)	5.00
84-31	Crime Prevention	3.00
84-32	Family Unity	3.00
84-33	Eleanor Roosevelt	3.00
84-34	Nation of Readers	3.00
84-35	Christmas, Madonna	4.00
84-36	Christmas, Santa Claus	4.00
84-37	Hispanic Americans	3.00
84-38	Vietnam Veterans Memorial	4.00

1985

85-1	Jerome Kern	5.00
85-2	7¢ Abraham Baldwin (3)	5.00
85-3	"D" (22¢) sheet and coil (3)	3.00
85-4	"D" (22¢) booklet pane (10)	5.00
85-5	"D" (22¢) Penalty Mail sheet and coil (3)	4.00
85-6	11¢ Alden Partridge (2)	3.00
85-7	33¢ Alfred Verville airmail	3.00
85-8	39¢ Lawrence & Elmer Sperry airmail	3.00
85-9	44¢ Transpacific airmail	3.00
85-10	50¢ Chester Nimitz	3.00
85-11	Mary McLeod Bethune	4.00
85-12	39¢ Grenville Clark	3.00
85-13	14¢ Sinclair Lewis (2)	3.00
85-14	Duck Decoys (4)	4.00
85-15	14¢ Iceboat coil (2)	5.00
85-16	Winter Special Olympics	3.00
85-17	Flag over Capitol sheet and coil (3)	4.00
05-18	Flag over Capitol booklet pane (5)	4.00
85-19	12¢ Stanley Steamer coil (2)	5.00
85-20	Seashells booklet pane (10)	5.00
85-21	Love	4.00
85-22	10.1¢ Oil Wagon coil (3)	5.00
85-23	12.5¢ Pushcart coil (2)	5.00
85-24	John J. Audubon	3.00
85-25	$10.75 Eagle booklet single	40.00
85-26	$10.75 Eagle booklet pane (3)	90.00
85-27	6¢ Tricycle coil (4)	5.00
85-28	Rural Electrification Administration	3.00
85-29	14¢ and 22¢ Penalty Mail sheet and coil (4)	5.00
85-30	AMERIPEX '86	3.00

85-31	9¢ Sylvanus Thayer (3)	3.00
85-32	3.4¢ School Bus coil (7)	6.00
85-33	11¢ Stutz Bearcat coil (2)	5.00
85-34	Abigail Adams	3.00
85-35	4.9¢ Buckboard coil (5)	6.00
85-36	8.3¢ Ambulance coil (3)	6.00
85-37	Frederic Bartholdi	3.00
85-38	8¢ Henry Knox (3)	3.00
85-39	Korean War Veterans	4.00
85-40	Social Security Act	3.00
85-41	44¢ Father Junipero Serra airmail	3.00
85-42	World War I Veterans	3.00
85-43	6¢ Walter Lippman (4)	3.00
85-44	Horses (4)	5.00
85-45	Public Education	3.00
85-46	International Youth Year (4)	3.00
85-47	Help End Hunger	3.00
85-48	21.1¢ Letters coil (2)	4.00
85-49	Christmas, Madonna	3.00
85-50	Christmas, Poinsettias	3.00
85-51	18¢ Washington/ Washington Monument coil (2)	4.00

1986

86-1	Arkansas Statehood	3.00
86-2	25¢ Jack London	2.50
86-3	Stamp Collecting booklet pane (4)	6.00
86-4	Love	3.00
86-5	Sojourner Truth	4.00
86-6	5¢ Hugo L. Black (5)	2.50
86-7	Republic of Texas (2)	2.50
86-8	$2 William Jennings Bryan	5.00
86-9	Fish booklet pane (5)	5.00
86-10	Public Hospitals	2.50
86-11	Duke Ellington	5.00
86-12	Presidents, Washington-Harrison (9)	6.00
86-13	Presidents, Tyler-Grant (9)	6.00
86-14	Presidents, Hayes-Wilson (9)	6.00
86-15	Presidents, Harding-Johnson (9)	6.00
86-16	Polar Explorers (4)	5.00
86-17	17¢ Belva Ann Lockwood (2)	3.50
86-18	1¢ Margaret Mitchell (3)	2.50
86-19	Statue of Liberty	3.00
86-20	4¢ Father Flanagan (3)	2.50
86-21	17¢ Dog Sled coil (2)	4.00
86-22	56¢ John Harvard	2.50
86-23	Navajo Blankets (4)	4.00
86-24	3¢ Paul Dudley White, MD (8)	2.50
86-25	$1 Bernard Revel	3.00
86-26	T.S. Eliot	2.50
86-27	Wood-Carved Figurines (4)	3.50
86-28	Christmas, Madonna	2.50
86-29	Christmas, Village Scene	2.50
86-30	5.5¢ Star Route Truck coil (4)	5.00
86-31	25¢ Bread Wagon coil	5.00

1987

87-1	8.5¢ Tow Truck coil (5)	4.00
87-2	Michigan Statehood	4.00
87-3	Pan American Games	4.00
87-4	Love	6.00
87-5	7.1¢ Tractor coil (5)	5.00
87-6	14¢ Julia Ward Howe (2)	3.00
87-7	Jean Baptiste Pointe Du Sable	10.00
87-8	Enrico Caruso	3.00
87-9	2¢ Mary Lyon (3)	2.50
87-10	Reengraved 2¢ Locomotive coil (6)	4.00
87-11	Girl Scouts	5.00
87-12	10¢ Canal Boat coil (5)	4.00
87-13	Special Occasions booklet pane (10)	6.00
87-14	United Way	2.50
87-15	Flag with Fireworks	2.50
87-16	Flag over Capitol coil, prephosphored paper (2)	4.00
87-17	Wildlife, Swallow-Squirrel (10)	6.00
87-18	Wildlife, Armadillo-Rabbit (10)	6.00
87-19	Wildlife, Tanager-Ladybug (10)	6.00

87-20	Wildlife, Beaver-Prairie Dog (10)	6.00
87-21	Wildlife, Turtle-Fox (10)	6.00
87-22	Delaware Statehood	3.00
87-23	U.S./Morocco Friendship	2.50
87-24	William Faulkner	2.50
87-25	Lacemaking (4)	4.00
87-26	10¢ Red Cloud (3)	2.50
87-27	$5 Bret Harte	12.00
87-28	Pennsylvania Statehood	3.00
87-29	Drafting of the Constitution booklet pane (5)	5.00
87-30	New Jersey Statehood	3.00
87-31	Signing of Constitution	3.00
87-32	Certified Public Accountants	3.00
87-33	5¢ Milk Wagon and 17.5¢ Racing Car coils (4)	4.00
87-34	Locomotives booklet pane (5)	10.00
87-35	Christmas, Madonna	2.50
87-36	Christmas, Ornaments	2.50
87-37	Flag with Fireworks booklet-pair	3.00

1988

88-1	Georgia Statehood	3.00
88-2	Connecticut Statehood	3.00
88-3	Winter Olympics	3.00
88-4	Australia Bicentennial	2.50
88-5	James Weldon Johnson	5.00
88-6	Cats (4)	5.00
88-7	Massachusetts Statehood	4.00
88-8	Maryland Statehood	4.00
88-9	3¢ Conestoga Wagon coil (8)	4.00
88-10	Knute Rockne	4.00
88-11	"E" (25¢) Earth sheet and coil (3)	5.00
88-12	"E" (25¢) Earth booklet pane (10)	6.00
88-13	"E" (25¢) Penalty Mail coil (2)	3.50
88-14	44¢ New Sweden airmail	3.00
88-15	Pheasant booklet pane (10)	6.00
88-16	Jack London booklet pane (6)	4.50
88-17	Jack London booklet pane (10)	6.00
88-18	Flag with Clouds	2.50
88-19	45¢ Samuel Langley airmail	3.00
88-19A	20¢ Penalty Mail coil (2)	3.00
88-20	Flag over Yosemite coil (2)	3.50
88-21	South Carolina Statehood	3.00
88-22	Owl & Grosbeak booklet pane (10)	6.00
88-23	15¢ Buffalo Bill Cody (2)	3.00
88-24	15¢ and 25¢ Penalty Mail coils (4)	4.00
88-25	Francis Ouimet	3.00
88-26	45¢ Harvey Cushing, MD	2.50
88-27	New Hampshire Statehood	3.00
88-28	36¢ Igor Sikorsky airmail	3.00
88-29	Virginia Statehood	3.00
88-30	10.1¢ Oil Wagon coil, precancel (3)	4.00
88-31	Love	3.00
88-32	Flag with Clouds booklet pane (6)	5.00
88-33	16.7¢ Popcorn Wagon coil (2)	4.00
88-34	15¢ Tugboat coil (2)	4.00
88-35	13.2¢ Coal Car coil (2)	4.00
88-36	New York Statehood	3.00
88-37	45¢ Love	3.00
88-38	8.4¢ Wheel Chair coil (3)	4.00
88-39	21¢ Railroad Mail Car coil (2)	4.00
88-40	Summer Olympics	3.00
88-41	Classic Cars booklet pane (5)	8.00
88-42	7.6¢ Carreta coil (4)	4.00
88-43	Honeybee coil (2)	4.00
88-44	Antarctic Explorers (4)	4.00
88-45	5.3¢ Elevator coil (5)	4.00

88-46	20.5¢ Fire Engine coil (2)	4.00
88-47	Carousel Animals (4)	3.50
88-48	$8.75 Eagle	25.00
88-49	Christmas, Madonna	2.50
88-50	Christmas, Snow Scene	2.50
88-51	21¢ Chester Carlson	2.50
88-52	Special Occasions booklet pane (6), Love You	10.00
88-53	Special Occasions booklet pane (6), Thinking of You	10.00
88-54	24.1¢ Tandem Bicycle coil (2)	5.00
88-55	20¢ Cable Car coil (2)	5.00
88-56	13¢ Patrol Wagon coil (2)	5.00
88-57	23¢ Mary Cassatt	3.00
88-58	65¢ H.H. "Hap" Arnold	3.00

1989

89-1	Montana Statehood	2.50
89-2	A. Philip Randolph	4.00
89-3	Flag over Yosemite coil, prephosphored paper (2)	3.00
89-4	North Dakota Statehood	3.00
89-5	Washington Statehood	3.00
89-6	Steamboats booklet pane (5)	6.00
89-7	WORLD STAMP EXPO '89	2.50
89-8	Arturo Toscanini	2.50
89-9	U.S. House of Representatives	3.00
89-10	U.S. Senate	3.00
89-11	Executive Branch	3.00
89-12	South Dakota Statehood	3.00
89-13	7.1¢ Tractor coil, precancel (4)	4.00
89-14	$1 Johns Hopkins	3.50
89-15	Lou Gehrig	5.00
89-16	1¢ Penalty Mail	3.00
89-17	45¢ French Revolution airmail	3.00
89-18	Ernest Hemingway	2.50
89-19	$2.40 Moon Landing	12.50
89-20	North Carolina Statehood	0.00
89-21	Letter Carriers	2.50
89-22	28¢ Sitting Bull	2.50
89-23	Drafting of the Bill of Rights	3.00
89-24	Prehistoric Animals (4)	6.00
89-25	25¢ and 45¢ PUAS-America (2)	3.00
89-26	Christmas, Madonna	6.00
89-27	Christmas, Antique Sleigh	6.00
89-28	Eagle and Shield, self-adhesive	4.00
89-29	$3.60 WORLD STAMP EXPO '89 souvenir sheet	10.00
89-30	Classic Mail Transportation (4)	3.50
89-31	$1.80 Future Mail Transportation souvenir sheet	6.00
89-32	45¢ Future Mail Transportation airmails (4)	6.00
89-33	$1 Classic Mail Transportation souvenir sheet	6.00

1990

90-1	Idaho Statehood	3.00
90-2	Love sheet and booklet pane (11)	6.00
90-3	Ida B. Wells	4.00
90-4	U.S. Supreme Court	3.00
90-5	15¢ Beach Umbrella booklet pane (10)	5.00
90-6	5¢ Luis Munoz Marin (5)	2.50
90-7	Wyoming Statehood	3.00
90-8	Classic Films (4)	5.00
90-9	Marianne Moore	2.50
90-10	$1 Seaplane coil (2)	5.00
90-11	Lighthouses booklet pane (5)	6.00
90-12	Plastic Flag stamp	3.00
90-13	Rhode Island Statehood	3.00

90-14	$2 Bobcat	5.00
90-15	Olympians (5)	7.00
90-16	Indian Headdresses booklet pane (10)	9.00
90-17	5¢ Circus Wagon coil (5)	3.00
90-18	40¢ Claire Lee Chennault	4.00
90-19	Federated States of Micronesia/ Marshall Islands (2)	3.00
90-20	Creatures of the Sea (4)	5.00
90-21	25¢ and 45¢ PUAS/America (2)	4.00
90-22	Dwight D. Eisenhower	2.50
90-23	Christmas, Madonna, sheet and booklet pane (11)	7.00
90-24	Christmas, Yule Tree, sheet and booklet pane (11)	7.00

1991

91-1	"F" (29¢) Flower sheet and coil (3)	3.00
91-2	"F" (29¢) Flower booklet panes (20)	12.50
91-3	4¢ Makeup	2.50
91-4	"F" (29¢) ATM booklet single	2.50
91-5	"F" (29¢) Penalty Mail coil (2)	3.00
91-6	4¢ Steam Carriage coil (7)	2.50
91-7	50¢ Switzerland	3.00
91-8	Vermont Statehood	2.50
91-9	19¢ Fawn (2)	3.00
91-10	Flag over Mount Rushmore coil (2)	2.50
91-11	35¢ Dennis Chavez	2.50
91-12	Flower sheet and booklet pane (11)	7.50
91-13	4¢ Penalty Mail (8)	3.00
91-14	Wood Duck booklet panes (20)	12.50
91-15	23¢ Lunch Wagon coil (2)	3.00
91-16	Flag with Olympic Rings booklet pane (10)	7.50
91-17	50¢ Harriet Quimby	3.00
91-18	Savings Bond	2.50
91-19	Love sheet and booklet pane, 52¢ Love (12)	9.00
91-20	19¢ Balloon booklet pane (10)	3.50
91-21	40¢ William Piper airmail	3.00
91-22	William Saroyan	2.50
91-23	Penalty Mail coil and 19¢ and 23¢ sheet (4)	3.00
91-24	5¢ Canoe and 10¢ Tractor-Trailer coils (4)	3.00
91-25	Flags on Parade	2.50
91-26	Fishing Flies booklet pane (5)	6.00
91-27	52¢ Hubert H. Humphrey	3.00
91-28	Cole Porter	3.50
91-29	50¢ Antarctic Treaty airmail	3.00
91-30	1¢ Kestrel, 3¢ Bluebird and 30¢ Cardinal (3)	3.00
91-31	Torch ATM booklet single	2.50
91-32	Desert Shield/ Desert Storm sheet and booklet pane (11)	7.50
91-33	Flag over Mount Rushmore coil, gravure printing (darker, 3)	3.00
91-34	Summer Olympics (5)	5.00
91-35	Flower coil, slit perforations (3)	3.00
91-36	Numismatics	3.00
91-37	Basketball	5.00
91-48	19¢ Fishing Boat coil (3)	3.00
91-49	Comedians booklet pane (10)	7.50
91-50	World War II miniature sheet (10)	9.00
91-51	District of Columbia	3.00
91-52	Jan Matzeliger	3.00
91-53	$1 USPS/ Olympic Logo	5.00

91-54	Space Exploration booklet pane (10)	7.50
91-55	50¢ PUASP/America airmail	3.00
91-56	Christmas, Madonna sheet and booklet pane (11)	7.50
91-57	Christmas, Santa Claus sheet and booklet pane (11)	7.50
91-58	5¢ Christmas coil, gravure printing (red, 6)	3.00
91-59	(10¢) Eagle and Shield, self-adhesive (3)	3.00
91-60	23¢ Flag presort	3.00
91-	$9.95 Express Mail	25.00
91-	$2.90 Priority Mail	9.00
91-	$14.00 Express Mail International	35.00

1992

92-01	Winter Olympic Games (5)	4.00
92-02	World Columbian Stamp Expo '92	3.50
92-03	W.E.B. Du Bois	3.00
92-04	Love	3.00
92-05	75¢ Wendell Willkie	3.00
92-06	29¢ Flower coil, round perforations (2)	3.00
92-07	Earl Warren	2.50
92-08	Olympic Baseball	3.00
92-09	Flag over White House, coil (2)	3.00
92-10	First Voyage of Christopher Columbus (4)	4.00
92-11	New York Stock Exchange	2.50
92-18	Space Adventures (4)	4.00
92-19	Alaska Highway	2.50
92-20	Kentucky Statehood	2.50
92-21	Summer Olympic Games (5)	5.00
92-22	Hummingbirds booklet pane (5)	5.00
92-23	Wildflowers (10)	7.50
92-24	Wildflowers (10)	7.50
92-25	Wildflowers (10)	7.50
92-26	Wildflowers (10)	7.50
92-27	Wildflowers (10)	7.50
92-28	World War II miniature sheet (10)	7.50
92-30	Dorothy Parker	2.50
92-31	Theodore von Karman	3.00
92-33	Minerals (4)	4.00
92-35	Juan Rodriguez Cabrillo	2.50
92-36	Wild Animals booklet pane (5)	5.00
92-38	Christmas Contemporary, sheet and booklet pane (8)	7.50
92-39	Christmas Traditional, sheet and booklet pane (11)	7.50
92-40	Pumpkinseed Sunfish	3.00
92-41	Circus Wagon	2.50
92-42	Happy New Year	2.50

1993

93-01	Elvis	3.00
93-02	Space Fantasy, booklet pane (5)	5.00

NOTE: Numbers and prices may be changed without notice, due to additional USPS stamp issues and/or different information that may become available on older issues.

Prices are courtesy of the American Society for Philatelic Pages and Panels, an organization specializing in Souvenir Pages.

American Commemorative Panels

The Postal Service offers American Commemorative Panels for each new commemorative stamp and special Christmas and Love stamp issued. The series began in 1972 with the Wildlife Commemorative Panel. The panels feature mint stamps complemented by fine reproductions of steel line engravings and the stories behind the commemorated subjects.

1972

1	Wildlife	9.00
2	Mail Order	8.00
3	Osteopathic Medicine	9.00
4	Tom Sawyer	8.00
5	Pharmacy	9.00
6	Christmas, Angels	11.00
7	Christmas, Santa Claus	11.00
7E	Same with error date (1882)	750.00
8	Stamp Collecting	8.00

1973

9	Love	12.00
10	Pamphleteers	10.00
11	George Gershwin	11.00
12	Posting of the Broadside	10.00
13	Copernicus	10.00
14	Postal People	9.00
15	Harry S. Truman	11.00
16	Post Rider	11.00
17	Boston Tea Party	32.00
18	Electronics	9.00
19	Robinson Jeffers	9.00
20	Lyndon B. Johnson	11.00
21	Henry O. Tanner	9.00
22	Willa Cather	9.00
23	Drummer	13.00
24	Angus Cattle	9.00
25	Christmas, Madonna	13.00
26	Christmas, Needlepoint Tree	13.00

1974

27	VFW	9.00
28	Robert Frost	9.00
29	EXPO '74	11.00
30	Horse Racing	11.00
31	Skylab	13.00
32	Universal Postal Union	9.00
33	Mineral Heritage	11.00
34	First Kentucky Settlement	9.00
35	Continental Congress	11.00
35A	Same with corrected logo	150.00
36	Chautauqua	9.00
37	Kansas Wheat	9.00
38	Energy Conservation	9.00
39	Sleepy Hollow	9.00
40	Retarded Children	9.00
41	Christmas, Currier & Ives	13.00
42	Christmas, Angel Altarpiece	13.00

1975

43	Benjamin West	9.00
44	Pioneer	13.00
45	Collective Bargaining	9.00
46	Contributors to the Cause	9.00
47	Mariner 10	13.00
48	Lexington & Concord	10.00
49	Paul Laurence Dunbar	9.00
50	D.W. Griffith	9.00
51	Bunker Hill	10.00
52	Military Uniforms	10.00
53	Apollo Soyuz	13.00
54	World Peace Through Law	9.00
54A	Same with August 15, 1975 date	150.00
55	Women's Year	9.00
56	Postal Service Bicentennial	11.00
57	Banking and Commerce	10.00
58	Christmas, Prang Card	13.00
59	Christmas, Madonna	13.00

1976

60	Spirit of '76	16.00
61	Interphil 76	15.00
62	State Flags	35.00
63	Telephone	12.00
64	Commercial Aviation	16.00
65	Chemistry	13.00
66	Benjamin Franklin	13.00
67	Declaration of Independence	13.00
68	Olympics	17.00
69	Clara Maass	13.00
70	Adolph Ochs	13.00
70A	Same with charter logo	18.00
71	Christmas, Winter Pastime	21.00
71A	Same with charter logo	21.00
72	Christmas, Nativity	17.00
72A	Same with charter logo	21.00

1977

73	Washington at Princeton	23.00
73A	Same with charter logo	18.00
74	Sound Recording	41.00

74A	Same with charter logo	33.00
75	Pueblo Pottery	110.00
75A	Same with charter logo	110.00
76	Solo Transatlantic Flight	120.00
77	Colorado Statehood	22.00
78	Butterflies	25.00
79	Lafayette	22.00
80	Skilled Hands	22.00
81	Peace Bridge	22.00
82	Battle of Oriskany	22.00
83	Alta, CA, Civil Settlement	22.00
84	Articles of Confederation	22.00
85	Talking Pictures	32.00
86	Surrender at Saratoga	22.00
87	Energy	27.00
88	Christmas, Valley Forge	27.00
89	Christmas, Mailbox	46.00

1978

90	Carl Sandburg	14.00
91	Captain Cook	23.00
92	Harriet Tubman	14.00
93	Quilts	25.00
94	Dance	18.00
95	French Alliance	18.00
96	Early Cancer Detection	14.00
97	Jimmie Rodgers	20.00
98	Photography	14.00
99	George M. Cohan	25.00
100	Viking Missions	44.00
101	Owls	44.00
102	Trees	44.00
103	Christmas, Madonna	20.00
104	Christmas, Hobby Horse	20.00

1979

105	Robert F. Kennedy	13.00
106	Martin Luther King, Jr.	12.00
107	International Year of the Child	12.00
108	John Steinbeck	12.00
109	Albert Einstein	13.00
110	Pennsylvania Toleware	12.00
111	Architecture	12.00
112	Endangered Flora	13.00
113	Seeing Eye Dogs	13.00
114	Special Olympics	17.00

115	John Paul Jones	15.00
116	15¢ Olympics	18.00
117	Christmas, Madonna	17.00
118	Christmas, Santa Claus	17.00
119	Will Rogers	16.00
120	Vietnam Veterans	17.00
121	10¢, 31¢ Olympics	18.00

1980

122	W.C. Fields	11.00
123	Winter Olympics	18.00
124	Benjamin Banneker	13.00
125	Frances Perkins	12.00
126	Emily Bissell	12.00
127	Helen Keller/ Anne Sullivan	12.00
128	Veterans Administration	12.00
129	General Bernardo de Galvez	12.00
130	Coral Reefs	14.00
131	Organized Labor	11.00
132	Edith Wharton	11.00
133	Education	11.00
134	Indian Masks	14.00
135	Architecture	11.00
136	Christmas, Epiphany Window	17.00
137	Christmas, Toys	17.00

1981

138	Everett Dirksen	12.00
139	Whitney Moore Young	12.00
140	Flowers	14.00
141	Red Cross	13.00
142	Savings & Loans	12.00
143	Space Achievement	16.00
144	Professional Management	18.00
145	Wildlife Habitats	17.00
146	Int'l. Year of Disabled Persons	10.00
147	Edna St. Vincent Millay	10.00
148	Architecture	11.00
149	Babe Zaharias/ Bobby Jones	13.00
150	James Hoban	11.00
151	Frederic Remington	11.00
152	Battle of Yorktown/ Virginia Capes	11.00
153	Christmas, Bear and Sleigh	16.00
154	Christmas, Madonna	16.00
155	John Hanson	10.00
156	U.S. Desert Plants	14.00

1982

157	Roosevelt	13.00
158	Love	16.00
159	George Washington	13.00
160	State Birds & Flowers	35.00
161	U.S./Netherlands	15.00
162	Library of Congress	16.00
163	Knoxville World's Fair	16.00
164	Horatio Alger	13.00
165	Aging Together	18.00
166	The Barrymores	20.00
167	Dr. Mary Walker	15.00
168	Peace Garden	18.00
169	America's Libraries	18.00
170	Jackie Robinson	45.00

171	Touro Synagogue	18.00
172	Architecture	18.00
173	Wolf Trap Farm Park	20.00
174	Francis of Assisi	20.00
175	Ponce de Leon	20.00
176	Christmas, Madonna	30.00
177	Christmas, Season's Greetings	30.00
178	Kitten & Puppy	30.00

1983

179	Science and Industry	9.00
180	Sweden/ USA Treaty	9.00
181	Balloons	12.00
182	Civilian Conservation Corps	9.00
183	40¢ Olympics	11.00
184	Joseph Priestley	9.00
185	Volunteerism	8.00
186	Concord/German Immigration	9.00
187	Physical Fitness	8.00
188	Brooklyn Bridge	10.00
189	TVA	9.00
190	Medal of Honor	12.00
191	Scott Joplin	14.00
192	28¢ Olympics	12.00
193	Babe Ruth	25.00
194	Nathaniel Hawthorne	9.00
195	13¢ Olympics	16.00
196	Treaty of Paris	11.00
197	Civil Service	11.00
198	Metropolitan Opera	11.00
100	Inventors	11.00
200	Streetcars	13.00
201	Christmas, Madonna	15.00
202	Christmas, Santa Claus	15.00
203	35¢ Olympics	16.00
204	Martin Luther	13.00

1984

205	Alaska Statehood	8.00
206	Winter Olympics	11.00
207	FDIC	8.00
208	Love	9.00
209	Carter G. Woodson	11.00
210	Soil and Water Conservation	8.00
211	Credit Union Act	8.00
212	Orchids	11.00
213	Hawaii Statehood	10.00
214	National Archives	8.00
215	20¢ Olympics	11.00
216	Louisiana World Exposition	10.00
217	Health Research	8.00
218	Douglas Fairbanks	8.00
219	Jim Thorpe	14.00
220	John McCormack	8.00
221	St. Lawrence Seaway	10.00
222	Preserving Wetlands	13.00
223	Roanoke Voyages	8.00
224	Herman Melville	8.00
225	Horace Moses	8.00
226	Smokey Bear	11.00
227	Roberto Clemente	27.50
228	Dogs	11.00
229	Crime Prevention	8.00

230	Family Unity	8.00
231	Christmas, Madonna	11.00
232	Christmas, Santa Claus	11.00
233	Eleanor Roosevelt	9.00
234	Nation of Readers	9.00
235	Hispanic Americans	9.00
236	Vietnam Veterans Memorial	12.00

1985

237	Jerome Kern	9.00
238	Mary McLeod Bethune	9.00
239	Duck Decoys	11.00
240	Winter Special Olympics	9.00
241	Love	9.00
242	Rural Electrification Administration	8.00
243	AMERIPEX '86	11.00
244	Abigail Adams	7.00
245	Frederic Auguste Bartholdi	13.00
246	Korean War Veterans	9.00
247	Social Security Act	8.00
248	World War I Veterans	8.00
249	Horses	11.00
250	Public Education	8.00
251	Youth	9.00
252	Help End Hunger	8.00
253	Christmas, Poinsettias	13.00
254	Christmas, Madonna	13.00

1986

255	Arkansas Statehood	7.00
256	Stamp Collecting Booklet	9.00
257	Love	9.00
258	Sojourner Truth	9.00
259	Republic of Texas	9.00
260	Fish Booklet	9.00
261	Public Hospitals	7.00
262	Duke Ellington	9.00
263	U.S. Presidents' Sheet #1	9.00
264	U.S. Presidents' Sheet #2	9.00
265	U.S. Presidents' Sheet #3	9.00
266	U.S. Presidents' Sheet #4	9.00
267	Polar Explorers	9.00
268	Statue of Liberty	10.00
269	Navajo Blankets	9.00
270	T.S. Eliot	7.00
271	Wood-Carved Figurines	9.00
272	Christmas, Madonna	9.00
273	Christmas, Village Scene	9.00

1987

274	Michigan Statehood	7.00
275	Pan American Games	7.00
276	Love	8.00
277	Jean Baptiste Pointe Du Sable	8.00
278	Enrico Caruso	8.00
279	Girl Scouts	9.00
280	Special Occasions Booklet	7.00

281	United Way	7.00	328	U.S. House of Representatives	10.00	
282	#1 American Wildlife	10.00	329	U.S. Senate	10.00	
283	#2 American Wildlife	10.00	330	Executive Branch	10.00	
284	#3 American Wildlife	10.00	331	South Dakota Statehood	10.00	
285	#4 American Wildlife	10.00	332	Lou Gehrig	20.00	
286	#5 American Wildlife	10.00	333	French Revolution	10.00	
287	Delaware Statehood	7.00	334	Ernest Hemingway	10.00	
288	Morocco/U.S. Diplomatic Relations	7.00	335	North Carolina Statehood	10.00	
289	William Faulkner	7.00	336	Letter Carriers	10.00	
290	Lacemaking	7.00	337	Drafting of the Bill of Rights	10.00	
291	Pennsylvania Statehood	7.00	338	Prehistoric Animals	17.50	
292	Constitution Booklet	7.00	339	25¢ and 45¢ America/PUAS	10.00	

Num	Item	Price
281	United Way	7.00
282	#1 American Wildlife	10.00
283	#2 American Wildlife	10.00
284	#3 American Wildlife	10.00
285	#4 American Wildlife	10.00
286	#5 American Wildlife	10.00
287	Delaware Statehood	7.00
288	Morocco/U.S. Diplomatic Relations	7.00
289	William Faulkner	7.00
290	Lacemaking	7.00
291	Pennsylvania Statehood	7.00
292	Constitution Booklet	7.00
293	New Jersey Statehood	7.00
294	Signing of the Constitution	7.00
295	Certified Public Accountants	17.50
296	Locomotives Booklet	10.00
297	Christmas, Madonna	9.00
298	Christmas, Ornaments	9.00

1988

Num	Item	Price
299	Georgia Statehood	7.00
300	Connecticut Statehood	7.00
301	Winter Olympics	9.00
302	Australia	7.00
303	James Weldon Johnson	7.00
304	Cats	9.00
305	Massachusetts Statehood	7.00
306	Maryland Statehood	7.00
307	Knute Rockne	9.00
308	New Sweden	7.00
309	South Carolina Statehood	7.00
310	Francis Ouimet	15.00
311	New Hampshire Statehood	7.00
312	Virginia Statehood	7.00
313	Love	7.00
314	New York Statehood	7.00
315	Classic Cars Booklet	9.00
316	Summer Olympics	9.00
317	Antarctic Explorers	7.00
318	Carousel Animals	7.00
319	Christmas, Madonna	9.00
320	Christmas, Village Scene	7.00

1989

Num	Item	Price
321	Montana Statehood	10.00
322	A. Philip Randolph	10.00
323	North Dakota Statehood	10.00
324	Washington Statehood	10.00
325	Steamboats Booklet	12.50
326	WORLD STAMP EXPO '89	10.00
327	Arturo Toscanini	10.00

Num	Item	Price
328	U.S. House of Representatives	10.00
329	U.S. Senate	10.00
330	Executive Branch	10.00
331	South Dakota Statehood	10.00
332	Lou Gehrig	20.00
333	French Revolution	10.00
334	Ernest Hemingway	10.00
335	North Carolina Statehood	10.00
336	Letter Carriers	10.00
337	Drafting of the Bill of Rights	10.00
338	Prehistoric Animals	17.50
339	25¢ and 45¢ America/PUAS	10.00
340	Christmas, Traditional and Contemporary	12.50
341	Classic Mail Transportation	10.00
342	Future Mail Transportation	10.00

1990

Num	Item	Price
343	Idaho Statehood	10.00
344	Love	10.00
345	Ida B. Wells	17.50
346	U.S. Supreme Court	10.00
347	Wyoming Statehood	10.00
348	Classic Films	15.00
349	Marianne Moore	10.00
350	Lighthouses Booklet	12.50
351	Rhode Island Statehood	10.00
352	Olympians	12.50
353	Indian Headdresses Booklet	12.50
354	Micronesia/ Marshall Islands	12.50
355	Creatures of the Sea	15.00
356	25c and 45c America/PUAS	12.50
357	Dwight D. Eisenhower	10.00
358	Christmas, Traditional and Contemporary	12.50

1991

Num	Item	Price
359	Switzerland	10.00
360	Vermont Statehood	10.00
361	Savings Bonds	10.00
362	29¢ and 52¢ Love	12.50
363	Saroyan	10.00
364	Fishing Flies Booklet	12.50
365	Cole Porter	12.50
366	Antartic Treaty	12.50
367	Desert Shield/ Desert Storm	27.50
368	Summer Olympics	12.50
369	Numismatics	12.50
370	Basketball	12.50
371	World War II Miniature Sheet	15.00
372	Comedians Booklet	12.50
373	District of Columbia	10.00
374	Jan Matzeliger	10.00
375	Space Exploration Booklet	15.00
376	America/PUASP	12.50

Num	Item	Price
377	Christmas, Traditional and Contemporary	12.50

1992

Num	Item	Price
378	Winter Olympics	12.50
379	World Columbian Stamp Expo '92	12.50
380	W.E.B. Du Bois	12.50
381	Love	10.00
382	Olympic Baseball	12.50
383	First Voyage of Christopher Columbus	12.50
384	Space Adventures	15.00
385	New York Stock Exchange	10.00
386	Alaska Highway	10.00
387	Kentucky Statehood	10.00
388	Summer Olympics	12.50
389	Hummingbirds Booklet	12.50
390	World War II Miniature Sheet	15.00
391	Dorothy Parker	10.00
392	Theodore von Karman	10.00
393	Minerals	12.50
394	Juan Rodriguez Cabrillo	10.00
395	Wild Animals Booklet	12.50
396	Christmas, Traditional and Contemporary	12.50
	Wildflowers	15.00
	Wildflowers	15.00
	Wildflowers	15.00
	Wildflowers	15.00
	Wildflowers	15.00
	Columbian Souvenir Sheets	20.00
	Columbian Souvenir Sheets	20.00
	Columbian Souvenir Sheets	20.00
405	Happy New Year	10.00

1993*

Num	Item	Price
406	Elvis	10.00
407	Space Fantasy	12.50
408	Percy Julian	10.00
409	Oregon Trail	10.00
410	World Univ. Games	10.00
411	Grace Kelly	10.00
412	Oklahoma	10.00
413	Circus	12.50
414	Cherokee Strip	10.00
415	Dean Acheson	10.00
416	Sport Horses	12.50
417	Garden Flowers	12.50
418	World War II	15.00
419	Hank Williams	10.00
420	Rock/Roll/R&B	15.00
421	Joe Louis	10.00
422	Broadway Musicals	12.50
423	National Postal Museum	12.50
424	Deaf Communication	12.50
425	Country Western	12.50
426	Youth Classics	12.50
427	Christmas	12.50
428	Mariana Islands	10.00

*1993 issues subject to change.

Prices are courtesy of the American Society for Philatelic Pages and Panels, an organization specializing in Commemorative Panels.

Subject Index

The numbers listed next to the stamp description are the Scott numbers. The numbers in parentheses are page numbers on which the stamp listing appears.

A

A Stamp, 1735-1736 (204)
Abbott & Costello, 2566 (296)
Abyssinian Cat, 2373 (276)
Acadia National Park, 746 (100), 762 (103)
Acheson, Dean, 2755 (316)
Acoma Pot, 1709 (203)
Adams
  Abigail, 2146 (251)
  John, 806 (108), 841 (111), 850 (111), 1687a (196), 2201 (256), 2216b (259)
  John Quincy, 811 (108), 846 (111), 2201 (256), 2216f (259)
Addams, Jane, 878 (112)
Admiralty Head Lighthouse (WA), 2470 (288), 2474 (288)
Adventures of Huckleberry Finn, The, (320)
African
  Americans, 873 (112), 902 (115), 953 (120), 1085 (135), 1233 (147), 1290 (152), 1361 (160), 1372 (160), 1486 (175), 1490-1491 (175), 1493 (175), 1495 (175), 1554 (180), 1560 (183), 1772 (211), 1790-1791 (212), 1860 (219), 1865 (219), 2027 (236), 2043 (239), 2051 (239), 2083-2084 (243), 2097 (244), 2164 (252), 2211 (256), 2223 (263), 2275 (267), 2420 (284), 2496 (291), 2746 (314), C97 (347), C102 (347), C103 (347), C105 (347)
  Elephant Herd, 1388 (163)
  Violet, (325)
Agave Cactus, 1943 (228)
Aging Together, 2011 (235)
AIDS Awareness, (322)
Air
  -Cushion Vehicle, C123 (348), C126 (351)
  Force, 1013 (127), 1067 (132), C49 (342)
  Mail Service, U.S., C74 (344)
  Save Our, 1413 (164)
  Service Emblem, C5 (339)
Aircraft Gun, 90mm, Anti-, 900 (115)
Airlift, 1341 (159)
Airliner, Hypersonic, C122 (348), C126 (351)
Alabama, 1654 (192), 1953 (231)
  Statehood, 1375 (160)
Alamo, The, 776 (104), 778 (104), 1043 (128)
Alaska, 1681 (195), 1954 (231)
  (Cook, Captain James), 1732-1733 (204)
  Highway, 2635 (304)
  Purchase, C70 (344)
  Statehood, 2066 (240), C53 (343)
  Territory, 800 (107)

-Yukon-Pacific Exposition, 370-371 (70)
Alaskan Malamute, 2100 (244)
Albania, 918 (116)
Alcoholism, You Can Beat It, 1927 (224)
Alcott, Louisa May, 862 (112)
Alexandria, C40 (340)
Alger, Horatio, 2010 (235)
Allegiance, Pledge of, 2594 (299)
Allen, Ethan, 1071 (132)
Alliance
  for Progress, 1234 (147)
  French, 1753 (207)
Allied
  Nations, 537 (83), 907 (115)
  Victory, 537 (83)
Alligator, 1428 (167)
Allosaurus, 1390 (163)
Alta, California, First Civil Settlement, 1725 (204)
Amateur Radio, 1260 (151)
Ambulance, 2128 (248), 2231 (263)
America
  Beautification of, 1318 (156), 1365-1368 (160)
  /PUAS, 2426 (284), 2512 (292), C121 (348), C127 (351)
  /PUASP, C131 (351)
America's Libraries, 2015 (235)
American, 1596-1599 (187), 1603-1606 (187), 1608 (187), 1610-1615 (187)
  Architecture, 1779-1782 (211), 1838-1841 (216), 1928-1931 (227), 2019-2021 (235), 2022 (235)
  Arts, 1484-1487 (175), 1553-1555 (180)
  Automobile Association, 1007 (124)
  Bald Eagle, 1387 (163)
  Bankers Association, 987 (123)
  Bar Association, 1022 (127)
  Bicentennial, 1432 (168), 1456 (171), 1458-1459 (171), 1476-1483 (172), 1543-1546 (180), 1559-1568 (183), 1629-1631 (191), 1633-1639 (191), 1640 (191), 1641-1644 (191), 1645-1665 (192), 1666-1674 (195), 1676-1682 (195), 1686 (196), 1687 (196), 1688 (199), 1689 (199), 1690-1694 (200), 1704 (200), 1716-1719 (203), 1722 (204), 1726 (204), 1728 (204), 1753 (207), 1789 (212), 1811 (215), 1813 (215), 1816 (215), 1937-1938 (227), 2052 (239)
  Cats, 2372-2375 (276)
  Chemical Society, 1002 (124)
  Circus, 1309 (155)
  Credo, 1139-1144 (140)
  Dance, 1750-1752 (207)
  Dance, Ballet, 1749 (207)
  Dogs, 2098-2101 (244)
  Flag, 1623 (188), 2116 (247)
  Folklore, 1317 (156), 1330 (156), 1357 (160), 1370 (160), 1470 (172)

Foxhound, 2101 (244)
Horses, 2155-2158 (252)
Indian, 565 (87), 695 (96), 1364 (160)
Institute of Architects, 1089 (136)
Kestrel, 2481 (291)
Legion, 1369 (160)
Militia, 1568 (183)
Music, 1252 (148)
Owls, 1760-1763 (208)
Philatelic Society, 730-731 (99), 750 (100), 766 (103), 770 (103)
Red Cross, 702 (96), 967 (120), 1910 (223)
Revolution, 551 (84), 645 (92), 651 (92), 653 (92), 657 (92), 689-690 (96), 727 (99), 734 (99), 752 (103), 1010 (127), 1729 (204), 1851 (219), 1937-1938 (227)
Revolution Battles, 617-618 (88), 619 (91), 629-630 (91), 643-644 (92), 646 (92), 688 (96), 1003 (124), 1361 (160), 1563-1564 (183), 1686 (196), 1722 (204), 1728 (204), 1826 (215)
Shoals Lighthouse (FL), 2473 (288)
Shorthair Cat, 2375 (276)
Society of Civil Engineers, 1012 (127)
Sports, 1932-1933 (227), 2046 (239), 2097 (244), 2376-2377 (276), 2417 (283)
Streetcar, First, 2059 (240)
Trees, 1764-1767 (208)
Turners Society, 979 (123)
Wildlife, 2286-2310 (268), 2311-2335 (271)
Woman, 1152 (143)
Wool Industry, 1423 (167)
Americana Issue, 1581-1582 (184), 1584-1585 (184), 1590-1594 (184), 1616-1619 (188), 1618C (188), 1622-1623 (188), 1625 (188)
Americans, African, 873 (112), 902 (115), 953 (120), 1085 (135), 1233 (147), 1290 (152), 1361 (160), 1372 (160), 1486 (175), 1490-1491 (175), 1493 (175), 1495 (175), 1554 (180), 1560 (183), 1772 (211), 1790-1791 (212), 1860 (219), 1865 (219), 2027 (236), 2043 (239), 2051 (239), 2083-2084 (243), 2097 (244), 2164 (252), 2211 (256), 2223 (263), 2275 (267), 2420 (284), 2496 (291), 2746 (314), C97 (347), C102 (347), C103 (347), C105 (347)
AMERIPEX '86, 2145 (251), 2198-2199 (256), 2200 (256), 2201 (256), 2216 (259), 2217 (259), 2218 (260), 2219 (260)
Amethyst, 1540 (180)
Angels, 1268 (151), 1276 (151), 1363 (160), 1471 (172)
Angus and Longhorn Cattle, 1504 (176)
Animals, Humane Treatment of, 1307 (155)
Annapolis Tercentary, 984 (123)

391

Antarctic
 Expedition, Byrd, 733 (99), 735 (100), 753 (103), 768 (103)
 Explorers, 2386-2389 (279)
 Treaty, 1431 (168), C130 (351)
Anthem, Flag and, 1890-1893 (220)
Anthony, Susan B., 784 (104), 1051 (131)
Anti-
 Aircraft Gun, 90mm, 900 (115)
 Pollution, 1410-1413 (164)
Antioch Dunes Evening Primrose, 1786 (211)
Apollo
 8, 1371 (160), 2633-2634 (304)
 Soyuz, 1569-1570 (183)
Appaloosa, 2158 (252)
Appleseed, Johnny, 1317 (156)
Appomattox, Civil War Centennial, 1182 (144)
Apprenticeship, 1201 (147)
Apte Tarpon Fly, 2547 (295)
Arbor Day, 717 (99)
Arc de Triomphe, 934 (119)
Architects, Institute of American, 1089 (136)
Architecture, American, 1779 (212), 1800-1802 (212), 1838-1841 (216), 1928-1931 (227), 2019-2022 (235)
Archives, National, 2081 (243)
Arctic Explorations, 1128 (139)
Arizona, 1680 (195), 1955 (231)
 National Park (Grand Canyon), 741 (100), 757 (103), 2512 (292)
 Statehood, 1192 (144)
Ark and The Dove, The, 736 (100)
Arkansas, 1657 (192), 1956 (231)
 River Navigation, 1358 (160)
 Statehood, 782 (104), 2167 (255)
Arlington Amphitheater, 570 (87), 701 (96)
Armed Forces, 926 (116), 929 (119), 934-936 (119), 939 (119), 1026 (127)
 Reserve, 1067 (132)
Armstrong, Edwin, 2056 (239)
Army Issue, 934 (119), 985 (123), 998 (124), 1013 (127), 1067 (132)
 and Navy, 900 (115)
 Continental, 1565 (183)
 Salvation, 1267 (151)
Arnold, Gen. H.H. "Hap," 2192 (255)
Arrival of Lafayette, 1010 (127)
"Arsenal of Democracy," 2559e (296)
Arthur, Chester A., 826 (108), 2218c (260)
Articles of Confederation, 1726 (204)
Artists, 884-888 (112), 1187 (144), 1207 (147), 1241 (148), 1243 (148), 1322 (156), 1335 (159), 1361 (160), 1370 (160), 1386 (163), 1433 (168), 1486 (175), 1553 (180), 1863 (219), 1934 (227), 2182 (255), C71 (344)
Asia, C131 (351)
Assiniboine Headdress, 2501 (291)
Astronauts, 1331 (156), 1434-1435 (168), 1912 (224), 2419 (284), 2632 (304), C76 (344)
Atlantic
 Cable, 1112 (139)
 Charter, 2559d (296)
 Cod, 2206 (256)
Atomic Energy Act, 1200 (147)
Atoms for Peace, 1070 (132)
Audubon, John James, 874 (112), 1241 (148), 1863 (219), C71 (344)
Austin, Stephen F., 776 (104), 778 (104)
Australia Bicentennial, 2370 (276)
Austria, 919 (116)
Authors, 859-863 (112), 980 (123), 1250 (148), 1281 (152), 1294 (152), 1327 (156), 1487 (175), 1731 (204), 1733 (204), 1832 (216), 1848 (219), 1856-1857 (219), 2010 (235), 2047 (239), 2073 (243), 2094 (244), 2168 (255), 2183 (255), 2196-2197 (255), 2350 (272), 2418 (283), 2538 (295)
Automobile, 296 (62), 1162 (143), 1286A (152), 1511 (179), 1906 (223), 2437 (287), 2438d (287)
 Electric, 1906 (223)

Aviation
 Commercial, 1684 (195)
 Naval, 1185 (144)
 Pioneers of, C91-C93 (347), C94 (347), C95 (347), C99 (347), C100 (347), C113 (348), C114 (348), C118 (348), C119 (348), C128 (351), C129 (351)
Azurite, 2700 (311)

B

B, (18¢) Stamp, 1819-1820 (215)
Baby Buggy, 1902 (223)
Badger, 1922 (224)
Balboa, Vasco Nunez de, 397 (73), 401 (74)
Bald Eagle, 1909 (223)
Baldwin, Abraham, 1850 (219)
Ballet, 1749 (207)
Balloon Jupiter, C54 (343)
Ballooning, 2530 (295)
Balloons, Hot Air, 2032-2035 (236)
Ballot Box, Early, 1584 (184)
Baltimore
 & Ohio Railroad, 1006 (124)
 Cathedral, 1780 (211)
Bankers Association, American, 987 (123)
Banking and Commerce, 1577-1578 (184)
Banneker, Benjamin, 1804 (212)
Bar Association, American, 1022 (127)
Barcelona, 235 (57)
Barred Owl, 1762 (208)
Barrel Cactus, 1942 (228)
Barry, John, 790 (107)
Barrymores, The, 2012 (235)
Bartholdi, Fredric Auguste, 2147 (251)
Barton, Clara, 967 (120)
Baseball, 855 (111)
 Professional, 1381 (163), 2016 (235), 2046 (239), 2097 (244), 2417 (283)
 Olympic, 2619 (300)
Basketball
 Centennial, 2560 (296)
 Naismith, 1189 (144)
Bass, Largemouth, 2207 (256)
Battle
 of Bennington, 643-644 (92)
 of Braddock's Field, 688 (96)
 of Brooklyn, 1003 (124)
 of Bunker Hill, 1361 (160), 1564 (183)
 of Fallen Timbers, 680 (95)
 of Fort Stanwix, 644 (92)
 of Lexington and Concord, 1563 (183)
 of Mobile, 1826 (215)
 of New Orleans, 1261 (151)
 of Oriskany, 644 (92), 1722 (204)
 of Saratoga, 644 (92)
 of White Plains, 629-630 (91)
Beach Umbrella, 2443 (287)
Beacon on Rocky Mountain, C11 (339)
Beagle, 2098 (244)
Beale, Boggs, Lincoln and Douglas Debating, 1115 (139)
Bear
 Brown, 1884 (220)
 Polar, 1429 (167), 1885 (220)
 Smokey the, 2096 (244)
Beau Geste, 2447 (288)
Beaugregory Fish, 1827 (215)
Beautification of America, 1318 (156), 1365-1368 (160)
Beavertail Cactus, 1944 (228)
Beecher Hall, UX172 (326)
Belgium, 914 (116)
Bell
 Alexander Graham, 893 (112), 1683 (195)
 Liberty, 1518 (179), C57 (343), C62 (343)
Bella
 Bella Tribe, Heiltsuk, 1834 (216)
 Coola Tribe, 1837 (216)
Bengal Tiger, White, 2709 (311)
Benny, Jack, 2564 (296)

Bergen
 & McCarthy, 2563 (296)
 Edgar, 2563 (296)
Bering Land Bridge, C131 (351)
Best
 Friend of Charleston, 2363 (275)
 Wishes, 2271 (264), 2396 (280)
Bethune, Mary McLeod, 2137 (251)
Bicycle, 1460 (171), 1901 (223)
 Tandem, 2266 (264)
Big Brothers, Big Sisters, 2162 (252)
Bighorn Sheep, 1467 (171), 1880 (220), 1949 (228)
Bill of Rights, 1312 (155)
 Drafting of the, 2421 (284)
Biltmore House, 1929 (227)
Biplane, 2436 (287), 2438 (287), 2438c (287)
 De Havilland, C6 (339)
Bird
 Treaty, Migratory, 1306 (155)
 & Flowers, State, 1954-1968 (231), 1969 (231), 1953 (231), 1970-1977 (231), 1978-1986 (232), 1988-1995 (232), 1996-2002 (232)
Bison, 1883 (220)
Bissell, Emily, 1823 (215)
Black
 and Tan Coonhound, 2101 (244)
 Heritage, 1744 (207), 1771 (211), 1804 (212), 1875 (220), 2016 (235), 2044 (239), 2073 (243), 2137 (251), 2203 (256), 2371 (276), 2402 (283), 2442 (287), 2567 (296), 2617 (300)
 Hugo L., 2172 (255)
Blacksmith, 1718 (203)
Blackwell, Elizabeth, 1399 (164)
Blair, Montgomery, C66 (343)
Bliss, Fort, 976 (123)
Blood Donor, 1425 (167)
Blue Jay, 1757 (208)
Bluebird, Eastern, 2482 (291)
Bluefin Tuna, 2208 (256)
Bobcat, 2476 (291)
"Bobtail" Horsecar, 2061 (240)
Bolivar, Simon, 1110-1111 (139)
Bon Homme Richard, 983 (123)
Bookmark and Eyeglasses, Books, 1585 (184)
Books
 Bookmark and Eyeglasses, 1585 (184)
 Youth Classics, (320)
Boone, Daniel, 904 (115), 1357 (160)
Borglum, Gutzon, Sculptured Head by, 1114 (139)
Boston
 State House, 1781 (211)
 Tea Party, 1480-1483 (172)
 Terrier, 2098 (244)
Botanic Congress, 1376-1379 (163)
Boulder Dam, 774 (104)
Boxing, 2766 (318)
Boy Scouts, 995 (124), 1145 (140), 2161 (252)
Boys' Clubs of America, 1163 (143)
Brain Coral, Beaugregory Fish, 1827 (215)
Bread Wagon, 2136 (248)
Brice, Fanny, 2565 (296)
Bridge, 293 (62), 297 (62), 961 (120), 1012 (127), 1109 (139), 1258 (151), 1721 (203)
 Brooklyn, 1012 (127), 2041 (239)
Broad-billed Hummingbird, 2643 (304)
Broadbill Decoy, 2138 (251)
Broadway Musicals, (319)
Brontosaurus, 1390 (163), 2425 (284)
Brooklyn
 Bridge, 1012 (127), 2041 (239)
 Battle of, 1003 (124)
Brother Jonathan, 2365 (275)
Brown
 Bear, 1884 (220)
 Pelican, 1466 (171)
Brussels Universal and International Exhibition, 1104 (136)
Bryan, William Jennings, 2195 (255)

Buchanan, James, 820 (108), 2217f
  (259)
  (Wheatland), 1081 (135)
Buck, Pearl, 1848 (219)
Buckboard, 2124 (248)
Buffalo, 287 (62), 569 (87), 700 (96),
  1392 (163), 1883 (220)
  Bill Cody, 2178 (255)
Buggy, 1360 (160), 1370 (160), 1505
  (176), 1902 (223)
  Baby, 1418 (167), 1902 (223)
Bulfinch, Charles, 1781 (211)
Bull, John, 2364 (275)
Bunche, Ralph, 1860 (219)
Bunker Hill, 1034 (128), 1056 (131)
  Flag, 1351 (159)
Burbank, Luther, 876 (112)
Burgoyne Campaign, 644 (92), 1728
  (204)
Burma Road, 2559a (296)
Burmese, 2374 (276)
Butterflies, 1712-1715 (203)
Byrd
  Antarctic Expedition II, 733 (99), 735
    (100), 753 (103), 768 (103)
  Richard E., 2388 (279)

C

C (20¢) Stamp, 1946-1948 (228)
Cab, Hansom, 1904 (223)
Cable Car, 1442 (168)
  San Francisco, 1442 (168), 2263
    (264)
Caboose, RR, 1905 (223)
Cabrillo, Juan Rodriguez, 2704 (311)
Cadillac, Landing of, 1000 (124)
Calico Scallop, 2120 (248)
California, 1663 (192), 1957 (231)
  Condor, 1430 (167)
  Gold, 954 (120)
  Pacific International Exposition, 773
    (104), 778 (104)
  Settlement, 1373 (160)
  Statehood, 997 (124)
  (Yosemite National Park), 740 (100),
    751 (100), 756 (103), 769 (103)
Calliope Hummingbird, 2446 (304),
  2643 (304)
Camel, 2392 (279)
Camellia, 1877 (220), 1935 (231)
Cameras, Motion Picture, 1555 (180)
Camp Fire Girls, 1167 (143), 2163 (252)
Canada, 1324 (156)
  Goose, 1757 (208)
  US Friendship, 961 (120)
Canal, 298 (62), 398 (73), 402 (74), 681
  (95), 856 (111)
  Boat, 2257 (264)
  Erie, 1325 (156)
Cancer
  Detection, Early, 1754 (207)
  Crusade Against, 1263 (151)
Candle, 1205 (147), 2395 (280)
  Holder, Rush Lamp and, 1610 (187)
Cannon, 629-630 (91), 1178 (144),
  1181 (144)
Canoe, 1356 (160), 2163 (252), 2453
  (288), 2353A (288)
Canvasback Decoy, 2140 (251)
Cape Hatteras, 1448-1451 (171), 2471
  (288)
CAPEX '78, 1757 (208), 1757a-h (208)
Capitol, 572-573 (87), 989 (124), 992
  (124), 1202 (147), 1365 (160), 1503
  (176), 1590-1591 (184), 1616 (188),
  1623 (188), 2114-2116 (247), 2561
  (296), C64 (343), C65 (343)
  National Sesquicentennial, 989-992
    (124)
  Statue of Freedom on Dome, 989
    (124)
Cardinal, 1465 (171), 1757 (208), 1965-
  1966 (231), 1969 (231), 1985 (232),
  1987 (232), 1998 (232), 2000 (232),
  2489 (291)
CARE, 1439 (168)
Carlson, Chester, 2180 (255)
Carlyle House, John, C40 (340)

Carmel, Man and Children of, 1485
  (175)
Carnegie, Andrew, 1171 (143)
Carolina Charter, 1230 (147)
  -Charleston, 683 (95)
Carousel Animals, 2390-2393 (279)
Carpenters' Hall, 1543 (180)
Carreta, 2255 (264)
Carriage, Steam, 2451 (288)
Carrier, Letter, 1238 (148), 1490 (175),
  1497 (175), 2420 (284)
Cars, Classic, 2381-2385 (279)
Carson
  Rachel, 1857 (219)
  Valley, NV, 999 (124)
Carteret, Philip, Landing of, 1247 (148)
Caruso, Enrico, 2250 (263)
Carver, Dr. George Washington, 953
  (120)
Cassatt, Mary, 1322 (156), 2182 (255)
Catfish, 2209 (256)
Cather, Willa, 1487 (175)
Cats, American, 2372-2375 (276)
Catt, Carrie C., 959 (120)
Cattle
  Angus and Longhorn, 1504 (176)
  Western, in Storm, 292 (62)
Century of Progress
  Exposition, 728-731(99)
  Flight, C18 (339)
Certified Public Accountants, 2361
  (275)
Chalice Coral, 1829 (215)
Champions of Liberty, 1096 (136),
  1110-1111 (139), 1117-1118 (139),
  1136-1137 (140), 1148 (140)
  Giusseppe Garibaldi, 1168-1169
    (143)
  Gustaf Mannerheim, 1165-1166 (143)
  Ignacy Jan Paderewski, 1159-1160
    (143)
  Mahatma Gandhi, 1174-1175 (144)
  Masaryk, 1147 (140)
  San Martin, 1125-1126 (139)
Chanute, Octave, C93 (347), C94 (347)
Charleston
  Best Friend of, 2363 (275)
  Carolina, 683 (95)
Charlotte Amalie Harbor, St.Thomas,
  Virgin Islands, 802 (107)
Charter, 2559 (296)
  Oak, 772 (104)
Chavez, Dennis, 2185 (255)
Checkerspot, 1713 (203)
Chemical Society, American, 1002 (124)
Chemistry, 1685 (195)
Chennault Claire Lee, 2186 (255)
Cherokee
  Seal, 972 (123)
  Strip, 1360 (160)
  Strip Land Run, 2754 (316)
Chesapeake Bay Retriever, 2099 (244)
Cheyenne Headdress, 2502 (291)
Chicago
  Century of Progress, Flight, C18
    (339)
  Century of Progress Exposition, 728-
    731 (99), 766 (103)
Chickasaw Seal, 972 (123)
Chief
  Joseph, 1364 (160)
  Shadoo, 683 (95)
Children, 230 (57), 235 (57), 651 (92),
  717 (99), 796 (107), 855 (111), 963
  (120), 995 (124), 1005 (124), 1007
  (124), 1015 (127), 1024 (127), 1073
  (135), 1082 (135), 1085 (135), 1087
  (136), 1093 (136), 1135 (140), 1149
  (140), 1152 (143), 1163 (143), 1167
  (143), 1199 (147), 1238 (148), 1273
  (151), 1321-1322 (156), 1336 (159),
  1342-1343 (159), 1385 (163), 1414
  (167), 1426 (167), 1444 (168), 1453
  (171), 1455 (171), 1468 (172), 1470
  (172), 1483 (172), 1485 (175), 1507
  (176), 1549 (180), 1559 (183), 1701-
  1703 (200), 1768-1769 (208), 1772
  (211), 1788 (212), 1799 (212), 1824
  (215), 1842 (216), 1910 (223), 1939
  (227), 2010-2011 (235), 2026-2030

  (236), 2063 (240), 2104 (247), 2106-
  2108 (247), 2153 (251), 2160-2165
  (252), 2199 (256), 2244 (263), 2251
  (263), 2275 (267), 2367 (275), 2399
  (280), 2427 (284)
  Children's Friendship, 1085 (135)
Chilkat Tlingit Tribe, 1835 (216)
China
  Clipper Over the Pacific, C20 (339),
    C21 (339), C22 (339), C115 (348)
  Republic of, 1188 (144)
Chinese Resistance, 906 (115)
Chipmunk, 1757 (208), 1757f (208)
Choctaw Seal, 972 (123)
Christmas
  4¢ '62, 1205 (147)
  5¢ '63, 1240 (148)
  5¢ '64, 1254-1270 (151)
  5¢ '65, 1276 (151)
  5¢ '66, 1321 (156)
  5¢ '67, 1336 (159)
  6¢ '68, 1363 (160)
  6¢ '69, 1384 (163)
  6¢ '70, 1414-1418 (167)
  8¢ '71, 1444-1445 (168)
  8¢ '72, 1471-1472 (172)
  8¢ '73, 1507-1508 (176)
  10¢ '74, 1550-1552 (180)
  10¢ '75, 1579-1580 (184)
  13¢ '76, 1701-1703 (200)
  13¢ '77, 1729-1730 (204)
  13¢ '82, 2025 (236)
  15¢ '78, 1768-1769 (208)
  15¢ '79, 1799-1800 (212)
  15¢ '80, 1842-1843 (216)
  20¢ '81, 1940 (227)
  20¢ '81, 1939 (227)
  20¢ '82, 2026-2030 (236)
  20¢ '83, 2063-2064 (240)
  20¢ '84, 2107-2108 (247)
  22¢ '87, 2367 (275)
  22¢ '85, 2165-2166 (252)
  22¢ '86, 2244-2245 (263)
  22¢ '87, 2368 (275)
  25¢ '88, 2399-2400 (280)
  25¢ '89, 2427-2429 (284)
  25¢ '90, 2514-2516 (292)
  29¢ '91, 2578-2585 (299)
  29¢ '92, 2710-2719 (312)
  29¢ '93, (321)
Churchill, Winston, 1264 (151), 2559
  (296), 2559d (296)
Cigar-Store Figure, 2243 (263)
Circuit Board, Printed, 1501 (176)
Circus, 2750-2753 (315)
  American, 1309 (155)
  Wagon, 2452 (288)
Cities, Save Our, 1411 (164)
City
  Mail Delivery, 1238 (148)
  of Alpena, 294 (62)
  of Refuge National Park, C84 (344)
Civil
  Aeronautics Conference, Inter-
    national, 649-650 (92)
  Defense, 2559 (296)
  Service, 2053 (239)
  War, Grand Army of the Republic,
    985 (123)
  War, United Confederate Veterans,
    998 (124)
  War Centennial, Appomattox, 1182
    (144)
  War Centennial, Fort Sumter, 1178
    (144)
  War Centennial, Gettysburg, 1180
    (144)
  War Centennial, Shiloh, 1179 (144)
  War Centennial, The Wilderness,
    1181 (144)
Civilian Conservation Corps, 2037 (236)
Clark
  Expedition, Lewis and, 1063 (132)
  George Rogers, 651 (92)
  Grenville, 1867 (219)
Classic
  Cars, 2381-2385 (279)
  Films, 2445-2448 (288), 2722 (315)
  Mail Transportation, 2434-2438 (287)

Clay, Henry, 140 (53), 151 (53), 162
(53), 173 (53), 198 (54), 227 (54), 259
(58), 274 (61), 284 (62), 309 (65),
1846 (219)
Clemens, Samuel L., 863 (112)
(Mark Twain), 1470 (172)
Clemente, Roberto, 2097 (244)
Clermont, 370-373 (70), 1270 (151)
Cleveland, Grover, 564 (87), 693 (96),
827 (108), 2218 (260), 2218d (260)
Cliff Palace, 743 (100), 759 (103)
Clown, 1390 (155)
Circus, 2752 (315)
Coal Car, 2259 (264)
Coast
and Geodetic Survey, 1088 (136)
Guard, 936 (119), 1067 (132)
Cobb, Col. David, 1686 (196), 1686d
(196)
Cocker Spaniel, 2099 (244)
Cod, Atlantic, 2206 (256)
Cody, Buffalo Bill, 2178 (255)
Coffeepot
Curved Spout, 1778 (211)
Straight-Spout, 1775 (211)
Cohan, George M., 1756 (207)
Collective Bargaining, 1558 (183)
College Football, 1382 (163), 2089 (244)
Collie, 2100 (244)
Colonial American Craftsmen, 1456-
1459 (171)
Colorado, 1670 (195), 1958 (231)
(Mesa Verde National Park), 743
(100), 759 (103)
River, 1374 (160)
Statehood, 1001 (124), 1711 (203)
Columbia
University, 1029 (127)
District of, 2561 (296)
Columbian Exposition, 230-245 (57),
2624-2629 (303)
World Stamp Expo '92, 2616 (300),
2624-2629 (303)
Columbus
Christopher, 118-119 (50), 230-245
(57), 2616 (300), 2620-2623 (300),
2624-2629 (303)
First Voyage of, 2620-2623 (300)
Landing, 118-119 (50)
Landing in Puerto Rico, (322)
Monument, 1076 (135)
Comanche Headdress, 2503 (291)
Comedians, 2562-2565 (296)
Commerce, Banking and, 1577-1578
(184)
Commercial Aviation, 1684 (195)
Common Dolphin, 2511 (291)
Communications
for Peace, Echo I-, 1173 (143)
in Colonial Times, 1476-1479 (172)
Composers, 879-883 (112), 962 (120),
1372 (160), 1484 (175), 1755-1756
(207), 1845 (219), 2044 (239), 2110
(247), 2177 (255), 2211 (256), 2371
(276), 2550 (295)
Comstock, Henry, 1130 (139)
Concord
/German Immigration, 2040 (236)
Lexington and, 617-618 (88), 619
(91), 1563 (183)
Condor, California, 1430 (167)
Conestoga Wagon, 2252 (264)
Congratulations!, 2267 (264)
Congress
Library of, 2004 (235)
US, 2559j (296)
Conifer, Sprig of, 1257 (151)
Connecticut 1637 (191), 1959 (231)
Settlement, 772 (104), 778 (104)
Statehood, 2340 (272)
Conservation
Corps, Civilian, 2037 (236)
Energy, 1547 (180), 1723 (204)
Forest, 1122 (139)
Range, 1176 (144)
Soil, 1133 (140)
Soil and Water, 2074 (243)
Water, 1150 (140)
Waterfowl, 1362 (160)

Wildlife, 1077-1079 (135), 1098
(136), 1392 (163), 1427-1430
(167), 1464-1467 (171), 1760-
1763 (208)
Constitution
Bicentennial, 2336-2348 (272), 2355-
2360 (275), 2412-2415 (283),
2421 (284)
Drafting of the, 2355-2359 (275)
Nineteenth Amendment, 1051 (131)
Nineteenth Amendment (Suffrage),
784 (104)
Ratification, 835 (111), 2336-2348
(272)
Signing of the, 798 (107), 2360 (275)
Thirteenth Amendment, 902 (115)
US Frigate, 951 (120)
Consumer Education, 2005 (235)
Contemplation of Justice, 1592 (184),
1617 (188)
Continental
Army, 1565 (183)
Congress, First, 1543-1546 (180)
Marines, 1567 (183)
Navy, 1566 (183)
Contra Costa Wallflower, 1785 (211)
Contributors to the Cause, 1559-1562
(183)
Cook, Captain James, 1732-1733 (204)
Coolidge, Calvin, 834 (111), 2219 (260),
2219b (260)
Coon Cat, Maine, 2374 (276)
Coonhound, Black and Tan, 2101 (244)
Cooper
Gary, 2447 (288)
James Fenimore, 860 (112)
Cooperative for American Relief Every-
where (CARE), 1439 (168)
Copernicus, Nicolaus, 1488 (175)
Copley
Elizabeth, 1273 (151)
John Singleton, 1273 (151)
Copper, 2701 (311)
Coral Reefs, 1827-1830 (215)
Cord, 2383 (279)
Cornwallis
at Yorktown, Surrender of, 703 (96)
Surrender of, 1686 (196)
Coronado Expedition, 898 (115)
Corregidor (Philippines), 925 (116)
Costa's Hummingbird, 2644 (304)
Country & Western Music, 2723 (318),
(320)
Crane, Ichabod, 1548 (180)
Crater Lake National Park, 745 (100),
761 (103)
Crazy Horse, 1855 (219)
Creatures of the Sea, 2508-2511 (291)
Credit Union Act, 2075 (243)
Crime Prevention, 2102 (247)
Crippled, Hope for the, 1385 (163)
Crockett, Davy, 1330 (156)
Crusade Against Cancer, 1263 (151)
Curtiss
Glenn, C100 (347)
Jenny, C1 (339), C2 (339), C3 (339),
C74 (344)
Curved-Spout Coffeepot, 1778 (211)
Cushing, Harvey, M.D., 2188 (255)
Cutler, Manasseh, 795 (107)
Czechoslovakia, 910 (116)

D

D (22¢) Stamp, 2111-2113 (247)
Daffodil, 2761 (317)
Dahlia, 1878 (220)
Dam
Boulder, 774 (104)
Grand Coulee, 1009 (127)
Norris, 1184 (144)
Dante, 1268 (151)
Dare, Virginia, 796 (107)
Dartmouth College Case, 1380 (163)
Davis
Alexander J., 1841 (216)
Jefferson, 1408 (164)
Daye Press, Stephen, 857 (111)
DC-4 Skymaster, C32 (340), C33 (340),
C37 (340), C39 (340), C41 (340)

de Grasse, Count, 703 (96)
De Havilland Biplane, C6 (339)
Decatur
House, 1440 (168)
Stephen, 791 (107)
Declaration
of Independence, 120 (50), 1545
(180), 1687 (196)
of Independence, by John Trumbull,
1691-1694 (200)
of Independence, Jefferson,
Thomas, 2184B (323)
of War, 2559j (296)
Deer, 2390 (279)
White-Tailed, 1888 (220)
DeForest Audions, C86 (344)
Delaware, 1633 (191), 1960 (231)
Statehood, 2336 (272)
Delta Wing Plane Silhouette, C77 (344)
Denmark, 920 (116)
Dental Health, 1135 (140)
Desert
Plants, 1942-1945 (228)
Shield\Desert Storm, 2551 (295)
Detroit, 1000 (124)
Development, Energy, 1724 (204)
Devils Tower National Monument, 1084
(135)
Dewey
George, 793 (107)
John, 1291 (152)
Diamond Head, HI, C46 (340)
Dickinson
Emily, 1436 (168)
John, 1687e (196), 1694 (200)
Dinosaurs (Prehistoric Animals), 2422-
2425 (284)
Dirksen, Everett, 1874 (220)
Disabled
American Veterans and Servicemen,
1421-1422 (167)
International Year of the, 1925 (224)
Discovery, 1733 (204)
Disney, Walt, 1355 (159)
District of Columbia, 2561 (296)
Dix, Dorothea, 1844 (219)
Doctors, 949 (120), 1138 (140), 1251
(148), 1399 (164), 1754 (207), 1865
(219), 2013 (235), 2038 (236), 2170
(255), 2188 (255)
Dogface, 1714 (203)
Dogs, 239 (57), 619 (91), 1128 (139),
1307 (155), 1468 (172), 2202 (256)
American, 2098-2101 (244)
Seeing Eye, 1787 (212)
Sled, 1128 (139), 2135 (248)
Dogwood, 2347 (272)
Blossoms Lace Design, 2354 (272)
Dolphin, Common, 2511 (291)
Dorchester, SS, 956 (120)
Douglas
Debates, Lincoln-, 1115 (139)
Fir, 1376 (163)
Douglass, Frederick, 1290 (152)
Draft, America's First Peacetime,
2559b (296)
Drafting
of the Bill of Rights, 2421 (284)
of the Constitution, 2355-2359 (275)
Drew, M.D., Charles R., 1865 (219)
Drug Abuse, Prevent, 1438 (168)
Drum, 1615 (187), 1629-1630 (191)
Drummer, 1479 (172), 1629-1630 (191)
Du Sable, Jean Baptiste Pointe, 2249
(263)
DuBois, W.E.B., 2617 (300)
Duck
Decoys, 2138-2141 (251)
Wood, 2493-2494 (291)
Duck Stamps
American Eider, RW24 (367)
American Merganser, RW23 (367)
Baldpates, RW9 (365)
Black Mallards, RW7 (365)
Black-Bellied Whistling Duck, RW57
(367)
Blue Geese, RW22 (365)
Blue-winged Teal, RW20 (365)
Buffleheads, RW15 (365)

Canada Geese, RW25 (367), RW3 (365), RW43 (367)
Canvasback Decoy, RW42 (367)
Canvasback Drake, RW32 (367)
Canvasbacks, RW2 (365), RW42 (367), RW49 (367)
Cinnamon Teal, RW38 (367), RW52 (367)
Duckling, RW28 (367)
Emperor Geese, RW39 (367)
Fulvous Whistling Duck, RW53 (367)
Gadwall Ducks, RW18 (365)
Goldeneye Ducks, RW16 (365)
Green-winged Teal, RW46 (367), RW6 (365)
Harlequin Ducks, RW19 (365)
Hawaiian Nene Geese, RW31 (367)
Hooded Merganser Drake, RW45 (367)
Hooded Mergansers, RW35 (367)
King Eider, RW58 (367)
Labrador Retriever, RW26 (367)
Lesser Scaup, RW56 (367)
Mallard Drake, RW26 (367)
Mallard Hen, RW28 (367)
Mallards, RW47 (367)
Mallards Alighting, RW1 (365)
Old Squaw Ducks, RW34 (367)
Pair of Brant, RW30 (367)
Pintail Drake and Hen Alighting, RW5 (365)
Pintail Drakes, RW29 (367)
Pintails, RW50 (367)
Readheads, RW54 (367)
Redhead Ducks, RW13 (365), RW27 (367)
Ring-necked Ducks, RW21 (365)
Ross's Geese, RW37 (367), RW44 (367)
Ruddy Ducks, RW48 (367), RW8 (365)
Scaup Ducks, RW4 (365)
Shoveller, RW12 (365)
Snow Geese, RW14 (365), RW55 (367)
Spectacled Eider, RW59 (367)
Steller's Eiders, RW40 (367)
Trumpeter Swans, RW17 (365)
Whistling Swans, RW33 (367)
White-fronted Geese, RW11 (365)
White-winged Scoters, RW36 (367)
Widgeons, RW51 (367)
Wood Ducks, RW10 (365), RW41 (367)
Duesenberg, 2385 (279)
Dulles
    Airport, 2022 (235)
    Memorial, John Foster, 1172 (143)
Dunbar, Paul Laurence, 1554 (180)

E

E (25¢) Stamp, 2277 (267), 2279 (267), 2282 (267)
Eagan, Eddie, 2499 (291)
Eagle, 1743 (207)
    and Shield, 116 (50), 1596 (187), 2431 (284), 2595 (299), 2604 (299)
    Bald, 303 (65), 775 (104), 909-921 (116), 1067 (132), 1090 (136), 1131 (139), 1140 (140), 1313 (155), 1341 (159), 1344 (159), 1387 (163), 1424 (167), 1831 (216), 1909 (223), 2111-2113 (247), 2122 (248), 2355-2359 (275), 2394 (280), 2431 (284), 2534 (295), 2540-2542 (295), 2605 (324), 314A (65), C67 (343)
    from Great Seal of the US, 1369 (160)
    in Flight, C48 (340), C50 (343)
    Weather Vane, 1344 (159)
    with Shield and Quill Pen, 2421 (284)
    with Shield, Olive Branch and Arrows, 2413 (283), C23 (339)
Eakins, Thomas, 1335 (159)
Earhart, Amelia, C68 (343)
Early
    Ballot Box, 1584 (184)
    Cancer Detection, 1754 (207)

Earth, 1173 (143), 1193 (144), 1371 (160), 1434 (168), 1569-1570 (183), 1913-1914 (224), 1917-1919 (224), 2277 (267), 2279 (267), 2282 (267), 2526 (295), 2535 (295), 2570 (299), C122 (348), C123 (348), C125 (348), C126 (351)
Eastern Bluebird, 2482 (291)
Eastman, George, 1062 (132)
Echo I-Communications for Peace, 1173 (143)
Edison
    Thomas A., 945 (119)
    Thomas (Electric Light's Golden Jubilee), 654-656 (92)
Education
    Consumer, 2005 (235)
    Higher, 1206 (147)
        (Land Grant Colleges), 1065 (132)
        (Learning Never Ends), 1833 (216)
        (Nation of Readers), 2106 (247)
        (Parent-Teachers Association), 1463 (171)
    Public, 2159 (252)
    Teachers of America, 1093 (136)
Educators, 869-873 (112), 1093 (136), 1291 (152), 1824 (215), 1850 (219), 1852 (219), 1854 (219), 1861 (219), 1920 (224), 2137 (251), 2169 (255), 2171 (255), 2194 (255)
Egalite, C120 (348)
Einstein, Albert, 1285 (152), 1774 (211)
Eisenhower, Dwight D., 1383 (163), 1393-1395 (164), 1401-1402 (164), 2219g (260), 2513 (292)
El Capitan, 740 (100), 751 (100), 756 (103), 769 (103)
Electric
    Auto, 1906 (223)
    Light's Golden Jubilee, 654-656 (92)
    Streetcar, Early, 2060 (240)
    Theories, 2055 (239)
Electronics, Progress in, 1500-1502 (176), C86 (344)
Elephant
    Herd, African, 1388 (163)
    Circus, 2751 (315)
Elevator, 2254 (264)
Eliot
    Charles W., 871 (112)
    T.S., 2239 (263)
Elk, 1886 (220)
Elkhorn Coral, 1828 (215)
Elks, Support Our Youth, 1342 (159)
Ellington, Duke, 2211 (256)
Ellsworth, Lincoln, 2389 (279)
Emancipation Proclamation, 1233 (147)
Emerson, Ralph Waldo, 861 (112)
Emigration, 290 (62)
Employ the Handicapped, 1155 (143)
Endangered Flora, 1783-1786 (211)
Energy, 1723-1724 (204)
    Conservation, 1547 (180), 1723 (204)
    Development, 1724 (204)
Engineering, 1012 (127)
Engineers, American Society of, 1012 (127)
Envelopes, Sealed, 2150 (251)
Environment, Preserve the, 1527 (179)
Ericsson Memorial, John, 628 (91)
Erie Canal, 1825 (150)
Erikson, Leif, 1359 (160)
Everglades National Park, 952 (120)
Ewry, Ray, 2497 (291)
Executive
    Branch, 2414 (283)
    Mansion, 990 (124)
Exotic Shorthair Cat, 2372 (276)
Experiment, 2405 (283)
Explorer II, 2035 (236)
Explorers, 285 (62), 288 (62),
    Antarctic, 2386-2389 (279)
    Armstrong, C76 (344)
    Balboa, 397 (73)
    Byrd, 733 (99), 735 (100), 768 (103), 2388 (279)
    Cabrillo, 2704 (311)
    Cadillac, 1000 (124)
    Cook, 1732-1733 (204)
    Coronado, 898 (115)

de Leon, 2024 (236)
Ellsworth, 2389 (279)
Erikson, 1359 (160)
Greely, 2221 (263)
Henson, 2223 (263)
Kane, 2220 (263)
Lewis and Clark, 1063 (132)
Marquette, 1356 (160)
Nicolet, 739 (100), 755 (103)
Palmer, 2386 (279)
Peary, 1128 (139), 2223 (263)
Polar, 2220-2223 (263)
Powell, 1374 (160)
Stefansson, 2222 (263)
Verrazano, 1258 (151)
Wilkes, 2387 (279)
Expo '74, 1527 (179)
Expositions, 230-245 (57), 285-290 (62), 292-299 (62), 323-330 (66), 370-371 (70), 397-400 (73), 401-404 (74), 630 (91), 728-731 (99), 735 (100), 750-751 (100), 766 (103), 773 (104), 778 (104), 852-853 (111), 948 (120), 1075-1076 (135), 1104 (136), 1196 (147), 1244 (148), 1310-1311 (155), 1340-1344 (159), 1527 (179), 1632 (191), 1757 (208), 2006-2009 (235), 2086 (243), 2410 (283), 2433 (284), 2616 (300), 2624-2626 (303), 2628-2629 (303)
Express
    International, 2542 (295)
    Mail, 1909 (223), 2122 (248), 2394 (280), 2541 (295)
Eyeglasses, Books, Bookmark, 1585 (184)

F

F Stamp, 2517-2520 (292), 2522 (292)
Fairbanks, Douglas, 2088 (244)
Fallingwater, 2019 (235)
Family
    Planning, 1455 (171)
    Unity, 2104 (247)
Famous Americans, 859-893 (112), 945 (119), 953 (120), 960 (120), 965 (120), 975 (123), 980 (123), 986 (123), 988 (123), 1062 (132), 1072 (132), 1121 (139), 1138 (140), 1170-1172 (143), 1177 (144)
Fantasy, Space, 2741-2745 (314)
Farmers of America, Future, 1024 (127)
Farming, 286 (62)
Farnsworth, Philo T., 2058 (239)
Farragut, David G., 311 (65), 792 (107)
Faulkner, William, 2350 (272)
Fawn, 2487 (291)
Federal
    Deposit Insurance Corporation, 2071 (240)
    Hall, 1086 (136)
Federated State of Micronesia, 2506 (291)
Fields, W.C., 1803 (212)
Fife Player, 1631 (191)
Fifth World Forestry Congress, 1156 (143)
Fiftieth Anniversary of Statehood (Montana, North Dakota, South Dakota, Washington), 858 (111)
Fifty
    -Star and 13-Star Flags, 1509 (176)
    -Star Runway, C72 (344), C73 (344)
    State Flags, 1633-1644 (191), 1645-1665 (192), 1666-1682 (195)
Fillmore, Millard, 818 (108), 2217d (259)
Films, Classic, 2445-2448 (288), 2722 (315)
Fine Arts, 1259 (151)
Finger Coral, 1830 (215)
Finland Independence, 1334 (156)
Finnish Settlement, Swedish-, 836 (111)
    (Stamp Collecting), 2200 (256)
Fir, Douglas, 1376 (163)
Fire
    Engine, 971 (123), 2264 (264)
    Pumper, 1908 (223)
    Truck, 971 (123)
Firemen, Volunteer, 971 (123)

395

Fireworks, 2276 (267)
First
    Automated Post Office, 1164 (143)
    Civil Settlement-Alta, California,
        1725 (204)
    Continental Congress, 1543-1546
        (180)
    Kentucky Settlement, 1542 (180)
    Navy Jack, 1354 (159), 1566 (183)
    Stars and Stripes, 1350 (159)
    Television Camera, 2058 (239)
    Voyage of Christopher Columbus,
        2620-2623 (300)
Fischer's Lovebirds, 2537 (295)
Fish, 2205-2209 (256)
    (Anti-Pollution), 1412 (164)
    (Louisiana World Exposition), 2086
        (243)
    (Wildlife Conservation), 1427 (167)
Fishing
    Boat, 2529 (292)
    Flies, 2545-2549 (295)
Flags, 231-233 (57), 329 (66), 372-373
    (70), 537 (83), 614 (88), 629-630 (91),
    690 (96), 775 (104), 778 (104), 909-
    921 (116), 923 (116), 938 (119), 942
    (119), 1000 (124), 1010 (127), 1034
    (128), 1069 (132), 1088 (136), 1123
    (139), 1239 (148), 1271 (151), 1275
    (151), 1407 (164), 1645-1665 (192),
    1666-1682 (195), 2097 (244), 2204
    (256), 2616 (300)
    and Anthem, 1890 (220), 1893 (220)
    50-Star, 1153 (143)
    49-Star, 1132 (140)
    on Parade, 2531 (295)
    Over Capitol, 1623 (188), 2114-2116
        (247)
    Over Mt. Rushmore, 2523 (292),
        2523A (292)
    Over Supreme Court, 1894-1895
        (220), 1896 (223)
    Over White House, 1208 (147), 1338
        (159), 2609 (299), 1338A (159),
        1338D (159), 1338F (159), 1338G
        (159)
    Over Yosemite, 2280 (267)
    Plane and Globes, C90 (344)
    US, 288 (62), 372 (70), 373 (70), 537
        (83), 629-630 (91), 690 (96), 727
        (99), 752 (103), 775 (104), 778
        (104), 929 (119), 938 (119), 944
        (119), 962 (120), 990-991 (124),
        1004 (124), 1010 (127), 1094
        (136), 1115 (139), 1132 (140),
        1153 (143), 1208 (147), 1249
        (148), 1261 (151), 1320 (156),
        1338 (159), 1338A (159), 1338D
        (159), 1338F (159), 1338G (159),
        1346 (159), 1348 (159), 1350
        (159), 1383 (163), 1406 (164),
        1447 (168), 1509 (176), 1519
        (179), 1597-1598 (187), 1618C
        (188), 1622 (188), 1630-1631
        (191), 1686d (196), 1688 (199),
        1890-1891 (220), 1893-1895
        (220), 1896 (223), 1952 (228),
        2103 (247), 2114-2115 (247),
        2216 (259), 2276 (267), 2278
        (267), 2280 (267), 2409 (283),
        2419 (284), 2421 (284), 2475
        (291), 2522 (292), 2523 (292),
        2523A (292), 2528 (292), 2531
        (295), 2607 (299), C34 (340), C54
        (343), C76 (344), C115 (348),
        C122 (348), C123 (348), C124
        (348), C125 (348), C126 (351)
    with Clouds, 2278 (267), 2285A (267)
    with Fireworks, 2276 (267)
    with Olympic Rings, 2528 (292)
Flags, State, 1633-1644 (191), 1645-
    1665 (192), 1666-1682 (195)
    Alabama, 1654 (192)
    Alaska, 1681 (195)
    Arizona, 1680 (195)
    Arkansas, 1657 (192)
    California, 1663 (192)
    Colorado, 1670 (195)
    Florida, 1659 (192)
    Hawaii, 1682 (195)

Idaho, 1675 (195)
Illinois, 1653 (192)
Indiana, 1651 (192)
Iowa, 1661 (192)
Kansas, 1666 (195)
Kentucky, 1647 (192)
Louisiana, 1650 (192)
Maine, 1655 (192)
Michigan, 1658 (192)
Minnesota, 1664 (192)
Mississippi, 1652 (192)
Missouri, 1656 (192)
Montana, 1673 (195)
Nebraska, 1669 (195)
Nevada, 1668 (195)
New Mexico, 1679 (195)
North Dakota, 1671 (195)
Ohio, 1649 (192)
Oklahoma, 1678 (195)
Oregon, 1665 (192)
Rhode Island, 1645 (192)
South Dakota, 1672 (195)
Tennessee, 1648 (192)
Texas, 1660 (192)
Utah, 1677 (195)
Vermont, 1646 (192)
Washington, 1674 (195)
West Virginia, 1667 (195)
Wisconsin, 1662 (192)
Wyoming, 1676 (195)
Flamingo, 2707 (311)
Flanagan, Father, 2171 (255)
Flathead Headdress, 2504 (291)
Flies, Fishing, 2545-2549 (295)
Flight, Powered, C47 (340)
Flora, Endangered, 1783-1786 (211)
Floral Piece, Lace, 2352 (272)
Florida, 1659 (192), 1961 (231)
    Huguenot-Walloon Monument, 616
        (88)
    Settlement, 1271 (151)
    Statehood, 927 (119)
Flowers, 1158 (143), 1183 (144), 1192
    (144), 1256 (151), 1318 (156), 1337
    (159), 1365-1367 (160), 1375 (160),
    1377-1379 (163), 1711 (203), 1737
    (204), 1783-1786 (211), 1807 (215),
    1876-1879 (220), 1942 (228), 1944
    (228), 1951 (228), 2014 (235), 2074
    (243), 2076-2079 (243), 2166 (252),
    2268 (264), 2273 (264), 2285 (267),
    2347 (272), 2378-2379 (276), 2395
    (280), 2416 (283), 2517 (292), 2524-
    2527 (292)
    Garden, 2760-2764 (317)
    State Birds and, 1978-1995 (232),
        1996-2002 (232)
Flushing Remonstrance, The, 1099
    (136)
Folk
    Art, American, 1706-1709 (203),
        1745-1748 (207), 1775-1778
        (211), 1834-1837 (216), 2138-
        2141 (261), 2235-2238 (263),
        2240-2243 (263), 2351-2352
        (272), 2354 (272), 2390-2393
        (279), 2501-2505 (291)
    Dance, 1751 (207)
Folklore, American, 1317 (156), 1330
    (156), 1357 (160), 1370 (160), 1470
    (172), 1548 (180), 1578 (184)
Food for Peace-Freedom from Hunger,
    1231 (147)
Football, College, 1382 (163), 2089
    (244), 2376 (276)
Forbes, Brig. Gen. John, 1123 (139)
Ford, Henry, 1286A (152)
Foreign Countries, 398 (73), 856 (111),
    906 (115), 909-921 (116), 925 (116),
    961 (120), 1021 (127), 1104 (136),
    1131 (139), 1157-1158 (143), 1188
    (144), 1313 (155), 1324 (156), 1334
    (156), 1431 (168), 1569-1570 (183),
    1721 (203), 1753 (207), 1757 (208),
    2003 (235), 2036 (236), 2040 (236),
    2091 (244), 2349 (272), 2370 (276),
    2532 (295), C120 (348)
Forest
    Congress, Fifth World, 1156 (143)
    Conservation, 1122 (139)

Fire Prevention, 2096 (244)
Fort
    Bliss, 976 (123)
    Dearborn (Chicago), 728 (99), 730
        (99), 766 (103)
    Duquesne (Pitt), 1123 (139)
    Harrod, 1542 (180)
    Kearny, 970 (123)
    McHenry, 962 (120)
    McHenry, Flag, 1346 (159), 1597-
        1598 (187), 1618C (188)
    Moultrie Flag, 962 (120), 1345 (159)
    Nisqually, 1604 (187)
    Orange, Landing at, 615 (88)
    Sackville, Surrender of, 651 (92)
    Snelling, 1409 (164)
    Stanwix, 644 (92)
    Sumter, Civil War Centennial, 1178
        (144)
    Ticonderoga, 1071 (132)
Fossil Fuels, 2009 (235)
Foster, Stephen Collins, 879 (112)
Four
    Chaplains, 956 (120)
    Freedoms, 908 (115)
4-H Clubs, 1005 (124)
49-Star Flag, 1132 (140)
Foxhound, American, 2101 (244)
France, 915 (116), 934 (119)
Francis of Assisi, 2023 (236)
Francisco, Peter, 1562 (183)
Franklin, Benjamin, 1 (45), 3 (45), 5-9
    (45), 5A (45), 8A (45), 18-24 (45), 38
    (46), 40 (46), 46 (46), 63 (49), 71 (49),
    81 (49), 85A (49), 86 (49), 92 (50),
    100 (50), 102 (50), 110 (50), 112 (50),
    134 (53), 145 (53), 156 (53), 167 (53),
    182 (53), 192 (54), 206 (54), 212 (54),
    219 (54), 246-247 (58), 264 (61), 279
    (62), 300 (65), 314 (65), 316 (65), 318
    (65), 331 (69), 343 (69), 348 (69), 352
    (69), 357 (70), 374 (70), 383 (73), 385
    (73), 387 (73), 390 (73), 392 (73), 414-
    418 (74), 419-423 (77), 431-435 (77),
    437-440 (77), 460 (78), 470-478 (79),
    497 (79), 508-518 (80), 523-524 (83),
    547 (84), 552 (84), 575 (87), 578 (87),
    581 (87), 594 (88), 596-597 (88), 604
    (88), 632 (91), 658 (95), 669 (95), 803
    (108), 947 (119), 948 (120), 1030
    (128), 1073 (135), 1140 (140), 1393D
    (164), 1474 (172), 1687b (196), 1690
    (200), 1693 (200), 1753 (207), 2036
    (236), 2052 (239), 2145 (251)
Franklinia, 1379 (163)
Fraternity, C120 (348)
Freedom
    from Hunger, Food for Peace, 1231
        (147)
    of the Press, 1119 (139), 1476-1477
        (172), 1593 (184)
    Wheels of, 1162 (143)
Freedoms, Four, 908 (115), 933 (119)
Fremont, John Charles, 288 (62)
French
    Alliance, 1753 (207)
    Revolution, C120 (348)
    Daniel Chester, 887 (112)
    Daniel Chester, Statue in Lincoln
        Memorial, 1116 (139)
Frequency Modulation, 2056 (239)
Friendship
    Apollo 7, 1193 (144)
    with Morocco, 2349 (272)
Frilled Dogwinkle, 2117 (248)
Frost, Robert, 1526 (179)
Fulton
    Celebration, Hudson-, 372-373 (70)
    Ferry House, 1003 (124)
    Robert, 1270 (151)
Fur Seals, 1464 (171)
Furness, Frank, 1840 (216)
Future
    Farmers of America, 1024 (127)
    Mail Transportation, C123 (348),
        C124 (348), C125 (348), C126
        (351)
    Spacecraft, 2543 (324)

G

Gable, Clark, 2446 (288)
Gadsby's Tavern, C40 (340)
Gadsden Purchase, 1028 (127)
Gaillard Cut, 856 (111)
Gallatin, Albert, 1279 (152)
Gallaudet, Thomas H., 1861 (219)
Galvez, General Bernardo de, 1826 (215)
Games, World University, 2748 (315)
Gandhi, Mahatma, 1174-1175 (144)
Garden
  Flowers, 2760-2764 (317)
  International Peace, 2014 (235)
Gardening-Horticulture, 1100 (136)
Garfield, James A., 205 (54), 205C (54), 216 (54), 224 (54), 256 (58), 271 (61), 282 (62), 305 (65), 558 (84), 587 (87), 638 (91), 664 (95), 675 (95), 723 (99), 825 (108), 2218b (260)
Garibaldi, Giuseppe, 1168-1169 (143)
Garland, Judy, 2445 (288)
Gehrig, Lou, 2417 (283)
Gemini 4, 1332 (156), 2634 (304)
General Federation of Women's Clubs, 1316 (156)
Geodetic, Coast and, Survey, 1088 (136)
Geophysical Year, International, 1107 (136)
George, Sen. Walter F., Memorial, 1170 (143)
Georgia, 726 (99), 1636 (191), 1962 (231)
  Statehood, 2339 (272)
German Immigration, Concord, 2040 (236)
Gershwin, George, 1484 (175)
Get Well!, 2268 (264)
Gettysburg
  Address, 978 (123)
  Battle of, 1180 (144)
Giannini, Amadeo P., 1400 (164)
Giant
  Panda, 2706 (311)
  Sequoia, 1764 (208)
Gilbreth, Lillian M., 1868 (219)
Giraffe, 2705 (311)
Girl Scouts, 974 (123), 1199 (147), 2251 (263)
Glacier National Park, 748 (100), 764 (103)
Glassblower, 1456 (171)
Globes, 650 (92), 702 (96), 1016 (127), 1066 (132), 1070 (132), 1112 (139), 1128-1129 (139), 1151 (140), 1156 (143), 1162 (143), 1410-1413 (164), 1439 (168), 1576 (184), 2535-2536 (295), C12 (339), C16 (339), C17 (339), C19 (339), C24 (340), C42 (340), C43 (340), C44 (340), C89 (344), C90 (344)
Goat, 2393 (279)
Goddard, Robert H., C69 (343)
Goethals, Gen. George W., 856 (111)
Gold Star Mothers, 969 (123)
Golden Gate, 399 (73), 403 (74), 567 (87), 698 (96)
  International Exposition, 852 (111)
Golf, 1932-1933 (227), 2377 (276)
Gompers, Samuel, 988 (123)
Gone with the Wind, 2446 (288)
Goode, Alexander D., 956 (120)
Gowan & Marx, 2366 (275)
Graces, The Three, 895 (115)
Graf Zeppelin, C13 (339), C14 (339), C15 (339), C18 (339)
Grand
  Army of the Republic, 985 (123)
  Canyon, 741 (100), 757 (103), 2512 (292)
  Coulee Dam, 1009 (127)
  Union Flag, 1352 (159)
Grange, National, 1323 (156)
Grant, Ulysses S., 223 (54), 255 (58), 270 (61), 281 (62), 303 (65), 314A (65), 560 (87), 589 (88), 640 (92), 666 (95), 677 (95), 787 (107), 823 (108), 2217i (259)

Grassland Habitats, 1922 (224)
Gray
  Birch, 1767 (208)
  Owl, 1760 (208)
Great Americans Issue, 1844-1869 (219), 2167-2173 (255), 2176-2180 (255), 2182-2186 (255), 2188 (255), 2190-2197 (255)
  Blue Heron, 1921 (224)
  Head, 746 (100), 762 (103)
  Horned Owl, 1763 (208)
  Lakes, 1069 (132)
  River Road, 1319 (156)
  Salt Lake, Valley of, 950 (120)
  Seal of the United States, 1194 (144)
  Smoky Mountains National Park, 749 (100), 765 (103), 797 (107)
  White Throne, 747 (100), 763 (103)
"Greatest Show on Earth," Circus, 2750-2753 (315)
Greece, 916 (116)
Greeley, Horace, 1177 (144)
Greely, Adolphus W., 2221 (263)
Green
  Bay (WI), 739 (100), 755 (103)
  Mountain Boys, 643 (92)
  Nathanael, 785 (107)
Griffith, D.W., 1555 (180)
Grizzly Bear, 1923 (224)
Gropius
  House, 2021 (235)
  Walter, 2021 (235)
Grosbeak, Owl, 2284 (267)
Grosvenor, Lt. Thomas, 1361 (160)
Guggenheim Museum, 1280 (152)
Guitar, 1613 (187)
Gunston Hall (Home of George Mason), 1108 (136)
Gutenberg Bible, 1014 (127)

H

Haida Ceremonial Canoe, Tlingit, Chief in, 1389 (163)
Hale, Nathan, 551 (84), 653 (92)
Half Moon, 370-371 (70)
Hamilton, Alexander, 143 (53), 154 (53), 165 (53), 175 (53), 190 (54), 201 (54), 217 (54), 1053 (131), 1086 (136), 1686e (196)
Hamilton's Battery, Alexander, 629-630 (91)
Hammarskjold, Dag, 1203-1204 (147)
Hancock, John, 1687d (196), 1694 (200)
Handcar, 1880s, 1898 (223)
Handicapped, Employ the, 1155 (143)
Handy, W.C., 1372 (160)
Hansom Cab, 1904 (223)
Hanson, John, 1941 (227)
Happy
  Birthday, 2272 (264), 2395 (280)
  New Year, 2720 (312)
Harbor
  NY, New Amsterdam, 1027 (127)
  Seal, 1882 (220)
Harding, Warren G., 553 (84), 576 (87), 582 (87), 598 (88), 605 (88), 610-613 (88), 633 (91), 659 (95), 670 (95), 684 (95), 686 (95), 833 (111), 2219a (260)
Hardy, Stan Laurel & Oliver, 2562 (296)
Harness Racing, 2758 (316)
Harnett, William M., 1386 (163)
Harris, Joel Chandler, 980 (123)
Harrison
  Benjamin, 308 (65), 622 (91), 694 (96), 828 (108), 1045 (131), 2218e (260)
  William Henry, 814 (108), 966 (124), 2201 (256), 2216i (259)
Harrod, Fort, 1542 (180)
Harte, Bret, 2196 (255)
Hartford, USS, 792 (107)
Hartley, David, 2052 (239)
Harvard, John, 2191 (255)
Hatter, 1459 (171)
Hatteras, Cape, 1448-1451 (171), 2471 (288)
Hawaii, 1682 (195), 1963 (231)
  City of Refuge National Park, C84 (344)

(Cook, Captain James), 1733 (204)
  Diamond Head, C46 (340)
  Discovery of, 647 (92)
  Statehood, 2080 (243), C55 (343)
  Territory, 799 (107)
Hawaiian Wild Broadbean, 1784 (211)
Hawthorne, Nathaniel, 2047 (239)
Hayes, Rutherford B., 563 (87), 692 (96), 824 (108), 2218a (260)
Head of Freedom, Capitol Dome, 573 (87), 989 (124)
Headdresses, 230 (57), 237 (57), 783 (104), C117 (348)
  Indian, 2501-2505 (291)
Headless Horseman, 1548 (180)
Health Research, 2087 (243)
Healy, George, Portrait by, 1113 (139)
Heiltsuk, Bella Bella Tribe, 1834 (216)
Help End Hunger, 2164 (252)
Hemingway, Ernest, 2418 (283)
HemisFair '68, 1340 (159)
Henry, Patrick, 1052 (131), 1144 (140)
Henson, Matthew, 2223 (263)
Herbert, Victor, 881 (112)
Herkimer
  at Oriskany, by Frederick Yohn, 1722 (204)
  Brig. Gen. Nicholas, 644 (92), 1722 (204)
Hermitage, The, 786 (107), 1037 (128), 1059 (131)
Higher Education, 1206 (147)
Highlander Figure, 2240 (263)
Himalayan Cat, 2373 (276)
Historical Flags, 1349 (159)
Hispanic Americans, 2103 (247)
Hispanics, 294-299 (62), 801 (107), 895 (115), 898 (115), 983 (123), 1031A (128), 1043 (128), 1110-1111 (139), 1125-1126 (139), 1157 (143), 1234 (147), 1271 (151), 1437 (168), 1826 (215), 2024 (236), 2097 (244), 2103 (247), 2173 (255), 2185 (255), 2247 (263), 2255 (264), 2704 (311), C56 (343), C104 (347), C116 (348)
Historic
  Flags, 1345-1348 (159), 1350-1354 (159)
  Preservation, 1440-1443 (168)
Hoban, James, 1935-1936 (227)
Holly, 1254 (151)
Holmes, Oliver Wendell, 1288 (152), 1288B (152), 1305E (155)
Homemakers, 1253 (148)
Homer, Winslow, 1207 (147)
Homestead Act, 1198 (147)
Honeybee, 2281 (267)
Honorable Discharge Emblem, 940 (119)
Hoover, Herbert, 1269 (151), 2219c (260)
Hope for the Crippled, 1385 (163)
Hopi Pot, 1708 (203)
Hopkins
  John, 2194A (255)
  Mark, 870 (112)
Horses
  American, 2155-2158 (252)
  Carousel, 2391 (279)
  Racing, 1528 (179)
  Sports, 2756-2759 (316)
Horticulture-Gardening, 1100 (136)
Hospitals, Public, 2210 (256)
Hot Air Ballooning, 2033-2034 (236)
House of Representatives, US, 2412 (283)
Houston, Sam, 776 (104), 778 (104), 1242 (148)
Howe
  Elias, 892 (112)
  Julia Ward, 2177 (255)
Hudson
  -Fulton Celebration, 372-373 (70)
  River, 372-373 (70), 752 (103)
Hughes, Charles Evans, 1195 (144)
Huguenot-Walloon Tercentary, 614-616 (88)
Hull, Cordell, 1235 (147)
Humane Treatment of Animals, 1307 (155)

Hummingbirds, 2642-2646 (304)
Humphrey, Hubert H., 2190 (255)
Hunger
　Freedom From-Food for Peace,
　　1231 (147)
　Help End, 2164 (252)
Hunt, Richard Morris, 1929 (227)
Huntington, Samuel, 1687 (196)
Hyacinth, 2760 (317)
Hyde Park, 930 (119)
Hypersonic Airliner, C122 (348), C126
　(351)

I

Iceboat, 2134 (248)
Idaho, 1675 (195), 1964 (231)
　Statehood, 896 (115), 2439 (287)
Illinois, 1653 (192), 1965 (231)
　Institute of Technology, 2020 (235)
　Statehood, 1339 (159)
　(Windmill), 1741 (207)
Independence
　Declaration of, 1687 (196)
　Finland, 1334 (156)
　Hall, 1044 (128), 1546 (180), 1622
　　(188), 1625 (188)
　Mexican, 1157 (143)
　Sesquicentennial Exposition, 627 (91)
　Skilled Hands for, 1717-1720 (203)
Indiana, 1651 (192), 1966 (231)
　Statehood, 1308 (155)
　Territory, 996 (124)
Indians, 230-231 (57), 237-238 (57),
　240 (57), 285 (62), 287 (62), 328 (66),
　565 (87), 680 (95), 682-683 (95), 695
　(96), 739 (100), 755 (103), 783 (104),
　972 (123), 1063 (132), 1187 (144),
　1360 (160), 1389 (163), 1426 (167),
　C117 (348)
　American, 1364 (160)
　American Art, Navajo Blanket, 2235
　　-2238 (263)
　Centennial, 972 (123)
　Chief Joseph, 1364 (160)
　Crazy Horse, 1855 (219)
　Head Penny, 1734 (204)
　Headdresses, 2501-2505 (291)
　Masks, Pacific Northwest, 1834-
　　1837 (216)
　Red Cloud, 2176 (255)
　Sequoyah, 1859 (219)
　Sitting Bull, 2184 (255)
　Thorpe, Jim, 2089 (244)
Induction Motor, 2057 (239)
Industry
　Agriculture for Defense, 899 (115)
　Petroleum, 1134 (140)
　Poultry, 968 (123)
　Science &, 2031 (236)
　Wool, 1423 (167)
Inkwell and Quill, 1535 (179), 1581
　(184), 1811 (215)
International
　Civic Aeronautics Conference, 649-
　　650 (92)
　Cooperation Year, 1266 (151)
　Geophysical Year, 1107 (136)
　Naval Review-Jamestown Festival,
　　1091 (136)
　Philatelic Exhibitions, 778 (104),
　　1075-1076 (135), 1310-1311 (155)
　Philatelic Exposition, 630 (91)
　Red Cross, 1016 (127), 1239 (148)
　Telecommunication Union, 1274
　　(151)
　Women's Year, 1571 (184)
　Year of the Child, 1772 (211)
　Year of the Disabled, 1925 (224)
　Youth Year, 2160-2163 (252)
Interphil 76, 1632 (191)
Intrepid, 2032 (236)
Inventors, 889-893 (112), 945 (119),
　1062 (132), 1270 (151), 1286A (152),
　2055 (239), 2567 (296), C113 (348),
　C114 (348), C118 (348), C119 (348),
　C45 (340), C69 (343), C91 (347), C92
　(347), C93 (347), C94 (347)
　American, 2056-2058 (239)

Iowa, 1661 (192), 1967 (231)
　Statehood, 942 (119)
　Territory, 838 (111)
Iris, 2763 (317)
Irving, Washington, 859 (112), 1548
　(180)
Isabella, Queen, 234 (57), 236-238 (57),
　241-244 (57), 2620 (300)
Islands, Northern Mariana, (321)
Iwo Jima (Marines), 929 (119)

J

Jack-in-the-Box, (321)
Jackson
　Andrew, 73 (49), 85B (49), 87 (50), 93
　　(50), 103 (50), 135 (53), 146 (53),
　　157 (53), 168 (53), 178 (53), 180
　　(53), 183 (53), 193 (54), 203 (54),
　　211D (54), 215 (54), 221 (54), 253
　　(58), 268 (61), 302 (65), 786 (107),
　　812 (108), 941 (119), 1209 (147),
　　1225 (147), 1286 (152), 2201
　　(256), 2216g (259)
　　(Battle of New Orleans), 1261 (151)
　Gen. Stonewall, 788 (107), 1408 (164)
　　(Hermitage), 1037 (128), 1059 (131)
James, USS Reuben, 2559f (296)
Jamestown
　Exposition, 328-330 (66)
　Festival, International Naval
　　Review, 1091 (136)
　Founding of, 329 (66)
Japan
　Opening of, 1021 (127)
　Treaty, US-, 1158 (143)
　US Declares War on, 2559j (296)
Japanese Bomb Pearl Harbor, 2559i
　(296)
Jay, John, 1046 (131), 2052 (239)
Jeffers, Robinson, 1485 (175)
Jefferson, Thomas, 12 (45), 27-28, 28A,
　29-30, 30A (46), 42 (46), 67-68 (49),
　75-76 (49), 80 (49), 95 (50), 105 (50),
　139 (53), 150 (53), 161 (53), 172 (53),
　187-188 (54), 197 (54), 209 (54), 228
　(54), 260 (61), 275 (61), 310 (65), 324
　(66), 561 (87), 590 (88), 641 (92), 667
　(95), 678 (95), 807 (108), 842 (111),
　851 (111), 1011 (127), 1033 (128),
　1055 (131), 1141 (140), 1278 (152),
　1299 (155), 1687b (196), 1693 (200),
　1779 (211), 2201 (256), 2216c (259),
　2523 (292), C88 (344)
　Memorial, 1510 (176), 1520 (179)
　(Monticello), 1047 (131)
Jet Liner, C51 (343), C52 (343), C60
　(343), C61 (343), C78 (344), C82 (344)
　Over Capitol, C64 (343), C65 (343)
Johnson
　Andrew, 822 (108), 2217h (259)
　James Weldon, 2371 (276)
　Lyndon B., 1503 (176), 2219i (260)
Joliet, Louis, 1356 (160)
Jones
　Bobby, 1933 (227)
　Casey, 993 (124)
　John Paul, 790 (107), 1789 (212)
Joplin, Scott, 2044 (239)
Joseph Pulitzer, 946 (119)
Journalism-Freedom of the Press, 1119
　(139), 1476-1477 (172), 1593 (184)
Julian, Percy Lavon, 2746 (314)
Jupiter, 2573 (299)
　Balloon, C54 (343)
　Pioneer 10, 1556 (183)
Justice, 313 (65)
　Contemplation of, 1592 (184), 1592a
　　(184)
　(Scales of), 1139 (140), 1186 (144)

K

Kamehameha, King, 799 (107)
Kane, Elisha Kent, 2220 (263)
Kansas, 1666 (195), 1968 (231)
　City, MO, 994 (124)
　Statehood, 1183 (144)
　Territory, 1061 (132)

Kearny
　Expedition, Gen. Stephen Watts,
　　944 (119)
　Fort, 970 (123)
Keep in Touch, 2274 (264)
Keller, Helen/Anne Sullivan, 1824 (215)
Kelly, Grace, 2749 (315)
Kennedy
　John F., 1287 (152), 2219h (260)
　Memorial, 1246 (148)
　Robert F., 1770 (211)
Kentucky, 1647 (192), 1969 (231)
　Settlement, First, 1542 (180)
　Statehood, 904 (115), 2636 (304)
Kern, Jerome, 2110 (247)
Kerosene Table Lamp, 1611 (187)
Kestrel, American, 2481 (291)
Key, Francis Scott, 962 (120), 1142
　(140)
Kii Statue, C84 (344)
Killer Whale, 2508 (291), 2511 (291)
King
　John's Crown, 1265 (151)
　Martin Luther, Jr., 1771 (211)
　Penguins, 2708 (311)
　Salmon, 1079 (135)
Kitten
　and Puppy, 2025 (236)
　Envelope
Knox, Henry, 1851 (219)
Knoxville World's Fair, 2006-2009 (235)
Koala, 2370 (276)
Korea, 921 (116)
Korean Veterans, 2152 (251)
Kosciuszko, General Thaddeus, 734
　(99)
Kossuth, Lajos, 1117-1118 (139)

L

La
　Fortaleza, PR, 801 (107)
　Rabida, 239 (57)
Labor Day, 1082 (135)
　(A. Philip Randolph), 2402 (283)
　(Collective Bargaining), 1558 (183)
　(Gompers, Samuel), 998 (124)
　Organized, 1831 (216)
　(Perkins, Francis), 1821 (215)
Lacemaking, 2351-2354 (272)
Lady's Slipper, 1377 (163), 2077 (243)
Lafayette, 1010 (127), 1097 (136)
　Indiana, C54 (343)
　Marquis de, 1686d (196), 1716 (203)
LaGuardia, Fiorello, 1397 (164)
Lake
　Erie, 1069 (132)
　Huron, 1069 (132)
　Michigan, 1069 (132)
　Ontario, 1069 (132)
　Placid, NY, Olympic-Winter
　　Games '32, 716 (99)
　Placid, NY, Olympic-Winter
　　Games '80, 1795-1798 (212)
　Superior, 1069 (132)
Lakes Steamer, 294 (62)
Lamps, 1206 (147), 1386 (163)
　Kerosene Table, 1611 (187)
　Rush, 1610 (187)
　Whale Oil, 1608 (187)
Land-Grant Colleges, 1065 (132)
Landing
　Craft, 1434 (168)
　of Cadillac, 1000 (124)
　of Carteret, 1247 (148)
　of the Pilgrims, 549 (84), 1420 (167)
Landset, 2570 (299)
Langley, Samuel P., C118 (348)
Lanier, Sidney, 1446 (168)
Lantern, Railroad, 1612 (187)
Latrobe, Benjamin, 1780 (211)
Laubach, Dr. Frank, 1864 (219)
Laurel
　& Hardy, 2562 (296)
　Stan, 2562 (296)
Laurens, John, 1686e (196)
Law
　and Order, 1343 (159)
　World Peace through, 1576 (184)
Leatherworker, 1720 (203)

398

Lee
  General Robert E., 788 (107), 982
    (123), 1049 (131), 1408 (164)
  Jason, 964 (120)
Lefty's Deceiver, 2548 (295)
Legend of Sleepy Hollow, The, 1548
  (180)
Leigh, Vivian, 2446 (288)
Lend-Lease Act, 2559c (296)
Leon, Ponce de, 2024 (236)
Letters, 1310 (155), 1511 (179), 2150
  (251), 2618 (300)
  Carrier, 1490 (175), 1497 (175)
  Carriers, 2420 (284)
  Lift Spirits, 1807 (215)
  Preserve Memories, 1805 (215)
  Shape Opinions, 1809 (215)
  Writing Issue, 1805-1810 (215)
Lewis
  and Clark Expedition, 1063 (132)
  Francis, 1687c (196)
  Meriwether, 1063 (132)
  Sinclair, 1856 (219)
Lexington and Concord, 617-618 (88),
  619 (91), 790 (107),1563 (183), 2618
  (300)
Liberte, C120 (348)
Liberty, 1034-1044 (128), 1045-1057
  (131), 1042A (128), 1044A (128),
  1054A (131), 1058-1059 (131),
  1059A (131)
  Bell, 627 (91), 1518 (179), 1595
    (187), 1618 (188), C57 (343), C62
    (343)
  Birth of, 618 (88)
  Head of, 1599 (187), 1619 (188)
  Statue of, 566 (87), 696 (96), 899
    (115), 908 (115), 946 (119), 995
    (124), 1035 (128), 1041-1042
    (128), 1044 (128), 1057 (131),
    1075 (135), 1320 (156), 1594
    (184), 1599 (187), 1619 (188),
    1816 (215), 2147 (251), 2224
    (263), C35 (340), C58 (343), C63
    (343), C80 (344), C87 (344)
  Torch, 1008 (127), 1594 (184), 1816
    (215), 2531A (295)
Libraries, America's, 2015 (235)
Library
  Low Memorial, 1029 (127)
  of Congress, 2004 (235)
Lighthouses, 1391 (163), 1449 (171),
  1605 (187), 1891 (220), 2470-2474
  (288)
  Sandy Hook, 1605 (187)
Lightning Whelk, 2121 (248)
Lilac, 2764 (317)
Lily, 1879 (220)
Lincoln
  Abraham, 77 (49), 85F (49), 91 (50),
    98 (50), 108 (50), 122 (50), 137
    (53), 148 (53), 159 (53), 170 (53),
    186 (54), 195 (54), 208 (54), 222
    (54), 254 (58), 269 (61), 280 (62),
    304 (65), 315 (65), 317 (65), 367-
    369 (70), 555 (84), 584 (89), 600
    (88), 635 (91), 661 (95), 672 (95),
    821 (108), 902 (115), 906 (115),
    978 (123), 1036 (128), 1058 (131),
    1113-1116 (139), 1143 (140),
    1233 (147), 1282 (152), 1303
    (155), 2081 (243), 2106 (247),
    2217g (259), 2410 (283), 2433
    (284), 2523 (292), 2523A (292),
    C59 (343), C88 (344)
  Gen. Benjamin, 1686b (196)
  Memorial, 571 (87)
  Tad, 2106 (247)
  -Douglas Debates, 1115 (139)
Lindbergh, Charles, 1710 (203), C10
  (339)
Lions International (Search for Peace),
  1326 (156)
Lippman, Walter, 1849 (219)
Literary Arts, 1773 (211), 1832 (216),
  2047 (239), 2094 (244), 2239 (263),
  2350 (272), 2418 (283), 2449 (288),
  2538 (295), 2698 (311)
Little

America (Antarctic), 733 (99), 735
  (100), 753 (103), 768 (103)
  House on the Prairie, (320)
  Women, (320)
Livingston, Robert R., 323 (66), 1020
  (127), 1687a (196), 1693 (200)
Lockheed Constellation, C35 (340)
Locks at Sault Ste. Marie, 298 (62)
Lockwood, Belva Ann, 2179 (255)
Locomobile, 2381 (279)
Locomotives, 114 (50), 295 (62), 922
  (116), 947 (119), 961 (120), 993
  (124), 1006 (124), 1415 (167), 1506
  (176), 1511 (179), 1573 (184), 1755
  (207), 1897A (223), 2226 (263), 2362-
  2366 (275), 2402 (283)
London, Jack, 2183 (255), 2197 (255)
Long, Dr. Crawford W., 875 (112)
Longfellow, Henry W., 864 (112)
Longhorn Cattle, Angus and, 1504 (176)
Los Angeles, CA, Olympic Issue '32,
  718-719 (99)
Louis
  XVI, King, 1753 (207)
  Joe, 2766 (318)
Louisiana, 1650 (192), 1970 (231)
  Purchase Exposition, 323-327 (66),
    1020 (127)
  Statehood, 1197 (147)
  World Exposition, 2086 (243)
Love, 1475 (172), 1951 (228), 2072
  (243), 2143 (251), 2202 (256), 2248
  (263), 2378-2379 (276), 2440-2441
  (287), 2535-2537 (295), 2618 (300)
Love You, 2398 (280)
  Dad!, 2270 (264)
  Mother!, 2273 (264)
Lovebirds, Fischer's, 2537 (295)
Low
  Juliette Gordon, 974 (123)
  Memorial Library, 1029 (127)
Lowell, James Russell, 866 (112)
Ludington, Sybil, 1559 (183)
Lunar
  Orbiter, 1435 (168), 2571 (299)
  Rover, 1435 (168)
Lunch Wagon, 2464 (288)
Luther, Martin, 2065 (240)
Luxembourg, 912 (116)
Lyndhurst, 1841 (216)
Lyon, Mary, 2169 (255)

M

Maass, Clara, 1699 (200)
MacArthur, Gen. Douglas, 1424 (167)
Macdonough, Thomas, 791 (107)
MacDowell, Edward A., 882 (112)
Mackinac Bridge, 1109 (139)
Madison
  Dolley, 1822 (215)
  Helene, 2500 (291)
  James, 262 (61), 277 (61), 312 (65),
    479 (79), 808 (108), 843 (111),
    2201 (256), 2216d (259)
Madonna and Child, della Robbia,
  1768 (208)
Magna Carta, 1265 (151)
Magsaysay, Ramon, 1096 (136)
Mail
  Car, 2265 (264)
  Car (Postal People), 1489 (175)
  Car (USPS), 1396 (164)
  Delivery, City, 1238 (148)
  Express, 1909 (223), 2122 (248),
    2394 (280), 2541 (295)
  International Express, 2542 (295)
  Order Business, 1468 (172)
  Overland, 1120 (139)
  Planes and US Map, Two, C7 (339),
    C8 (339), C9 (339)
  (Pony Express), 894 (115), 1154 (143)
  Priority, 2419 (284), 2540 (295)
  Railroad, 2265 (264)
  Transportation, Future, C122 (348),
    C123 (348), C125 (348), C126
    (351)
  Wagon, 1903 (223)
Mailbox, Rural, 1703 (200), 1730 (204)
Main Coon Cat, 2374 (276)

Maine, 1655 (192), 1971 (231)
  (Christmas), 1384 (163)
  (Great Head National Park), 746
    (100), 762 (103)
  Statehood, 1391 (163)
Makeup Rate, 2521 (292)
Malamute, Alaskan, 2100 (244)
Malaria Eradication, 1194 (144)
Mallard, 1757b (208)
  Decoy, 2139 (251)
Mann, Horace, 869 (112)
Mannerheim, Gustaf, 1165-1166 (143)
Maps, 327 (66), 733 (99), 735 (100), 753
  (103), 768 (103), 783 (104), 795
  (107), 858 (111), 906 (115), 927
  (119), 933 (119), 942 (119), 952
  (120), 955 (120), 957 (120), 984
  (123), 1018 (127), 1028 (127), 1067
  (132), 1069 (132), 1071 (132), 1092
  (136), 1112 (139), 1120 (139), 1131
  (139), 1154 (143), 1206 (147), 1232
  (147), 1247-1248 (148), 1258 (151),
  1274 (151), 1306 (155), 1308 (155),
  1319 (156), 1340 (159), 1431 (168),
  1690 (200), 1937-1938 (227), 2220-
  2223 (263), 2386-2389 (279), 2620
  (300), C7 (339), C8 (339), C9 (339),
  C10 (339), C14 (339), C53 (343), C55
  (343), C116 (348), C117 (348)
Marbois, Marquis Francois de Barbe,
  1020 (127)
Marconi's Spark Coil and Spark Gap,
  1500 (176)
Marin, Luis Munoz, 2173 (255)
Marine Corps, 1013 (127)
  Reserve, 1315 (156)
Mariner
  2, 2569 (299)
  10, 2568 (299)
  10/Venus, Mercury, 1557 (183)
Marines, 929 (119)
  Continental, 1567 (183)
Marquette, Jacques, 285 (62), 1356
  (160)
Mars, 2572 (300), 2631-2632 (304)
  Viking Missions to, 1759 (208)
Marshall
  George C., 1289 (152)
  Islands, Republic of the, Federated
    States of Micronesia, 2506-2507
    (291)
  James W., 954 (120)
  John, 263 (61), 278 (61), 313 (65),
    480 (79), 1050 (131), 2415 (283)
  Plan, Acheson, Dean, 2755 (316)
Marx, Gowan &, 2366 (275)
Maryland, 1639 (191), 1972 (231)
  Settlement, 736 (100)
  Statehood, 2342 (272)
Masaryk, Thomas G., 1147 (140), 1148
  (140)
Masks, Pacific Northwest Indian, 1834-
  1837 (216)
Mason, George, 1858 (219)
  (Gunston Hall), 1108 (136)
Massachusetts, 1638 (191), 1973 (231)
  Bay Colony, 682 (95)
  Flag, 1034 (128), 1056 (131)
  Hall, UX173 (326)
  Statehood, 2341 (272)
  Windmill, 1740 (207)
Masters, Edgar Lee, 1405 (164)
Matzeliger, Jan, 2567 (296)
Maybeck, Bernard, 1930 (227)
Mayflower, 548 (84)
  Compact, Signing of, 550 (84)
  (Landing of the Pilgrims), 549 (84),
    1420 (167)
Mayo, Doctors William J. and Charles
  H., 1251 (148)
Mazzei, Philip, C98 (347)
McCarthy
  & Bergen, 2563 (296)
  Charlie, 2563 (296)
McCormack, John, 2090 (244)
McCormick, Cyrus Hall, 891 (112)
McDowell, Dr. Ephraim, 1138 (140)
McGruff the Crime Dog, 2102 (247)
McHenry Flag, Fort, 1346 (159)

McKinley, William G., 326 (66), 559 (87), 588 (87), 639 (92), 665 (95), 676 (95), 829 (108), 2218f (260)
McLoughlin, John, 964 (120)
McMahon, Sen. Brien, 1200 (147)
Medal of Honor, 2013 (235), 2045 (239), 2103 (247)
Mellon, Andrew W., 1072 (132)
Melville, Herman, 2094 (244)
Memorial, 1318 (156)
  Poppy, 977 (123)
Merchant Marine, 939 (119)
Mercury, 1557 (183), 2568 (299), 2634 (304)
  Project, 1193 (144)
Mermaid, 1112 (139)
Mesa Verde National Park, 743 (100), 759 (103)
Metropolitan Opera, 2054 (239)
Mexican Independence, 1157 (143)
Michael, Moina, 977 (123)
Michigan, 1658 (192), 1974 (231)
  Landing of Cadillac, 1000 (124)
  State College, 1065 (132)
  Statehood, 775 (104), 778c (104), 2246 (263)
Micronesia, Federated States of/ Republic of the Marshall Islands, 2506-2507 (291)
Microphone, 1502 (176)
Microscope, 1080 (135), 1263 (151), 1754 (207), 1925 (224)
Migratory
  Bird Hunting & Conservation Stamp Act, 2092 (244)
  Bird Treaty, 1306 (155)
Miguel Locks, Pedro, 398 (73), 402 (74)
Military Uniforms, 1565-1568 (183)
Militia, American, 1568 (183)
Milk Wagon, 2253 (264)
Millay, Edna St. Vincent, 1926 (224)
Millikan, Robert, 1866 (219)
Mineral Heritage, 1538-1541 (180)
Minerals, 2700-2703 (311)
Minnesota, 1664 (192), 1975 (231)
  (Hubert Humphrey), 2190 (255)
  Statehood, 1106 (136)
  Territory, 981 (123)
Minute Man, The, 619 (91)
Mirror Lake, 742 (100), 750 (100), 758 (103), 770 (103)
Mission Belfry, CA, 1373 (160)
Missions, 1373 (160), 1443 (168), C116 (348)
Mississippi, 1652 (192), 1976 (231)
  (Great River Road), 1319 (156)
  River, 285 (62), 1356 (160)
  River Bridge, 293 (62)
  Statehood, 1337 (159)
  Territory, 955 (120)
Missouri, 1656 (192), 1977 (231)
  Kansas City, 994 (124)
  River, 1063 (132)
  Statehood, 1426 (167)
Mistletoe, 1255 (151)
Mitchell
  Margaret, 2168 (255)
  Pass, NE, 1060 (132)
Mobile, Battle of, 1826 (215)
Modern Dance, 1752 (207)
Monmouth, Battle of (Molly Pitcher), 646 (92)
Monongahela River, 681 (95)
Monorail, 1196 (147)
Monroe, James, 325 (66), 562 (87), 591 (88), 603 (88), 642 (92), 668 (95), 679 (95), 810 (108), 845 (111), 1020 (127), 1038 (128), 1105 (136), 2201 (256), 2216e (259)
Montana, 1673 (195), 1978 (232)
  (Glacier National Park), 748 (100), 764 (103)
  Statehood, 858 (111), 2401 (283)
Monticello, 1047 (131)
Monument, George Washington, 2149 (251)
Moon, 124 (348), 126 (351), 1021 (127), 1192 (144), 1345 (159), 1371 (160), 1434-1435 (168), 1548 (180), 1909 (223), 2122 (248), 2246 (263), 2394

(280), 2404 (283), 2419 (284), 2571 (299), 2631-2634 (304)
  Landing, 2419 (284), C76 (344)
  Rover, 1435 (168)
Moore
  John Bassett, 1295 (155)
  Marianne, 2449 (288)
Moorish Idol, 1829 (215)
Moose, 1757e (208), 1887 (220)
Morgan
  Charles W., 1441 (168), 2340 (272)
  Horse, 2156 (252)
  Silver Dollar, 1557 (183)
Morning Light, S.S., 1239 (148)
Morocco, Friendship with, 2349 (272)
Morris, Robert, 1004 (124)
Morro Castle, San Juan, Puerto Rico, 1437 (168)
Morse, Samuel F.B., 890 (112), 924 (116)
Morton, Julius Sterling, (Arbor Day), 717 (99)
Moses
  Grandma, 1370 (160)
  Horace A., 2095 (244)
Mothers
  Gold Star, 969 (123)
  of America, 737-738 (100), 754 (103)
Motion Pictures, 926 (116), 1355 (159), 1555 (180), 1727 (204)
Motion-Picture Camera, 1555 (180)
Motorcycle, 1899 (223)
Mott, Lucretia, 959 (120)
Moultrie Flag, Fort, 1345 (159)
Mount
  Davidson, 1130 (139)
  Hood, 1124 (139)
  McKinley National Park, 800 (107), 1454 (171)
  Rainier, 2404 (283)
  Rainier National Park, 742 (100), 750 (100), 758 (103), 770 (103)
  Rockwell (Mt. Sinopah), 748 (100), 764 (103)
  Rushmore, 2523 (292), 2523A (292), C88 (344)
  Rushmore Memorial, 1011 (127)
  Surabachi, 929 (119)
  Vernon, 785 (107), 1032 (128)
Mountain
  Bluebird, 2439 (287)
  Habitats, 1923 (224)
Muddler Minnow, 2549 (295)
Muir, John, 1245 (148)
Muscogee Seal, 972 (123)
Museum, National Postal, (319)
Music, American, 1252 (148)
Musicals, Broadway, (319)
Musicians, Rock and Roll, 2721 (314), 2724-2730 (318)
Muskellunge, 2205 (256)
My
  Fair Lady, (319)
  Old Kentucky Home State Park, 2636 (304)
Myron's Discobolus, 719 (99)

N

Naismith-Basketball, 1189 (144)
Narrows Bridge, Verrazano-, 1258 (151)
Nassau Hall (Princeton University), 1083 (135), 1704 (200)
Nation of Readers, A, 2106 (247)
National
  Apprenticeship Program, 1201 (147)
  Archives, 227 (54), 2081 (243)
  Capitol, 990-992 (124)
  Cathedral, Postal Card, UX166 (326)
  Defense, 899-901 (115)
  Education Association, 1093 (136)
  Farmer's Bank, 1931 (227)
  Grange, 1323 (156)
  Guard, 1017 (127)
  Park Service, 1314 (155)
  Parks, 740-751 (100), 756-759 (103), 761-765 (103), 769-770 (103), 952 (120), 1448-1451 (171), 1453-1454 (171), 2018 (235), C84 (344)
  Postal Museum, (319)

Recovery Act, 732 (99)
  Stamp Exhibition, 735 (100), 768 (103)
Nativity, by John Singleton Copley, 1701 (200)
NATO, 1008 (127), 1127 (139)
Natural History, 1387-1390 (163)
Nautical Figure, 2242 (263)
Nautilus, 1128 (139)
Navajo Blanket, 2235-2238 (263)
Naval
  Academy, US, 794 (107)
  Aviation, 1185 (144)
  Review, International, 1091 (136)
Navy, 790-794 (107)
  Continental, 1556 (183)
  US, 935 (119), 1013 (127), 1067 (132)
Nebraska, 1669 (195), 1979 (232)
  Statehood, 1328 (156)
  Territory, 1060 (132)
Nelson, Thomas, Jr., 1686d (196), 1687c (196)
Neptune, 1112 (139), 2576 (299)
  New England, 2119 (248)
Netherlands, 913 (116), 2003 (235)
Nevada, 1668 (195), 1980 (232)
  Settlement, 999 (124)
  Statehood, 1248 (148)
Nevin, Ethelbert, 883 (112)
New Amsterdam Harbor, NY, 1027 (127)
New England Neptune, 2119 (248)
New Hampshire, 1068 (132), 1641 (191), 1981 (232)
  Statehood, 2344 (272)
New Jersey, 1635 (191), 1982 (232)
  Settlement, 1247 (148)
  Statehood, 2338 (272)
New Mexico, 1679 (195), 1983 (232)
  (Chavez, Dennis), 2185 (255)
  Statehood, 1191 (144)
New Orleans, 2407 (283)
New Sweden, C117 (348)
New Year, Happy, 2720 (312)
New York, 1643 (191), 1984 (232), C38 (340)
  City, 1027 (127)
  City Coliseum, 1076 (135)
  Newburgh, 727 (99), 731 (99), 752 (103), 767 (103)
  Skyline, C35 (340)
  Statehood, 2346 (272)
  Stock Exchange, 2630 (304)
  World's Fair '39, 853 (111)
  World's Fair '64, 1244 (148)
Newspaper Boys, 1015 (127)
Niagara Falls, 297 (62), 568 (87), 699 (96)
  Railway Suspension Bridge, 961 (120)
Nicolet, Jean, 739 (100), 755 (103)
Nie Nederland, 614 (88)
Nimitz, Chester W., 1869 (219)
Nineteenth Amendment, 1406 (164)
  (Suffrage), 784 (104), 1051 (131), 1406 (164)
Nisqually, Fort, 1604 (187)
Norris
  Dam, 1184 (144)
  Sen. George W., 1184 (144)
Norse-American, 620-621 (91)
North Carolina, 1644 (191), 1985 (232)
  (Great Smoky Mountains National Park), 749 (100), 765 (103)
  Statehood, 2347 (272)
North Dakota, 1671 (195), 1986 (232)
  Statehood, 858 (111), 2403 (283)
North Pole, 1128 (139)
Northern
  Mariana Islands, (321)
  Sea Lion, 2509 (291)
Northwest Territory
  Ordinance, 795 (107)
  Sesquicentennial, 837 (111)
Norway, 911 (116)
Numismatics, 2558 (296)
Nurse, 702 (96), 1699 (200), 1910 (223)
Nursing, 1190 (144)
NYU Library, 1928 (227)

O

O'Kane Hall, Postal Card, UX171 (326)
O'Neill
    Capt. William O. "Bucky," 973 (123)
    Eugene, 1294 (152), 1305C (155)
Oakland Bay Bridge, Plane Over, C36
    (340)
Ochs, Adolph S., 1700 (200)
Ocotillo, 1378 (163)
Ohio, 1649 (192), 1987 (232)
    River Canalization, 681 (95)
    Statehood, 1018 (127)
Oil
    Derrick, 1134 (140)
    Wagon, 2130 (248)
Oklahoma!, 2722 (315)
Oklahoma, 1678 (195), 1988 (232)
    (Cherokee Strip), 1360 (160)
    Statehood, 1092 (136)
Old
    Faithful, 744 (100), 760 (103), 1453
        (171)
    Man of the Mountain, 1068 (132),
        2344 (272)
    North Church, 1603 (187)
Olgethorpe, General, 726 (99)
Olympians, 2496-2500 (291)
Olympic Games, 84 (347), 1696 (200)
    '32, 716 (99), 718-719 (99)
    '60, 1146 (140)
    '72, 1460-1462 (171), C85 (344)
    '76, 1695 (200), 1697 (200), 1698
        (200)
    '80, 1790-1798 (212), C97 (347)
    '84, 2048-2051 (239), 2068-2070
        (240), 2082-2085 (243), C101
        (347), C102 (347), C103 (347),
        C104 (347), C105 (347), C106
        (347), C107 (347), C108 (347),
        C109 (347), C110 (347), C112
        (347)
    '88, 2369 (276), 2380 (276)
    '92, 2553-2557 (296), 2611-2615
        (300), 2637-2641 (304)
    Baseball, 2619 (300)
    Diver, 1695 (200)
    Rings and Snowflake, 1146 (140)
    Rings, 2539-2542 (295)
    Rings, Flag with, 2528 (292)
    Runner, 1697 (200)
    Special, 1788 (212)
    Special, Winter, 2142 (251)
    Skater, 1698 (200)
    Skier, 1696 (200)
Omnibus, 1897 (223), 2225 (263)
One-Room Schoolhouse, 1606 (187)
Opening of Japan, 1021 (127)
Opera, Metropolitan, 2054 (239)
Orange
    Landing at Fort, 615 (88)
    -Tip, 1715 (203)
Orbiter
    Lunar, 2571 (299)
    Viking, 2572 (299)
Orchids, 2076-2079 (243)
Order, Law and, 1343 (159)
Ordinance, Northwest Territory, 795
    (107)
Oregon, 1665 (192), 1989 (232)
    (Crater Lake National Park), 745
        (100), 761 (103)
    SS, 997 (124)
    Statehood, 1124 (139)
    Territory, 783 (104), 964 (120)
    Trail, 964 (120), 2747 (314)
Organized Labor, 1831 (216)
Oriskany, 644 (92)
    Herkimer at, 1722 (204)
    Mail Transportation, C124 (348)
Osteopathic Medicine, 1469 (172)
Otter, Sea, 2510 (291)
Ouimet, Francis, 2377 (276)
Overland Mail, 1120 (139)
Overrun Countries, 129 (116), 909-911
    (116), 913-921 (116)
Owens, Jesse, 2496 (291)
Owl/Grosbeak, 2284-2285 (267)
Owls, American, 1760-1763 (208)

Oxen, 950 (120), 958 (120), 964 (120),
    970 (123), 981 (123), 997 (124), 1019
    (127), 1028 (127), 1061 (132), 1426
    (167), 1487 (175), 1542 (180)

P

P.S. Write Soon, 1806 (215), 1808
    (215), 1810 (215)
Pacific
    Calypso, 2079 (243)
    Northwest Indian Masks, 1834-1837
        (216)
    Trust Territories, Northern Mariana
        Islands, (321)
Pacific Exposition
    Alaska-Yukon-, 370-371 (70)
    California, 773 (104), 778 (104)
Packard, 2384 (279)
Paddlewheel Steamer, 1187 (144),
    2435 (287), 2438 (287)
Paderewski, Ignacy Jan, 1159-1160
    (143)
Paine, Thomas, 1292 (152)
Painting, American, 1187 (144), 1207
    (147), 1241 (148), 1243 (148), 1273
    (151), 1322 (156), 1335 (159), 1361
    (160), 1386 (163), 1433 (168), 1553
    (180), C71 (344)
Palace
    of the Arts, 1930 (227)
    of the Governors, Santa Fe, NM,
        1031A (128), 1054A (131)
Palmer, Capt. Nathaniel B., 2386 (279)
Palomar Mountain Observatory, 966
    (120)
Pamphleteers, 1476 (172)
Pan American
    Games, 2247 (263), C56 (343)
    Union, 895 (115)
    Union Building, C34 (340)
    Exposition, 294-299 (62)
Panama
    Canal, 398 (73), 402 (74), 856 (111)
    Pacific Expedition, 401-404 (74)
    Pacific Exposition, 397-400 (73),
        400A (73)
Panda, Giant, 2706 (311)
Papanicolaou, Dr. George, 1754 (207)
Parent Teacher Association, 1463 (171)
Paris, Treaty of, 2052 (239)
Parker, Dorothy, 2698 (311)
Parkman, Francis, 1281 (152), 1297
    (155)
Partridge, Alden, 1854 (219)
Pass, NE, Mitchell, 1060 (132)
Patrol Wagon, Police, 2258 (264)
Patton, Jr., General George S., 1026
    (127)
Peace
    Atoms for, 1070 (132)
    Bridge, 1721 (203)
    Corps, 1447 (168)
    Garden, International, 2014 (235)
    of 1783, 727 (99), 731 (99), 752
        (103), 767 (103)
    Through Law, World, 1576 (184)
    Through World Trade, World, 1129
        (139)
Peale, Charles Wilson, 1789 (212)
Pearl Harbor, 2559i (296)
Peary, Admiral Robert, 1128 (139),
    2223 (263)
Pelican, Brown, 1466 (171)
Penguins, King, 2708 (311)
Penn
    Academy, 1840 (216)
    William, 724 (99)
Pennsylvania, 1634 (191), 1990 (232)
    Academy of Fine Arts, 1064 (132),
        1840 (216)
    Avenue, 2561 (296)
    State University, 1065 (132)
    Statehood, 2337 (272)
    Toleware, 1775-1778 (211)
Performing Arts, 1755-1756 (207), 1801
    (212), 1803 (212), 2012 (235), 2088
    (244), 2090 (244), 2110 (247), 2211
    (256), 2250 (263), 2411 (283), 2550
    (295)

Perisphere, 853 (111)
Perkins, Frances, 1821 (215)
Perry
    Commodore, 144 (53), 155 (53), 166
        (53), 177 (53), 191 (54), 202 (54),
        218 (54), 229 (54)
    Matthew C., 1021 (127)
    Oliver Hazard, 261 (61), 261A (61),
        276 (61), 276A (61)
Pershing, Gen. John J., 1042A (128)
Persian Cat, 2375 (276)
Persistent Trillium, 1783 (211)
Petrified Wood, 1538 (180)
Petroleum Industry, 1134 (140)
Pharmacy, 1473 (172)
Pheasant, 2283 (267)
Philadelphia
    Exchange, 1782 (211)
    Light Horse Flag, 1353 (159)
Philatelic
    Americans, Society of, 797 (107)
    Society, American, 730-731 (99),
        750 (100), 766 (103), 770 (103)
Philatelic Exhibitions, 948 (120), 1632
    (191), 1757 (208), 2145 (251), 2216-
    2217 (259), 2218-2219 (260)
    Centenary International, 948 (120)
    Fifth National, 1075-1076 (135)
    International Centenary, 948 (120)
    Third International, 778 (104)
    Trans-Mississippi, 751 (100)
Philippines (Corregidor), 925 (116)
Phoenix, 2406 (283)
Photography, 1758 (208)
    George Eastman, 1062 (132)
Physical Fitness, 2043 (239)
    -Sokols, 1262 (151)
Piano, 1615C (187)
Pierce
    Arrow, 2382 (279)
    Franklin, 819 (108), 2217e (259)
Pilgrims, 548-550 (84)
    Landing of the, 1420 (167)
    Tercentenary, 548-550 (84)
Pine Cone, (326)
Pioneer
    II, 1916 (224)
    10 Jupiter, 1556 (183)
    11, 2573 (299)
Pioneers of Aviation, C91 (347), C92
    (347), C93 (347), C94 (347), C95
    (347), C96 (347), C99 (347), C100
    (347), C113 (348), C114 (348), C118
    (348), C119 (348), C128 (351), C129
    (351)
Piper
    Cub, C129 (351)
    William T., C129 (351)
Pitcher, Molly (Battle of Monmouth),
    646 (92)
Plane, C77 (344)
    and Globes, C89 (344)
    Globes and Flag, C90 (344)
Playmakers Theatre, Postal Card,
    UX170 (326)
Pledge of Allegiance, 2594 (299)
Pluto, 2577 (299)
Pocahontas, 330 (66)
Poe, Edgar Allan, 986 (123)
Poets, 864-868 (112), 986 (123), 1405
    (164), 1436 (168), 1446 (168), 1485
    (175), 1526 (179), 1554 (180), 1926
    (224), 2239 (263), 2449 (288)
Poinsettia, 1256 (151)
Poland, 909 (116)
    (von Steuben, General), 689 (96)
Poland's Millennium, 1313 (155)
Polar
    Bear, 1429 (167), 1885 (220)
    Explorers, 1128 (139), 1431 (168),
        2220-2223 (263)
Police, Patrol Wagon, 2258 (264)
Poling, Clark V., 956 (120)
Polio, 1087 (136)
Polk, James K., 816 (108), 2217b (259)
Polo, 2759 (316)
Pony Express, 894 (115), 1154 (143)
Poor, Salem, 1560 (183)
Popcorn Wagon, 2261 (264)
Porgy & Bess, 1484 (175)

401

Porkfish, 1828 (215)
Porter
　Cole, 2550 (295)
　David D., 792 (107)
Post
　Office Dept. Bldg., C42 (340)
　Office, First Automated, 1164 (143)
　Rider, 113 (50), 1478 (172)
　Wiley, C95 (347), C96 (347)
Postage Stamp Centenary, 947 (119), 948 (120)
Postal
　Conference, International, C66 (343)
　Service, 1164 (143), 1238 (148), 1396 (164), 1489-1498 (175), 1572-1575 (184), 2420 (284), 2539 (295)
Posting a Broadside, 1477 (172)
Potomac River, 1366 (160)
Poultry Industry, 968 (123)
Powatan, USS, 792 (107)
Powell, John Wesley, 1374 (160)
Powered Flight, C47 (340)
POWs-MIAs, 1422 (167)
Preamble to the Constitution, 2355-2359 (275)
Prehistoric Animals, 2422-2425 (284)
Preservation of Wildlife Habitats, 1921-1924 (224)
Preserve the Environment (Expo '74), 1527 (179)
Presidential Issue, '38, 803-831 (108), 832-834 (111), 839-851 (111)
Presidents Miniature Sheets, '86, 2216-2217 (259), 2218-2219 (260), (Stamp Collecting), 2201 (256)
Presley, Elvis, 2721 (314)
Prevent Drug Abuse, 1438 (168)
Priestley, Joseph, 2038 (236)
Princeton
　George Washington at, 1704 (200)
　University (Nassau Hall), 1083 (135)
Printed Circuit Board, 1501 (176)
Printing, 857 (111)
　Press, 857 (111), 1014 (127), 1119 (139), 1476 (172), 1593 (184)
Priority Mail, 2419 (284), 2540 (295)
Proclamation
　Emancipation, 1233 (147)
　of Peace, American Revolution, 727 (99), 752 (103)
Professional
　Baseball, 1381 (163)
　Management, 1920 (224)
Progress
　Alliance for, 1232 (147), 1234 (147)
　in Electronics, 1500-1502 (176), C86 (344)
　of Women, 959 (120)
Project Mercury, 1193 (144)
Prominent Americans, 1278-1283 (152), 1283B (152),1284-1286 (152), 1286A (152), 1287-1288 (152), 1288B (152), 1289-1294 (152), 1299 (155), 1303-1304 (155), 1304C (155), 1305 (155), 1305C (155), 1393-1395 (164), 1397-1402 (164)
Pronghorn Antelope, 1078 (135), 1889 (220)
Propeller, Wooden, and Airplane Radiator, C4 (339)
Providence, RI, 1164 (143)
Pteranodon, 2423 (284)
PUAS, America/, 2426 (284), 2512 (292), C121 (348), C127 (351)
PUASP, America/, C131 (351)
Public
　Education, 2159 (252)
　Hospitals, 2210 (256)
Pueblo Pottery, 1706-1709 (203)
Puerto Rico
　(Clemente, Roberto), 2097 (244)
　Columbus Landing in, (322)
　(de Leon, Ponce), 2024 (236)
　Election, 983 (123)
　(Marin, Luis Munoz), 2173 (255)
　San Juan, 1437 (168)
　Territory, 801 (107)
Pulaski, General, 690 (96)
Pulitzer, Joseph, 946 (119)

Puma, 1881 (220)
Pumper, Fire, 1908 (223)
Puppy and Kitten, 2025 (236)
Pure Food and Drug Laws, 1080 (135)
Pushcart, 2133 (248)
Putnam, Rufus, 795 (107)
Pyle, Ernie, 1398 (164)

Q

Quarter
　Horse, 2155 (252)
　Seated, 1578 (184)
Quill
　Inkwell and, 1535 (179), 1581 (184), 1811 (215)
　Pen, 1099 (136), 1119 (139), 1230 (147), 1250 (148), 2360 (275), 2421 (284)
Quilts
　American, 1745-1748 (207)
　Basket Design, 1745 (207)
Quimby, Harriet, C128 (351)

R

Raccoon, 1757h (208)
Racing
　Car, 2262 (264)
　Horse, 1528 (179)
Radiator, Airplane, and Wooden Propeller, C4 (339)
Radio
　Amateur, 1260 (151)
　Waves, 1260 (151), 1274 (151), 1329 (156)
Railroad
　Baltimore & Ohio, 1006 (124)
　Engineers, 993 (124)
　Lantern, 1612 (187)
　Mail Car, 2265 (264)
　Transcontinental, 922 (116)
Randolph, A. Philip, 2402 (283)
Range Conservation, 1176 (144)
Ratification of the Constitution, 835 (111), 2336-2348 (272)
Rayburn, Sam, 1202 (147)
Read, George, 1687e (196), 1694 (200)
Readers, A Nation of, 2106 (247)
Rebecca of Sunnybrook Farm, (320)
Recognizing Deafness, (320)
Red
　Cloud, 2176 (255)
　Fox, 1757g (208)
　-Nosed Reindeer, (321)
　Squirrel, 2478 (324)
Red Cross
　American, 702 (96), 967 (120), 1910 (223)
　International, 1016 (127), 1239 (148)
Redhead Decoy, 2141 (251)
Reed, Dr. Walter, 877 (112)
Refuge National Park, City of, C84 (344)
Register and Vote, 1249 (148), 1344 (159)
Religious Freedom in America, 1099 (136)
Remington, Frederic, 888 (112), 1187 (144), 1934 (227)
Renwick, James, 1838 (216)
Representatives, House of, 2412 (283)
Republic of
　China, 1188 (144)
　Texas, 776 (104), 778 (104), 2204 (256)
　the Marshall Islands, 2507 (291)
Research, Health, 2087 (243)
Resolution, 1733 (204)
Restaurantionen, 620 (91)
Retarded Children, 1549 (180)
Reticulated Helmet, 2118 (248)
Retriever, Chesapeake Bay, 2099 (244)
Reuter, Ernst, 1136-1137 (140)
Revel, Bernard, 2194 (255)
Revere, Paul, 1048 (131), 1059A (131)
Rhode Island, 1645 (192), 1991 (232)
　Flag, 1349 (159)
　Settlement, 777 (104)
　Statehood, 2348 (272)
　Windmill, 1739 (207)

Rhodochrosite, 1541 (180)
Rhythm & Blues/Rock & Roll, 2724-2737 (318)
Ribalt Monument, 616 (88)
Richardson, Henry Hobson, 1839 (216)
Riley, James Whitcomb, 868 (112)
Ring Master, Circus, 2753 (315)
Rise of the Spirit of Independence, 1476-1479 (172)
Roanoke
　Island Settlement, Virginia Dare, 796 (107)
　Voyages, 2093 (244)
Robinson, Jackie, 2016 (235)
Rochambeau, Count de, 703 (96)
Rock & Roll
　Musicians, 2721 (314)
　/Rhythm & Blues, 2724-2737 (318)
Rockne, Knute, 2376 (276)
Rocky Mountains, 288 (62)
　Beacon on, C11 (339)
Rodgers, Jimmie, 1755 (207)
Rogers
　Will, 975 (123), 1801 (212)
Roosevelt
　Eleanor, 1236 (148), 2105 (247)
　Franklin D., 930-933 (119), 1284 (152), 1298 (155), 1305 (155), 1950 (228), 2219d (260), 2559d (296)
　(Rough Riders), 973 (123)
　(Sagamore Hill), 1023 (127)
　Theodore, 557 (84), 586 (87), 602 (88), 637 (91), 648 (92), 663 (95), 674 (95), 830 (108), 856 (111), 1011 (127), 1039 (128), 2218g (260), 2523 (292), C88 (344)
Roses, 1737 (204), 1876 (220), 2378-2379 (276)
Ross
　Betsy, 1004 (124)
　George, 1004 (124)
Rotary International, 1066 (132)
Rough Riders, 973 (123)
Rover
　Lunar, 1435 (168)
　Surface, C124 (348), C126c (351)
Royal Wulf, 2545 (295)
RR Caboose, 1905 (223)
Ruby-Throated Hummingbird, 2642 (304)
Ruffled Grouse, 1924 (224)
Rufous Hummingbird, 2645 (304)
Rural
　America, 1504-1506 (176)
　Electrification Administration, 2144 (251)
　Mailbox, 1730 (204)
Rush Lamp and Candle Holder, 1610 (187)
Rushmore, Mount, 1011 (127), 2523 (292), 2523A (292), C88 (344)
Russell
　Charles M., 1243 (148)
　Richard, 1853 (219)
Ruth, Babe, 2046 (239)
Rutledge, Edward, 1687e (196), 1694 (200)

S

Saarinen, Eeno, 2022 (235)
Sabertooth Blenny, 1830 (215)
Santa Fe, NM, 1031A (128)
Sacagawea, 1063 (132)
Sackville, Surrender of Fort, 651 (92)
Saddlebred Horse, 2157 (252)
Safety, 1007 (124)
　Traffic, 1272 (151)
Sagamore Hill (Home of Theodore Roosevelt), 1023 (127)
Saguaro Cactus, 1192 (144), 1945 (228), 1955 (231)
Saint
　Augustine, 927 (119)
　Charles Streetcar, 2062 (240)
　-Gaudens, Augustus, 886 (112)
　Lawrence Seaway, 1131 (139), 2091 (244)
Salem, Peter, 1361 (160)

Salomon, Haym, 1561 (183)
Salute to Youth, 963 (120)
Salvation Army, 1267 (151)
Sampson, William T., 793 (107)
San Diego, CA, 773 (104), 778 (104)
San Francisco
  Bay, 400 (73), 400A (73)
  Cable Car, 1442 (168), 2263 (264)
  Discovery of, 404 (74), 400A (73)
  (Golden Gate), 567 (87), 698 (96)
  -Oakland Bay Bridge, Plane over,
    C36 (340)
San Gabriel Mission, CA, C116 (348)
San Ildefonso Pot, 1707 (203)
San Juan, Puerto Rico, 1437 (168)
San Martin, Jose De, 1125-1126 (139)
San Xavier del Bac Mission, 1443 (168)
Sandburg, Carl, 1731 (204)
Sandy Hook Lighthouse, 1605 (187),
  2474 (288)
Santa
  Claus, 1472 (172), 1508 (176), 1800
    (212), 2064 (240), 2108 (247),
    2579-2585 (299)
  Maria, 232 (57)
Santa Fe, NM, 944 (119), 1054A (131)
Saratoga
  Battle of, 1728 (204)
  US, 791 (107)
Sargent, Gov. Winthrop, 955 (120)
Saroyan, William, 2538 (295)
Satellite, 1575 (184)
Saturn, 1916 (224), 2574 (299)
Sault Ste. Marie, 298 (62), 1069 (132)
Savannah, 923 (116)
Save Our
  Air, 1413 (164)
  Cities, 1411 (164)
  Soil, 1410 (164)
  Water, 1412 (164)
Savings
  and Loans, 1911 (223)
  Bonds US, 2534 (295)
  Bonds-, Servicemen, 1320 (156)
Saw-Whet Owl, 1761 (208), 2284 (267)
Sawtooth Mountain, ID, 2439 (287)
Sawyer, Tom, 1470 (172)
Saxhorns, 1614 (187)
Schloy, Winfield S., 793 (107)
School
  Bus, 2123 (248)
  Teachers, 1093 (136)
Schoolhouse, One-Room, 1606 (187)
Schurz, Carl, 1847 (219)
Science & Industry, 2031 (236)
Sciences, The, 1237 (148)
Scientists, 874-878 (112), 953 (120),
  1074 (135), 1080 (135), 1285 (152),
  1488 (175), 1774 (211), 2699 (311),
  2746 (314)
Scott
  Blanche Stuart, C99 (347)
  General Winfield, 153 (53), 164 (53),
    175 (53), 200 (54), 786 (107)
  Jock, 2546 (295)
Scotts Bluff, NE, 1060 (132)
Sea
  Creatures of the, 2508-2511 (291)
  Lion, Northern, 2509 (291)
  Otter, 2510 (291)
Seal, 683 (95), 775 (104), 778 (104),
  794 (107), 897 (115), 927 (119), 940
  (119), 955 (120), 972 (123), 974
  (123), 979 (123), 995 (124), 1001-
  1002 (124), 1005 (124), 1015 (127),
  1018 (127), 1066 (132), 1091 (136),
  1095-1096 (136), 1127 (139), 1131
  (139), 1151 (140), 1156 (143), 1167
  (143), 1194 (144), 1234 (147), 1266
  (151), 1308 (155), 1314 (155), 1419
  (167), 1421 (167), 1432 (168), 1525
  (179), 1559-1561 (183), 1565-1570
  (183), 1825 (215), 2142 (251), 2336
  (272), C40 (340)
  Fur, 1464 (171)
  Harbor, 1882 (220)
Sealed Envelopes, 2150 (251)
Seamstress, 1717 (203)
Seaplane, 2468 (288)

Search for Peace (Lions International),
  1326 (156)
Seashells, 2117-2121 (248)
Seated Liberty Quarter, 1578 (184)
SEATO, 1151 (140)
Seattle World's Fair, 1196 (147)
Seeing Eye Dogs, 1787 (212)
Seminole Seal, 972 (123)
Senate, US, 2413 (283)
Sequoyah, 1859 (219)
Serra, Father Junipero, C116 (348)
Service Women, 1013 (127)
Servicemen
  Disabled American Veterans and,
    1421-1422 (167)
  Savings Bonds, 1320 (156)
Sevier, Gov. John, 941 (119)
Seward, William H., 370-371 (70)
Shadoo, Chief, 683 (95)
Shakespeare, William, 1250 (148)
Sheridan, General Philip, 787 (107)
Sherman
  General William T., 225 (54), 257
    (58), 272 (61), 787 (107)
  Roger, 1687a (196), 1693 (200)
Shield, Eagle and Flags, 121 (50)
Shiloh, Civil War Centennial, 1179 (144)
Ship, 2559h (296)
  Figurehead, 2241 (263)
Shipbuilding, 1095 (136)
Shiprock, NM, 1191 (144)
Shorthair Cat
  American, 2375 (276)
  Exotic, 2372 (276)
Shoshone Headdress, 2505 (291)
Show Boat, (319)
Shuttle, 1913-1914 (224), 1917-1919
  (224), C125 (348), C126a (351),
  C126d (351)
Siamese Cat, 2372 (276)
Sign Language, American, (320)
Signing of the
  Constitution, 798 (107), 2360 (275)
  Mayflower Compact, 550 (84)
Sikorsky, Igor, C119 (348)
Silver Centennial, 1130 (139)
Silversmith, 1457 (171)
SIPEX, 1310-1311 (155)
Sitting Bull, 2184 (255)
Skilled Hands for Independence, 1717-
  1720 (203)
Skylab, 1915 (224)
  I, 1529 (179)
Sled, Dog, 1128 (139), 2135 (248)
Sleepy Hollow, Legend of, 1548 (180)
Sleigh, 1384 (163), 1551 (180), 1900
  (223), 2400 (280), 2428 (284)
Sloan, John, 1433 (168)
Smith
  Alfred E., 937 (119)
  Captain John, 328 (66)
Smithsonian Institution, 943 (119),
  1838 (216)
Smokey the Bear, 2096 (244)
Snelling, Fort, 1409 (164)
Snowman, (321)
Social Security Act, 2153 (251)
Society of Philatelic Americans, 797
  (107)
Soil
  Conservation, 1133 (140)
  Save Our, 1410 (164)
  Water and, 2074 (243)
Sokols, Physical Fitness-, 1262 (151)
Solar Energy, 2006 (235)
Solo Transatlantic Flight, Lindbergh's,
  1710 (203), C10 (339)
Soo Locks, 298 (62), 1069 (132)
Sound Recording, 1705 (200)
Sousa, John Philip, 880 (112)
South Carolina, 1640 (191), 1992 (232)
  Settlement, 1407 (164)
  Statehood, 2343 (272)
South Dakota, 1672 (195), 1993 (232)
  Statehood, 858 (111), 2416 (283)
South-East Asia Treaty Organization
  (SEATO), 1151 (140)
Southeast Carved Wood Figure, 2426
  (292), C121 (348)
Soyuz, Apollo, 1569-1570 (183)

Space
  Accomplishment in, 1331-1332 (156)
  Accomplishment in (Apollo 8), 1371
    (160)
  Achievement Decade, 1434-1435
    (168)
  Achievements, 1912-1919 (224)
  Adventure, 2631-2634 (304)
  (Apollo Soyuz), 1569 (183), 1570
    (183)
  (Echo I-Communications for Peace),
    1173 (143)
  Exploration, 2568-2577 (299)
  Fantasy, 2741-2745 (314)
  (Fort Bliss), 976 (123)
  (Future Mail Transportation), C122
    (348), C123 (348), C124 (348),
    C125 (348), C126 (351)
  (Goddard, Robert H.), C69 (343)
  (Mariner 10/Venus, Mercury), 1557
    (183)
  (Moon Landing), 2419 (284), C76
    (344)
  Needle, 1196 (147)
  (Palomar Mountain Observatory),
    966 (120)
  (Pioneer 10/Jupiter), 1556 (183)
  (Project Mercury), 1193 (144)
  Shuttle, 2631 (304), C125 (348),
    C126a (351), C126d (351)
  (Skylab I), 1529 (179)
  Vehicle, 2543 (324)
  (Viking Missions), 1759 (208)
  (von Karman, Theodore), 2699 (311)
Spacecraft, C122 (348), C125 (348),
  C126 (351)
  Future, 2543 (324)
Spaniel, Cocker, 2099 (244)
Speaker, 1502 (176)
Speaker's Stand, 1582 (184)
Special Occasions, 2267-2274 (264),
  2395-2398 (280)
Special Olympics, 1788 (212)
  Winter, 2142 (251)
Sperry, Lawrence and Elmer, C114
  (348)
"Spirit of St. Louis," Lindbergh's, 1710
  (203), C10 (339)
Spirit of '76, 1629-1631 (191)
Sportin' Life, 1484 (175)
Sports, 716 (99), 718-719 (99), 855
  (111), 1146 (140), 1189 (144), 1262
  (151), 1381-1382 (163), 1460-1462
  (171), 1528 (179), 1695-1698 (200),
  1702-1703 (200), 1788 (212), 1790-
  1798 (212), 1932-1933 (227), 2016
  (235), 2027 (236), 2029 (236), 2033-
  2034 (236), 2043 (239), 2046 (239),
  2048-2051 (239), 2067-2070 (240),
  2082-2085 (243), 2089 (244), 2097
  (244), 2142 (251), 2247 (263), 2369
  (276), 2377 (276), 2380 (276), 2417
  (283), 2496-2500 (291), 2560 (296),
  2756-2759 (316), C56 (343), C85
  (344), C97 (347), C101-C112 (347)
  American, 2376-2377 (276)
Spreading Pogonia, 2078 (243)
Squash Blossoms Lace, Design, 2351
  (272)
Squirrel, Red, 2478 (324)
SS Adriatic, 117 (50)
Stagecoach, 1120 (139), 1572 (184),
  1898A (223), 2228 (263), 2434 (287),
  2438a (287), 2448 (288)
Stamp
  Collecting, 1474 (172), 2198-2201
    (256), 2410 (283), 2433 (284)
  Expo '89, 2410 (283), 2433 (284),
    2433a-d (284)
  Expo '92, World Columbian, 2616
    (300)
Stanley Steamer, 2132 (248)
Stanton
  Edwin M., 138 (53), 149 (53), 160
    (53), 171 (53), 196 (54)
  Elizabeth, 959 (120)
Stanwix, Battle of Fort, 644 (92)
Star Route Truck, 2125 (248)
Stars and Stripes, 2531 (295)

State
  Birds & Flowers, 1953-1977 (231),
    1978-2002 (232)
  Capitols, 782 (104), 838 (111), 896
    (115), 903 (115), 927 (119), 941
    (119), 957 (120), 996 (124), 1001
    (124), 1232 (147), 1308 (155),
    1407 (164), 2337 (272), 2342 (272)
Statehood
  Alabama, 1375 (160)
  Alaska, 2066 (240), C53 (343)
  Anniversary, 858 (111)
  Arizona, 1192 (144)
  Arkansas, 2167 (255)
  California, 997 (124)
  Colorado, 1001 (124), 1711 (203)
  Connecticut, 2340 (272)
  Florida, 927 (119)
  Georgia, 2339 (272)
  Hawaii, 2080 (243), C55 (343)
  Idaho, 896 (115), 2439 (287)
  Illinois, 1339 (159)
  Indiana, 1308 (155)
  Iowa, 942 (119)
  Kansas, 1183 (144)
  Kentucky, 904 (115), 2636 (304)
  Louisiana, 1197 (147)
  Maine, 1391 (163)
  Maryland, 2342 (272)
  Massachusetts, 2341 (272)
  Michigan, 775 (104), 778 (104),
    2246 (263)
  Minnesota, 1106 (136)
  Mississippi, 1337 (159)
  Missouri, 1426 (167)
  Montana, 858 (111), 2401 (283)
  Nebraska, 1328 (156)
  Nevada, 1248 (148)
  New Hampshire, 2344 (272)
  New Jersey, 2338 (272)
  New Mexico, 1191 (144)
  New York, 2346 (272)
  North Carolina, 2347 (272)
  North Dakota, 858 (111), 2403 (283)
  Ohio, 1018 (127)
  Oklahoma, 1092 (136)
  Oregon, 1124 (139)
  Rhode Island, 2348 (272)
  South Carolina, 2343 (272)
  South Dakota, 858 (111), 2416 (283)
  Tennessee, 941 (119)
  Texas, 938 (119)
  Vermont, 903 (115), 2533 (295)
  Virginia, 2345 (272)
  Washington, 858 (111), 2404 (283)
  West Virginia, 1232 (147)
  Wisconsin, 957 (120)
  Wyoming, 897 (115), 2444 (288)
Statesman, Acheson, Dean, 2755 (316)
Statue of Liberty, 566 (87), 696 (96),
  899 (115), 908 (115), 946 (119), 995
  (124), 1035 (128), 1041-1042 (128),
  1044 (128), 1057 (131), 1075 (135),
  1320 (156), 1594 (184), 1599 (187),
  1619 (188), 1816 (215), 2147 (251),
  2224 (263), C35 (340), C58 (343),
  C63 (343), C80 (344), C87 (344)
Steam Carriage, 2451 (288)
Steamboats, 2405-2409 (283), 2435
  (287), 2438b (287)
Steamer, 294 (62)
Steamship
  (City of Apena), 294 (62)
  (St. Paul), 299 (62)
  (Savannah), 923 (116)
Steel Industry, 1090 (136)
Steeplechase, 2756 (316)
Stefansson, Vilhjalmur, 2222 (263)
Stegosaurus, 1390 (163), 2424 (284)
Steinbeck, John, 1773 (211)
Steinmetz, Charles, 2055 (239)
Stevenson, Adlai E., 1275 (151)
Stewart, Walter, 1686e (196)
Stock Exchange, New York, 2630 (304)
Stone
  Harlan F., 965 (120)
  Lucy, 1293 (152)
  Mountain Memorial, 1408 (164)
Stourbridge Lion, 2362 (275)
Straight-Spout Coffeepot, 1775 (211)

Stratford Hall, 788 (107)
Stravinsky, Igor, 1845 (219)
Streetcars, 2059-2062 (240)
Strickland, William, 1782 (211)
Stuart, Gilbert Charles, 884 (112)
Stutz Bearcat, 2131 (248)
Stuyvesant, Peter, 971 (123)
Suffrage, Woman, 1406 (164)
  (Belva Ann Lockwood), 2179 (255)
  (Lucy Stone), 1293 (152)
  (Susan B. Anthony), 784 (104),
    1051 (131)
Sugar Bowl, 1777 (211)
Sullivan
  Ann & Helen Keller, 1824 (215)
  Expedition, Maj. Gen. John, 657 (92)
  Louis, 1931 (227)
Sun, 616 (88), 906 (115), 950 (120), 968
  (123), 1016 (127), 1188 (144), 1434
  (168), 1710 (203), 1723-1724 (204),
  1915 (224), 2340 (272)
  Tower of the, 852 (111)
  Yat-Sen, 906 (115), 1188 (144)
Support Our Youth-Elks, 1342 (159)
Supreme Court, 991 (124), 1895 (220),
  1896 (223), 2415 (283)
  (Black, Hugo), 2172 (255)
  Flag Over, 1894 (220)
  Frieze (American Bar Association),
    1022 (127)
  (Holmes, Oliver Wendell), 1288 (152),
    1288B (152), 1305E (155)
  (Jay, John), 1046 (131)
  (Marshall, John), 312 (65), 479 (79),
    1050 (131)
  (Moore, John Bassett), 1295 (155)
  (Warren, Earl), 2184A (255)
Surface Rover, C124 (348), C126c (351)
Surrender
  at Saratoga, 644 (92), 1728 (204)
  of Cornwallis at Yorktown, 703 (96),
    1686 (196)
Surrey, 1907 (223)
Sutter's Mill, 954 (120)
Swallowtail, 1712 (203)
Swedish
  -Finnish Landing, 836 (111)
  Pioneer, 958 (120)
  (Stamp Collecting), 2200 (256)
Switzerland, 2532 (295)
Synthetic Fuels, 2007 (235)

T

Taft
  Sen. Robert A., Memorial, 1161 (143)
  William H., 685 (95), 687 (95), 831
    (108), 2218h (260)
Talking Pictures, 1727 (204)
Tandem Bicycle, 2266 (264)
Tanner, Henry O., 1486 (175)
Taylor, Zachary, 179 (53), 181 (53), 185
  (54), 204 (54), 817 (108), 2217c (259)
Tea Caddy, 1776 (211)
Teachers of America, 1093 (136)
Telecommunication Union, Inter-
  national, 1274 (151)
Telegraph, 890 (112), 924 (116)
Telephone, 893 (112), 1683 (195)
Telescope, 1919 (224)
Television Camera, First, 2058 (239)
Tennessee, 1648 (192), 1994 (232)
  Statehood, 941 (119)
  Valley Authority, 2042 (239)
Terrier, Boston, 2098 (244)
Territorial Issues, 799-802 (107)
Territories, Pacific Trust, Northern
  Mariana Islands, (321)
Tesla, Nikola, 2057 (239)
Texas, 1660 (192), 1995 (232)
  (HemisFair '68), 1340 (159)
  Republic of, 776 (104), 778 (104),
    2204 (256)
  Statehood, 938 (119)
  Windmill, 1742 (207)
Thank you!, 2269 (264)
Thayer, Sylvanus, 1852 (219)
Theater Dance, 1750 (207)
Thinking of You, 2397 (280)

13-Star Flags, 50-Star and, 1509 (176),
  1704 (200), 2216 (259), 2552 (295),
  2608 (299)
Thirteenth Amendment, 902 (115)
Thomas A. Edison, 945 (119)
Thomson, Charles, 1687 (196),
  1694 (200)
Thoreau, Henry David, 1327 (156)
Thorpe, Jim, 2089 (244)
Three Graces, 895 (115)
Ticonderoga, Fort, 1071 (132)
Tidal Basin, 1318 (156)
Tiger, White Bengal, 2709 (311)
Tlingit
  Chief in Haida Ceremonial Canoe,
    1389 (163)
  Tribe, 1836 (216)
Tokyo Bay, 1021 (127)
Toleware, Pennsylvania, 1775-1778
  (211)
Torch, 978-979 (123), 1015 (127), 1066
  (132), 1096 (136), 1110-1111 (139),
  1117-1118 (139), 1125-1126 (139),
  1136-1137 (140), 1144 (140), 1147-
  1148 (140), 1159-1160 (143), 1165-
  1166 (143), 1168-1169 (143), 1174-
  1175 (144), 1234 (147), 1308 (155),
  2336 (272)
  Liberty, 1594 (184), 1816 (215),
    2531A (295)
  of Enlightenment, 901 (115)
Toscanini, Arturo, 2411 (283)
Tourmaline, 1539 (180)
Touro Synagogue, 2017 (235)
Tow Truck, 2129 (248)
Tower of the Sun, 852 (111)
Toy Soldier, (321)
Track Racing, 2757 (316)
Tractor, 1162 (143), 2127 (248)
  Trailer, 2457 (288)
Traffic Safety, 1272 (151)
Trail, Oregon, 2747 (314)
Trans-Mississippi
  Exposition, 285-293 (62)
  Philatelic Exposition, 751 (100), 769
    (103)
Transatlantic
  Airmail, C24 (340)
  Flight, Solo, 1710 (203), C10 (339)
Transcontinental Railroad, 922 (116)
Transistors, 1501 (176)
Transpacific Airmail, C20 (339), C21
  (339), C22 (339), C115 (348)
Transport Plane, Twin-Motor, C25 (340)
Transportation, 1897 (223), 1897A
  (223), 1898 (223), 1898A (223), 1899-
  1908 (223), 2252-2266 (264), 2451-
  2453 (288), 2457 (288), 2464 (288),
  2468 (288)
  Air-Cushion Vehicle, C123 (348),
    C125 (348), C126b (351)
  Airplane, 649-650 (92), 934 (119),
    947 (119), 1185 (144), 1511 (179),
    1574 (184), 1684 (195), 1710
    (203), 2433 (284), 2436 (287),
    2438c (287), 2468 (288), C1-C11
    (339), C20-C22 (339), C25-C41
    (340), C44-C47 (340), C68 (343),
    C74 (344), C91-C96 (347), C99-
    C100 (347), C113-C115 (348),
    C118-C119 (348), C128-C129
    (351)
  Ambulance, 2128 (248), 2231 (263)
  Automobile, 296 (62), 1162 (143),
    1286A (152), 1511 (179), 1511a
    (179), 1906 (223), 2131-2132
    (248), 2262 (264), 2381-2385
    (279), 2437-2438 (287)
  Balloons, 2032-2035 (236), 2530
    (295), C54 (343)
  Bicycle, 1460 (171), 1901 (223), 2266
    (264), C110 (347)
  Buggy, 1360 (160), 1370 (160), 1505
    (176), 1902 (223), 2124 (248)
  Bus, 1897 (223), 2123 (248), 2225
    (263)
  Cable Car, 1442 (168), 2263 (264)
  Caboose, RR, 1905 (223)
  Canoe, 2453 (288)
  Carriage, Steam, 2451 (288)

Cart, 981 (123), 2133 (248)
Classic, 2434-2438 (287)
Classic Mail, 2434-2438 (287)
Coal Car, 2259 (264)
Elevator, 2254 (264)
Fire Engine, 971 (123), 1908 (223), 2264 (264)
Future Spacecraft, 2543 (324)
Handcar, 1898 (223)
Horses, 235 (57), 240 (57), 287 (62), 289 (62), 400 (73), 400A (73), 404 (74), 618 (88), 645 (92), 783 (104), 835 (111), 894 (115), 898 (115), 944 (119), 947 (119), 950 (120), 973 (123), 1001 (124), 1003 (124), 1006 (124), 1012 (127), 1028 (127), 1061 (132), 1120 (139), 1123 (139), 1130 (139), 1154 (143), 1176 (144), 1243 (148), 1261 (151), 1360 (160), 1384 (163), 1408 (164), 1416 (167), 1478-1479 (172), 1505 (176), 1528 (179), 1548 (180), 1551 (180), 1559 (183), 1686 (196), 1689 (199), 1794 (212), 1934 (227), 2059 (240), 2341 (272), 2345-2346 (272), 2391 (279), 2400 (280), 2401 (283), 2448 (288)
Jeep, 2559c (296)
Jet, 1017 (127), 1574 (184), 2022 (235), C47 (340), C49 (343), C51 (343), C52 (343), C57-C65 (343), C75 (344), C77-C78 (344), C81-C82 (344), C87 (344), C89-C90 (344), C98 (347), C122 (348), C126a (351)
Locomotive, 295 (62), 922 (116), 947 (119), 961 (120), 993 (124), 1006 (124), 1506 (176), 1511 (179), 1573 (184), 1755 (207), 1897A (223), 1905 (223), 2226 (263), 2362-2366 (275), 2402 (283)
Lunar Rover, 1435 (168)
Lunch Wagon, 2464 (288)
Mail Car, 2265 (264)
Monorail, 1196 (147)
Motorcycle, 1899 (223)
Series, 2123-2136 (248)
Ships and Boats, 230-233 (57), 235 (62), 293-294 (62), 299 (62), 329 (66), 372-373 (70), 398-399 (73), 402-403 (74), 548-549 (84), 567 (87), 614-615 (88), 620-621 (91), 683 (95), 698 (96), 736 (100), 739 (100), 746 (100), 755 (103), 762 (103), 790 (107), 792-793 (107), 802 (107), 836 (111), 856 (111), 923 (116), 936 (119), 939 (119), 947 (119), 951 (120), 956 (120), 984 (123), 994 (124), 997 (124), 1000 (124), 1003 (124), 1010 (127), 1017 (127), 1021 (127), 1027 (127), 1063 (132), 1069 (132), 1088 (136), 1091 (136), 1095 (136), 1109 (139), 1128 (139), 1197 (147), 1207 (147), 1239 (148), 1258 (151), 1270-1271 (151), 1322 (156), 1325 (156), 1335 (159), 1356 (160), 1358 (160), 1374 (160), 1389 (163), 1409 (164), 1420 (167), 1433 (168), 1441-1442 (168), 1448 (171), 1480-1483 (172), 1567-1568 (183), 1688 (199), 1733 (204), 1793 (212), 1937-1938 (227), 2040 (236), 2080 (243), 2085 (243), 2091 (244), 2093 (244), 2134 (248), 2163 (252), 2200 (256), 2220 (263), 2260 (264), 2336 (272), 2340 (272), 2342 (272), 2386-2387 (279), 2404-2409 (283), 2435 (287), 2438b (287), 2453 (288), 2506-2507 (291), 2529 (292), 2559 (296), 2621 (300), 2623 (300), C130 (351)
Shuttle, C125 (348), C126d (351)
Sled, 1128 (139), 1461 (171), 1702-1703 (200), 2027 (236), 2135 (248)

Sleigh, 1384 (163), 1551 (180), 1900 (223), 1940 (227), 2400 (280)
Stagecoach, 1120 (139), 1572 (184), 1898A (223), 2228 (263), 2434 (287), 2438 (287), 2448 (288)
Steam Carriage, 2451 (288)
Streetcar, 2059-2062 (240)
Surface Rover, C124 (348), C126 (351)
Tank, 1026 (127), 2559e (296)
Tractor, 1162 (143), 2127 (248)
Tractor-Trailer, 2457 (288)
Tricycle, 2126 (248)
Truck, 1025 (127), 1162 (143), 1572 (184), 2125 (248), 2129 (248), 2457 (288), 2559a (296), 2635 (304)
Wagon, 240 (57), 286 (62), 289-290 (62), 323 (66), 783 (104), 950 (120), 958 (120), 964 (120), 970 (123), 981 (123), 997 (124), 1018-1019 (127), 1028 (127), 1061 (132), 1120 (139), 1124 (139), 1360 (160), 1426 (167), 1487 (175), 1542 (180), 1744 (207), 1897 (223), 1903 (223), 1907 (223), 2124 (248), 2128 (248), 2130 (248), 2136 (248), 2253 (264), 2255 (264), 2258 (264), 2261 (264), 2341 (272), 2345-2346 (272), 2403 (283), 2448 (288), 2452 (288), 2464 (288)
Wheelchair, 1155 (143), 1385 (163), 2153 (251), 2256 (264)
Zeppelin, C13 (339), C14 (339), C15 (339), C18 (339)
Trapeze, Circus, 2750 (315)
Treaty
    Antarctic, 1431 (168), C130 (351)
    of Paris, 2052 (239)
    US-Japan, 1158 (143)
Trees, 1240 (148), 1245 (148), 1376 (163)
    American, 1764-1767 (208)
Trego, William T., 1689 (199)
Tricycle, 2126 (248)
Trinity Church, 1839 (216)
Trout, 1427 (167)
Truck
    Star Route, 2125 (248)
    Tow, 2129 (248)
Trucking Industry, 1025 (127)
Truman, Harry S., 1499 (176), 1862 (219), 2219 (260), 2219f (260)
Trumbull, John, 1361 (160), 1686d (196)
Truth, Sojourner, 2203 (256)
Tyrannosaurus, 2422 (284)
Trylon, 853 (111)
Tube, TV, 1502 (176)
Tuberculosis, 1823 (215)
Tubman, Harriet, 1744 (207)
Tugboat, 2260 (264)
Tulip, 2425-2427 (292), 2517-2520 (292), 2524 (292), 2762 (317)
Tuna, Bluefin, 2208 (256)
Turners Society, American, 979 (123)
TV Camera Tube, 1502 (176)
(Twain, Mark), Samuel L. Clemens, 863 (112), 1470 (172)
$20 Gold Piece, 1578 (184), 1577b (184)
Twin-Motored Transport Plane, C25-C31 (343)
Two Medicine Lake, 748 (100), 764 (103)
Tyler, John, 815 (108), 847 (111), 2217a (259)

U
Umbrella, Beach, 2443 (287)
United
    Confederate Veterans, 998 (124)
    (Dag Hammarskjold), 1203-1204 (147)
    Headquarters, 1203-1204 (147)
    International Cooperation Year, 1266 (151)
    Nations, 907 (115), 1419 (167)
    Nations Conference, 928 (119)

Nations Memorial (Stevenson, Adlai E.), 1275 (151)
    Way, 2275 (267)
Universal
    (Classic Mail Transportation), 2434-2437 (287)
    (Future Mail Transportation), C126 (351)
    Postal Union, 1530-1537 (179), C42 (340), C43 (340), C44 (340)
    Postal Union (Future Mail Transportation), C122 (348), C123 (348), C124 (348), C125 (348)
Uranus, 2575 (299)
Urban Planning, 1333 (156)
US
    Air Mail Service, C74 (344)
    -Canada Friendship, 961 (120)
    Capitol, 572-573 (87), 649-650 (92), 989 (124), 992 (124), 1013 (127), 1152 (143), 1202 (147), 1365 (160), 1368 (160), 1503 (176), 2114-2116 (247), 2532 (295), 2561 (296), C64 (343)
    Congress, 2559j (296)
    Frigate Constitution, 951 (120)
    House of Representatives, 2412 (283)
    -Japan Treaty, 1158 (143)
    Map and Two Mail Planes, C7 (339)
    Military Academy, 780 (107)
    (Morocco, Friendship With), 2349 (272)
    Naval Academy, 794 (107)
    Postage Stamp Centenary, 947 (119)
    Savings Bonds, 2534 (295)
    Senate, 2413 (283)
    Servicemen, 1421-1422 (167)
    -Sweden Treaty, 2036 (236)
USA, 2193 (255), 2608B (323)
    and Jet, C75 (344), C81 (344)
    /Netherlands, 2003 (235)
Utah, 950 (120), 1677 (195), 1996 (232)
    Settlement, 950 (120)
    (Zion National Park), 747 (100), 763 (103)

V
Valley
    Carson, NV, 999 (124)
    Forge, 645 (92), 1689 (199), 1729 (204)
    of the Great Salt Lake, 950 (120)
Van
    Buren, Martin, 813 (108), 2201 (256), 2216h (259)
    der Rohe, Mies, 2020 (235)
Varicoito, 2702 (311)
Vehicle, Space, 2543 (324)
Venus, 2569 (299)
    Mercury, Mariner 10/, 1557 (183)
Vermont, 1646 (192), 1997 (232)
    Battle of Bennington and Independence, 643 (92)
    Statehood, 903 (115), 2533 (295)
Verrazano-Narrows Bridge, 1258 (151)
Verville, Alfred, C113 (348)
Veterans
    Administration, 1825 (215)
    Administration of Foreign Wars, 1525 (179)
    Civil War, 985 (123), 998 (124)
    Disabled American, 1421 (167)
    Korean, 2152 (251)
    of World War I, 2154 (252)
    of World War II, 940 (119)
    Vietnam, 1802 (212), 2109 (247)
Victory, Allied, 537 (83)
Vietnam Veterans, 1802 (212)
    Memorial, 2109 (247)
Viking
    Missions to Mars, 1759 (208)
    Orbiter, 2572 (299)
    Ship, 621 (91)
Vincennes, 651 (92)
Violet, African, (325)
Violins, Weaver, 1813 (215)
Virgin Islands, 802 (107)
Virginia, 1642 (191), 1998 (232)

Capes, Battle of the, 1938 (227)
of Sagadahock, 1095 (136)
Rotunda, 1779 (211)
Windmill, 1738 (207)
Voice of America, 1329 (156)
Voluntarism, 2039 (236)
Volunteer Firemen, 971 (123)
von
Karman, Theodore, 2699 (311)
Steuben, Gen. Friedrich, 689 (96),
1686d (196)
Vote, Register and, 1249 (148), 1344
(159)
Voyager 2, 2574-2576 (299)

W

Wagon
Bread, 2136 (248)
Circus, 2452 (288)
Lunch, 2464 (288)
Mail, 1903 (223)
Oil, 2130 (248)
Walk in the Water, 2409 (283)
Walker, Dr. Mary, 2013 (235)
Walloon, Huguenot, 614-616 (88)
Wapiti, 1886 (220)
War, Win the, 905 (115)
Warren, Earl, 2184A (255)
Washington
and Lee University, 982 (123)
at Cambridge, 617 (88)
at Princeton, 1704 (200)
at Valley Forge, 645 (92), 1729 (204)
Bicentennial Issue, 704-715 (96)
Booker T., 873 (112), 1074 (135)
Bridge, 1012 (127)
Crossing the Delaware, 1688 (199)
Cruisers Flag, 1347 (159)
D.C., 943 (119), 989-992 (124)
(Executive Branch), 2414 (283)
George, 2 (45), 4 (45), 10-11 (45), 13-
17 (45), 25-26 (45), 31-37 (46), 39
(46), 41 (46), 43 (46), 44-45 (46),
47 (46), 64-62 (49), 62B (46), 66
(49), 69 (49), 70 (49), 72 (49), 74
(49), 78-79 (49), 82-83 (49), 85
(49), 85C (49), 85D (49), 85E (49),
88-90 (50), 94 (50), 96-97 (50), 99
(50), 101 (50), 104 (50), 106-107
(50), 109 (50), 111 (50), 115 (50),
136 (53), 147 (53), 158 (53), 169
(53), 184 (54), 194 (54), 207 (54),
210 (54), 211B (54), 213-214 (54),
219D (54), 220 (54), 248-252 (58),
265-267 (61), 279B (62), 301 (65),
319 (65), 320-322 (66), 332-342
(69), 344-347 (69), 349-351 (69),
353-356 (70), 358-366 (70), 375
(70), 377-382 (73), 384 (73), 386
(73), 388-389 (73), 391 (73), 393-
396 (73), 405-413 (74), 424-429
(77), 430 (77), 441-450 (78), 452-
459 (78), 461-469 (78), 481-482
(79), 482A (79), 483-496 (79), 498-
507 (80), 519 (83), 525-528 (83),
528A (83), 528B (83), 529-534
(83), 534A (83), 534B (83), 535-
536 (83), 538-546 (84), 554 (84),
577 (87), 579 (87), 583 (87), 595
(88), 599 (88), 599A (88), 606 (88),
634 (91), 634A (91), 645-647 (92),
660 (95), 671 (95), 688 (96), 703-
715 (96), 720-722 (99), 785 (107),
804 (108), 839 (111), 848 (111),
947 (119), 948 (120), 982 (123),
1003-1004 (124), 1011 (127),
1031 (128), 1054 (131), 1123
(139), 1139 (140), 1213 (147),
1229 (147), 1283 (152), 1283B
(152), 1304 (155), 1304C (155),
1686c (196), 1688b (199), 1689b
(199), 1729 (204), 1952 (228),
2081 (243), 2201 (256), 2216a
(259), 2523 (292), C88 (344)
Headquarters, 727 (99), 730 (99),
752 (103), 766 (103)
Inauguration, 854 (111), 2414 (283)
John P., 956 (120)

Martha, 306 (65), 556 (84), 585 (87),
601 (88), 636 (91), 662 (95), 673
(95), 805 (108), 840 (111), 849
(111)
Monument, 649-650 (92), 1158
(143), 1366 (160)
(Mount Rainier National Park), 742
(100), 750 (100), 758 (103), 770
(103)
State, 1674 (195), 1999 (232)
Statehood, 858 (111), 2404 (283)
(Steamboat), 2408 (283)
Territory, 1019 (127)
(Touro Synagogue), 2017 (235)
Water
Conservation, 1150 (140)
Conservation, Soil and, 2074 (243)
Save our, 1412 (164)
Waterfowl Conservation, 1362 (160)
Wayne
Gen. Anthony, 680 (95)
John, 2448 (288)
Weaver Violins, 1813 (215)
Webster
Daniel, 141 (53), 152 (53), 163 (53),
174 (53), 189 (54), 199 (54), 226
(54), 258 (58), 273 (61), 283 (62),
307 (65), 725 (99), 1380 (163),
282C (62)
Noah, 1121 (139)
Wells, Ida B., 2442 (287)
West
Benjamin, 1553 (180)
Gen. Joseph, 683 (95)
Point, US Military Academy, 789
(107)
Quoddy Head (ME), 2472 (288)
West Virginia, 1667 (195), 2000 (232)
Statehood, 1232 (147)
Western, Country &, (320)
Westport Landing, MO, 994 (124)
Wetland Habitats, 1921 (224)
Whale Oil Lamp, 1608 (187)
Killer, 2508 (291)
Wharton
Edith, 1832 (216)
Joseph, 1920 (224)
Wheatland (Home of James Bucha-
nan), 1081 (135)
Wheelchair, 1155 (143), 1385 (163),
2153 (251), 2256 (264)
Wheels of Freedom, 1162 (143)
Wheelwright, 1719 (203)
Whistler's Mother, 737-738 (100), 754
(103)
Whistler, James A. McNeill, 737-738
(100), 754 (103), 885 (112)
White
Bengal Tiger, 2709 (311)
Dr. Paul Dudley, 2170 (255)
House, 809 (108), 844 (111), 932
(119), 990 (124), 1208 (147), 1240
(148), 1338 (159), 1338A (159),
1338D (159), 1338F (159), 1338G
(159), 1935-1936 (227), 2219
(260), 2609 (299)
House, Little, 931 (119)
Mountain, 2661 (307)
Oak, 1766 (208)
Pine, 1765 (208)
Plains, Battle of, 629 (91), 630 (91)
Sanford, 1928 (227)
-Tailed Deer, 1888 (220)
William Allen, 960 (120)
Whitman, Walt, 867 (112)
Whitney, Eli, 889 (112)
Whittier, John Greenleaf, 865 (112)
Whooping Cranes, 1098 (136)
Wightman, Hazel, 2498 (291)
Wigmaker, 1458 (171)
Wild
Animals, 2705-2709 (311)
Pink, 2076 (243)
Turkey, 1077 (135)
Wilderness, Civil War Centennial, 1181
(144)
Wildflower, 2647-2671 (307),
2672-2696 (308)
Wildlife, 757 (208), 1880-1889 (220),
2476 (291)

American, 2286-2310 (268), 2311-
2335 (271)
Conservation, 1077-1078 (135),
1098 (136), 1392 (163), 1427-
1430 (167), 1464-1467 (171),
1760-1763 (208)
Habitats, Preservation of, 1921-1924
(224), 1924a (224)
Wiley, Harvey W., 1080 (135)
Wilkes, Lt. Charles, 2387 (279)
Wilkie, Wendell, 2193 (255)
Willard, Frances E., 872 (112)
Williams
Hank, 2723 (318)
Roger, 777 (104)
Wilson, Woodrow, 623 (91), 697 (96),
832 (111), 1040 (128), 2218i (260)
Win the War, 905 (115)
Windmills, 1738-1742 (207)
Winged
Airmail Envelope, C79 (344), C83
(344)
Globe, C12 (339), C16 (339), C17
(339), C19 (339), C24 (340)
Winter
Olympic Games '84, 2067 (240)
Pastime, by Nathaniel Currier, 1702
(200)
Special Olympics, 2142 (251)
Wisconsin, 1662 (192), 2001 (232)
Statehood, 957 (120)
Tercentary, 739 (100), 755 (103)
(Workman's Compensation Law),
1186 (144)
Witherspoon, John, 1687c (196)
Wizard of Oz, The, 2445 (288)
Wolf Trap Farm National Park, 1452
(171), 2018 (235)
Woman
American, 1152 (143)
Clubs, General Federation of, 1316
(156)
Progress of, 959 (120)
Service, 1013 (127)
Suffrage, 1406 (164)
Wood
-Carved Figurines, 2240-2243 (263)
Duck, 2493-2494 (291)
Wooden Propeller, Airplane Radiator
and, C4 (339)
Woodland Habitats, 1924 (224)
Woodson, Carter G., 2073 (243)
Wool Industry, American, 1423 (167)
Workmen's Compensation, 1186 (144)
World
Columbian Stamp Expo '92, 2616
(300), 2624-2629 (303)
Exposition, Louisiana, 2086 (243)
Forestry Congress, Fifth, 1156 (143)
Health Organization, 1194 (144)
Peace Through Law, 1576 (184)
Peace Through World Trade, 1129
(139)
Refugee Year, 1149 (140)
STAMP EXPO '89, 2410 (283), 2433
(284)
STAMP EXPO '92, Columbian, 2616
(300), 2624-2629 (303)
University Games, 2748 (315)
War I, 537 (83), 2154 (252)
War II, 899 901 (115), 905 (115), 907-
908 (115), 909-921 (116), 925-926
(116), 929 (119), 934-936 (119),
939-940 (119), 956 (120), 969
(123), 1026 (127), 1289 (152),
1424 (167), 1869 (219), 2186
(255), 2192 (255), 2559 (296),
2697 (311), 2765 (317)
World's Fair
'64, 1244 (148)
Expo '74, 1527 (179)
Expo Seattle '62, 1196 (147)
Knoxville '82, 2006-2009 (235)
New York, 853 (111)
Wreath and Toys, 1843 (216)
Wright
Airplane, 649 (92), C45 (340), C47
(340), C91 (347)
Brothers, C45 (340), C47 (340), C91
(347), C92 (347)

Frank Lloyd, 1280 (152), 2019 (235), 1280b (152)
Wulfenite, 2703 (311)
Wyoming, 1676 (195), 2002 (232)
   Statehood, 897 (115), 2444 (288)
   (Yellowstone National Park), 744 (100), 760 (103), 1453 (171)

Y

Yat-Sen Sun, 906 (115), 1188 (144)
Year
   International Women's, 1571 (184)
   of the Child, International, 1772 (211)
   of the Disabled, International, 1925 (224)
Yellow Lady's-Slipper, 2077 (243)
Yellowstone National Park, 744 (100), 760 (103), 1453 (171)
YMCA Youth Camping, 2160 (252)
Yorktown
   Battle of, 703 (96), 1937 (227)
   Surrender of Cornwallis at, 703 (96), 1686 (196)
   -Virginia Capes, Battle of, 703 (96), 1937-1938 (227)
Yosemite
   National Park, 740 (100), 751 (100), 756 (103), 769 (103)
   Flag Over, 2280 (267)
Young, Whitney Moore, 1875 (220)
Youth
   Camping, YMCA, 2160 (252)
   Classics, (320)
   Salute to, 963 (120)
   Support our, 1342 (159)
   Year, International, 2160-2163 (252)
Yugoslavia, 917 (116)
Yukon-Pacific, Exposition, Alaska-, 370-371 (70)

Z

Zaharias, Babe, 1932 (227)
Zeppelin
   Between Continents, C14 (339)
   Century of Progress, C18 (339)
   Over Atlantic, C13 (339)
   Passing Globe, C15 (339)
Zia Pot, 1706 (203)
Zion National Park, 747 (100), 763 (103)
ZIP Code, 1511 (179)

Postmasters General
of the United States

Appointed by the Continental Congress

1775 Benjamin Franklin, PA
1776 Richard Bache, PA
1782 Ebenezer Hazard, NY

Appointed by the President with the advice and consent of the Senate

1789 Samuel Osgood, MA
1791 Timothy Pickering, PA
1795 Joseph Habersham, GA
1801 Gideon Granger, CT
1814 Return J. Meigs, Jr., OH
1823 John McLean, OH
1829 William T. Barry, KY
1835 Amos Kendall, KY
1840 John M. Niles, CT
1841 Francis Granger, NY
1841 Charles A. Wickliffe, KY
1845 Cave Johnson, TN
1849 Jacob Collamer, VT
1850 Nathan K. Hall, NY
1852 Samuel D. Hubbard, CT
1853 James Campbell, PA
1857 Aaron V. Brown, TN
1859 Joseph Holt, KY
1861 Horatio King, ME
1861 Montgomery Blair, DC
1864 William Dennison, OH
1866 Alexander W. Randall, WI
1869 John A.J. Creswell, MD
1874 James W. Marshall, NJ
1874 Marshall Jewell, CT
1876 James N. Tyner, IN
1877 David McK. Key, TN
1880 Horace Maynard, TN
1881 Thomas L. James, NY
1882 Timothy O. Howe, WI
1883 Walter Q. Gresham, IN
1884 Frank Hatton, IA
1885 William F. Vilas, WI
1888 Don M. Dickinson, MI
1889 John Wanamaker, PA
1893 Wilson S. Bissell, NY
1895 William L. Wilson, WV
1897 James A. Gary, MD
1898 Charles Emory Smith, PA
1902 Henry C. Payne, WI
1904 Robert J. Wynne, PA
1905 George B. Cortelyou, NY
1907 George von L. Meyer, MA
1909 Frank H. Hitchcock, MA
1913 Albert S. Burleson, TX
1921 Will H. Hays, IN
1922 Hubert Work, CO
1923 Harry S. New, IN
1929 Walter F. Brown, OH
1933 James A. Farley, NY
1940 Frank C. Walker, PA
1945 Robert E. Hannegan, MO
1947 Jesse M. Donaldson, IL
1953 Arthur E. Summerfield, MI
1961 J. Edward Day, CA
1963 John A. Gronouski, WI
1965 Lawrence F. O'Brien, MA
1968 W. Marvin Watson, TX
1969 Winton M. Blount, AL

Selected by the Presidentially appointed U.S. Postal Service Board of Governors

1971 Elmer T. Klassen, MA
1975 Benjamin Franklin Bailar, MD
1978 William F. Bolger, CT
1985 Paul N. Carlin, WY
1986 Albert V. Casey, MA
1986 Preston R. Tisch, NY
1988 Anthony M. Frank, CA
1992 Marvin Runyon, TN